Capitalism Is Past Its Sell-By Date

From Incredible Success To Enabling Environmental and Resource Unsustainability

by

KATE —
Looking forward
to your comments
KW

Kit Webster

Table of Contents

DEDICATION I

INTRODUCTION I

PART I – CAPITALISM - FROM INCREDIBLE SUCCESS TO DETERIORATION AND DYSFUNCTION 1

Incredible Prosperity 1
   Four Things Have Been Critical to This Incredible Prosperity 5

Capitalism 6
   A Quick Comparison of Socialism and Capitalism 8
   Cultural Pressure on Capitalism 10
   What we Have Today Is Not Unfettered Capitalism 12
      Is the U.S. Going to Become a Socialist State? 12
   The Downsides of Capitalism 19
      Capitalism's Inherent Flaws 21
         Capitalism will take itself to extremes and destroy itself 22
         Capitalism leaves behind those who cannot keep up 23
         Business cycles, which at times can be extreme, are inherent within capitalism 24
         The system can be gamed by its participants, including cronyism, regulation, regulatory capture, administrative interference and monopoly power. 27
         Capitalism creates inequalities in income and wealth that can become so extreme that they destabilize the culture. 31
         Because capitalism demands and drives change, including creative destruction, and the creation of technologies, it is inherently destabilizing 34
         Capitalism deemphasizes the future by analyzing it using a "discount rate" 35
         We are in a strange time during which the Federal Reserve is destroying capitalism 37
         Capitalism raises issues of sustainability 41
      Headwinds 42
         The law of diminishing returns 43
         A changing cultural environment 45
         Attempts to implement social and political values through corporations 46
         Regulators Have Vacated the Field 52

The Triffin Dilemma 52
The Fourth Turning 54
The Rise of the Robots 57
Fighting Climate Change 58
Mortgaging and Hamstringing the Future 60
Demographics 62

Tradeoffs **63**

Compounding – A Digression **65**

Back to Tradeoffs **66**

All Trends Exhaust Themselves **68**

So, What Is The Best Way to Organize an Economy? **72**

When Was the Actual Sell-By Date? **73**

What to Do? **85**

PART II – UNSUSTAINABILITY – THE END GAME 90

The Environmentalists Are Right (Sort Of) **91**

I Really Did Not Want To Be Here **92**

Technology and Abundance **93**

Climate Change Will Affect, but is not Critical to, the Discussion About Overpopulation and Consumption **95**

Before We Get Started **97**
Data 97
Complexity 98
Contentiousness 99
Prediction 99
Peak Resources 101
EROI 105
The Future – A New Definition of Peak Oil 106
Yet Another Twist 108
And, The Final Twist 110

Back to Prediction 110

The U.N. Intergovernmental Science-Policy Platform on Biodiversity and
Ecosystem Services (IPBES) 110

Carrying Capacity 112
   The Limits to Growth 117
   Eco-Footprint 120
   Rigorous Analysis 123
   Other Predictions 124
   The opposing view – the technological cavalry 128
   My View on Carrying Capacity 129

Planetary Boundaries 130

Consumption 132
   The Magnitude of the Consumption Challenge 132
   Food 133
      Water 134
         Rivers That Run Dry 139
         Disappearing Aquifers 141
         The Great Lakes 146
         Seas That are Drying Up 146
         Polluted Water 146
         Water is Being Taken Out of Circulation 148
         Seasonality 148
         Complications From Fighting Climate Change 148
         Peak Water 148
         Ownership of Water 149
         How Bad Is It? 152
         The Good News 153
         Conservation 154
         Recycling 155
         Pricing 156
         Regulation 157
         Summary 157
      Topsoil 158
         Desertification 159
         Competition for arable land 160
         Peak Phosphorus 160
      Fish 163
         The bottom of the food chain 167
      Technology and Food 168
         GMOs 169

Herbicides and pesticides.. 171
Precise use of resources 173
Meat grown in the lab and processed from plants...................... 173
Vertical farms 175
Additional Steps to Increase the Food Supply 175
Reduce waste... 175
Reduce obesity... 177
Don't plant organically 177
Climate change 178
Stop planting crops for biofuels... 178
Employ some of the principles of regenerative agriculture 178
Re-think the definition of food 179
Then, the Bad News.. 179
A Conundrum 180

Energy...**181**
Revisiting EROI... 181
The Cost of Conversion to Renewable Energy.................................. 185
The Irony of Inexpensive, Renewable Energy.................................... 185

Materials **186**
The Parable of Maxite 191
Projections of Depletion... 194
Solutions... 196

Waste...**196**

Climate Change and the Population / Consumption Challenge...........**203**

The Price Conundrum...**205**

So, Where Are We? **206**

Achieving Sustainability **210**
Personal Responsibility... 211
Two Alternative Scenarios 212
Intentional Sustainability.. 213

Growth...**214**
How Growth Overwhelms... 216
What To Do About Population? 217
What To Do About Consumption?... 220

Pricing **224**

Gross Ecosystem Product 228
Hail Mary 229

The Future **230**
The Good News 230
The Dream 231
Change is Very Hard 232
    The Climate Change Example 233

Quality of Life **233**

The End Game **237**

Winners and Losers **240**

The Cultural Conundrum of Growth **241**
How Much of What is Enough? 243
Social Instead of Economic Goals 244
Utopia Versus Dystopia 246
    Signs of Dystopia 248

The Bottom Line **253**

What to Do? **255**

It Gets Worse **255**

A NO-GROWTH ECONOMY **256**

The Story, So Far **256**

Revisiting Growth **257**

A No-Growth Economy **258**

Steady State for the Long Run **261**
Everything is Connected 262
Employment in a No-Growth Economy 263
Components of a No-Growth Economy 265

CONCLUSION **266**

Scorpions, Greek Tragedy, Overpopulation and the Human Condition ...**266**

Things to Think About 268

In the End 269

Dealing with the Sell-By Date 270

SPECIAL OFFER 273

ACKNOWLEDGEMENTS 274

ABOUT THE AUTHOR...275

REFERENCES – PARTIAL LIST..276

ENDNOTES...286

Dedication

To Beth – wife, soul mate, partner, muse, friend and lover

Introduction

The elevation of the material conditions of humanity has been extraordinary, enabled by

- the Enlightenment, which freed Western humans to explore explanations outside of the framework of religion;
- the availability of cheap energy;
- the exploitation of natural resources; and
- capitalism and free markets, as a framework for the productive allocation of savings and resources.

The three hundred years since the beginning of the Industrial Revolution and the evolution and maturation of modern capitalism have created incredible increases in lifespans and wellbeing, a profusion of consumer goods and a dramatic reduction in poverty. Human existence, at least for the developed world, and increasingly for the developing world, has been transformed from being "solitary, poor, nasty, brutish and short,[1]" to encompassing technology, the arts, travel and myriad avenues of self-fulfillment, education and communication, all within a significantly longer lifespan.

I do not know whether I am related to the great 19th century statesman and orator, Daniel Webster. However, I was strongly influenced by a story about him in which he successfully defended the defendant in a trial and then successfully prosecuted the appeal on behalf of the plaintiff.

From that time forward, I have been determined to understand an issue such that I could argue it from either side.

I have spent a lifetime pursuing the goal of attempting to understand. I began by learning about the physical universe, based on my masters of electrical engineering degree. I then turned my attention to humans – to history, philosophy, religion and psychology - to attempt to understand human behavior. I have read hundreds of books on these subjects over the decades and have attempted to integrate the knowledge I gained into a conceptual framework about the way humans, in the aggregate, have created cultures, institutions, nations and empires. Since essentially all the many humans, cultures, institutions, nations and empires of history no longer exist, that conceptual framework must include an understanding of why almost all are gone, except for those which have been relatively recently created.

(Interestingly, it is some religions which have persisted the longest. Hinduism, which has evolved over time, goes back into the mist of pre-history, Judaism perhaps began around 1800 BCE and Buddhism dates from the sixth century BCE.)

My studies and decades of work life gave me some success in my understanding of the physical world. However, I despair of ever understanding the incredible complexity and variety of human behavior. I did, however, begin to gather some broad generalizations that describe human behavior at a high level. These thoughts can best be considered as a framework within which to contemplate human behavior and therefore the evolution of human institutions. These thoughts revolved around the following principles.

Before I detail the principles, I would like to list fundamental, underlying axioms about the physical world:

- Resources are scarce.
- Over a reasonable timeframe, life is, at best, a zero-sum game. The ecosystem is bounded and the second law of thermodynamics exists. Until and unless we can incorporate other planets into our resource base, we are depleting a closed system.
- Life is not fair. There are outsized returns to the strong, the swift and the cunning. And to the small and numerous, such as viruses and bacteria.
- Humans have increased in numbers and in their ability and inclination to consume and transform resources to the point that they have become a plague species – a proposition we will explore in detail in Part II of this book.

An extraordinary amount of physical resources and energy are required to keep reality at bay.

Following are my "laws" that provide a framework for thinking about human nature:

- Humans are very creative, but will take all trends to their extremes. In pursuit of progress and novelty, each chain in a trend or process becomes the foundation for building the new and the novel in an endless progression. These extremes are not sustainable and facilitate the destruction of cultures, institutions, countries and empires. This profound tendency is captured in quotes, such as Eric Hoffer's "Every great cause begins as a movement, becomes a business, and eventually degenerates into a racket," and Karl Marx's "history repeats itself, first as tragedy, then as farce."

- In a Jungian sense, everything we have created is a projection of our inner nature – governments, institutions, cultures.

- All human endeavors and creations have "good" attributes and "bad" attributes. When creating a culture, it is important to determine what its values and goals are and to understand the implicit and explicit tradeoffs required in the decision-making toward achieving those goals. There is no decision that does not include tradeoffs.

- The average human has an IQ of 100; half the human race has an IQ of less than 100. According to the Myers-Briggs classification of human communication (which may or may not be entirely valid, but is indicative), approximately 40% of humans think employing an analytical component, approximately 27% include a conceptual component and 10% include both. Not only do the vast majority of humans not understand complexity and nuance, they cannot understand complexity and nuance.

- 10-20% of people will and do believe anything.

- You cannot do just one thing. Every decision can affect multiple people and institutions. Unintended consequences of every action are inherent in most human decisions.

- The most important question in decision-making is, what are my goals and objectives? The second-most-important question is, compared to what?

- Contrarianism is a useful rule of thumb. Whenever a large majority of a group strongly holds an opinion, it is either wrong or will change significantly.

- The road to hell is paved with good intentions. Humanity's desire for the good and the nice – for puppies, unicorns and rainbows – is at odds with the "brutality" of nature, variations in human behavior and the reality of the laws of thermodynamics.

- Nature abhors a vacuum. When people have their needs met and have time on their hands, they will fill that time. Some will fill it with reading; some with video games; and some, particularly the well-educated, upper-middle-class-and-above, will fill it with the purpose of social issues.

- Humans will not agree, and are genetically and culturally disposed to be different in a significant variety of ways. This sets up a perpetual, unstoppable dynamic of change in culture and institutions and disagreement among its participants. This change is well expressed in the Hegelian, thesis, antithesis, synthesis (however, as a process, without teleology). Or in the concept of yin, yang and the resolution of opposites. At times, it is expressed in riots, revolution and war.
- Because humans have differing and often opposite opinions, there is a social and political version of scientist Isaac Newton's third law. His third law of motion is, "for every action there is an equal and opposite reaction." The social / political equivalent is, every political or social act will meet resistance; the larger, more forceful or more meaningful the act, the greater the magnitude of the resistance.
- History unfolds in cycles and not in straight lines. However, as Mark Twain is said to have noted, "History does not repeat itself, but it often rhymes." This rhyming is the expression of human nature in the context of a changing history, technology and social structure.
- One of those historical cycles is from rational to romantic and back again. We are in a romantic age during which justification is primarily based on feelings and not facts.
- Humans require and make myths. Myths are stories that need not be factually true, but which embody eternal truths. (The loss of traditional myths in the modern age and their replacement by politics represents a profound change in the foundations of human behavior.)
- A quest for novelty becomes an increasing component of human motivation as income, security and leisure time increase.
- In the short term, and often in the medium and long terms, denial and reality avoidance significantly contribute to peace of mind and quality of life, making them dominant in human thinking and behavior. Reality avoidance is primarily facilitated by wealth.
- There are times when things fall apart and humans fall into dark ages and world wars. Although homo sapiens is a violent species, extreme collapse and widespread, extreme violence are the exceptions.
- Not every problem has a solution.

The point of these thoughts is to lay the foundation for a discussion of why capitalism is past its sell-by date and to consider what comes next. Capitalism is, after all, a set of human principles and practices, and therefore subject to these "laws."

As a result of this thought process and after having laid the groundwork in the 70s and 80s, I began developing a view in the early 1990s that the U.S. would enter a cyclical, and potentially a secular, decline in the early 2000s. I began an email list and later a website. You can join me at http://www.pastsellbydate.com to discuss and help to further develop these thoughts.

In the late 1990s, I read *The Fourth Turning* by Strauss and Howe[2], which expressed some of my thoughts much better than I could (although I was not, and am not, developing my thoughts in the context of generations as Strauss and Howe did). Strauss and Howe developed our mutual themes that trends lead to extreme excesses that must be resolved prior to a rebirth or regeneration, creating a new cycle – a new First Turning in their view. But also that the current Fourth Turning, which began in 2008 and should last about 20 years, will be a time of destruction of the old, and an exceedingly dangerous period of time. While not the way to bet, the probability of calamity and war increases during a Fourth Turning as the old is destroyed, cultures and institutions become unstable and the new is created.

The advent of the Covid-19 pandemic has created a Fourth Turning on steroids and arguably accelerated many of the trends that were already under way.

This book, on the end of capitalism, was born during the process of writing a different book.

I write to "find out what I think."[3]

In the 1970s I read *The Limits to Growth*[4], and was profoundly affected by its portrayal of a future in which we humans will bring catastrophe on ourselves by unrelenting increases in population and consumption of resources. Then I lived through the 80s and 90s, a time of incredible economic growth that seemed to have no limits. I began to believe that the authors of *Limits* were like some environmentalists - overstating problems upon which action must be taken NOW.

Sometime in the 90s I first heard about climate change, back when it was global warming. The sound bites in newspapers and on television just did not add up.

I was dismayed by the misinformation around the subject of climate change, the incomplete explanations from the media, and by books that presented only one side of the issue.

All of the focus was on the bad things that would result from climate change, with no discussion of the tradeoffs associated with fighting it. Since there are no decisions without downsides and there are always unintended consequences of significant actions, there was a great deal not being said by the popular press, movie stars and politicians.

I wondered why, if fighting climate change was going to be easy and positive for the economy, we did not just do it.

Then climate change became politically correct and the probability of getting unbiased analysis from politicians and the popular press fell to close to zero.

I spent more than a decade reading everything I could find on the subject, from scientific papers to books to internet rants - from Al Gore to Rush Limbaugh - in order to understand the issues around climate change for myself.

As I began writing a book on climate change and following the facts and data to discover what I thought, I came to a completely unexpected conclusion, albeit one that was reached in *The Limits to Growth*: climate change is a symptom of an underlying disease. We are trying to fix symptoms while leaving the underlying problem alone. We are trying to manage a fever with aspirin while the underlying cancer continues to grow.

Climate change is a symptom of a more profound, underlying disease.

I became aware that something more fundamental, more existential than even climate change, is at stake. While my interest in climate change was primarily academic, my expanding thoughts on population and consumption grew into a compelling concern. Ultimately, it became important that I directly address THE underlying problem: capitalism has enabled too many people to consume too many resources, exhausting the Earth's resources and nature's ability to cleanse and renew itself. This underlying problem manifests itself in several symptoms, one of which is climate change.

If all energy were renewable tomorrow and the problem of climate change were solved tomorrow, we would still face the existential problem of the limits to human population and to the consumption and depletion of global resources. The associated crisis will likely begin within the next 40 years, however it probably has already begun.

Capitalism and its consumerism variant have been too successful in turning natural resources and energy into humans and goods. They are now reaching or have reached their natural limits.

Then, it seemed that the Great Financial Crisis (GFC) marked the beginning of the current Fourth Turning (with which Howe agrees), and I wrote a book about the GFC in order to fundamentally understand what it was and why it happened.

It is important to realize that news provided by the media, particularly in an era of political correctness and significantly divided political opinions, does not provide an adequate basis for the understanding of complex subjects. And nothing is more complicated than the non-linear, multifaceted, complex system that is the political economy. These social and political divisions lead to not only inadequate discussions, but also inaccurate and biased discussions of, among other things, climate change, capitalism and sustainability.

My book on climate change led to thoughts on the subject of sustainability, which led to thoughts on the viability of capitalism.

You receive a free copy of my book on climate change, which was described by Dr. David Collum, professor at Cornell University, as "a fabulous 110 page write-up on global warming, more moderate than my own but right on the maximum in my opinion," for free by signing up for my free, weekly newsletter at http://www.pastsellbydate.com/subscribe.

I have been a life-long, free-market capitalist and have held the positions of Chief Executive Officer, President and Chief Financial Officer in various privately- and publicly-held companies. It is clear to me that capitalism, while having its challenges (remembering that everything has both "good" and "bad" characteristics), provides the most efficient allocation of resources to, in turn, provide the highest standard of living for the most people. There are no words sufficient to describe capitalism's ability to deploy savings, energy and natural resources to elevate the lives of many, and recently, the vast majority, of humans.

And that is the problem. That trend – deploying ever-more resources to the world's rapidly-expanding population - is now creating the excesses that are providing the foundation for the end of capitalism. The primary excesses from capitalism today are inequality, crony capitalism, regulatory capture and the demise of environmental sustainability. By far, the most important and existential challenge is environmental sustainability, which is a primary topic of this book.

The critical importance of environmental sustainability to a discussion about capitalism makes this a difficult book for me to write.

I have two objectives to achieve within this book. The first is a general discussion of the strengths and weaknesses of capitalism, leading to the conclusion that it is a trend that has been taken too far. The second is to establish that a primary result of capitalism, the loss of sustainability, is a part of our current reality and is an existential challenge.

While sustainability is an occasional topic of discussion, it generally does not receive widespread coverage. To the extent serious attention is paid to environmental issues, discussion is usually framed in terms of climate change and loss of biodiversity. Essentially no one is making the case that, in effect, the economic successes enabled by capitalism are leading to catastrophe relating to sustainability. Perhaps the most recent, influential book on the subject was Naomi Klein's *This Changes Everything*.[5] Ms. Klein's book primarily addresses capitalism's effect on climate change.

Those that do discuss sustainability generally do not address the difficult issues associated with fixing the problem. Instead, they forecast a coming together of humanity that will generally pursue intangible, spiritual and social improvement as opposed to material improvement. A spontaneous, global outbreak of "kumbaya."

I will make the case that sustainability is no less than the primary challenge facing humanity. Sustainability is a challenge primarily because capitalism enables the efficient taking, use and re-formation of the Earth's resources.

Because the case for sustainability is not part of popular discussion, I will spend some time establishing the details and urgency of the loss of sustainability.

This book addresses the end of capitalism, first by reviewing capitalism's successes, challenges and end game, and second by undertaking a comprehensive discussion of the state of, and implications for, sustainability. Accordingly, this book is divided into two parts: an examination of capitalism, generally, concentrating on the trends which are bringing about its significant change, if not demise, and a detailed examination of the principal trend due to capitalism, which is the loss of sustainability. The book ends with a discussion of a particularly non-capitalistic, no growth world, which is the end game of re-attaining sustainability through a no-growth economy.

I will contemplate humanity's future on the "other side" of capitalism, and it is not pretty. The excesses have become extreme, and we have severely compromised our future, economically and environmentally. We have become accustomed to unsustainable standards of living, which will be very difficult to give up.

Importantly, as capitalism is dismantled as the culture demands more equality, "fairness" and social responsibility, standards of living will decrease for most in the West, reinforcing the demand for change. Standards of living will decline for several reasons, one of which will be that we are at the boundaries for sufficient cheap energy and for inexpensive materials. Another is that whatever economic system is adopted will unlikely be able to generate the material returns of capitalism.

Capitalism is a juggernaut, transforming all before it at an increasing rate, utilizing energy to turn the Earth's natural resources into humans, infrastructure and goods.

And that is the problem.

Peak capitalism will coincide with the current Fourth Turning, which is occurring now. There is an argument to be made that the Great Recession of

2008-2009 and the continuing economic and social issues, including the election of former president Donald Trump, the pronounced increase in credibility of socialist ideas, increasing rates of suicide and opioid use, and extensive social unrest, are the first symptoms of a world that is reaching its limits beyond climate change and the loss of biodiversity. This is a world that has become unsustainable and is beginning to fray around its edges.

The challenges associated with adequately addressing sustainability are daunting. In summary, the average citizen of the U.S. must decrease their levels of consumption by approximately 75%.

This book is not intended to be either a critique or defense of capitalism. The objective of this book is to examine the logical results and implications of capitalism as we have implemented it.

I will address very complex, interconnected ideas, each of which could be the subject of its own book. I will do so in such a way as to make this book widely accessible by simplifying complexity.

Importantly, I will address all issues head-on. The chips are allowed to fall where they may. Uncertainty is ok, so long as it reflects the state of current knowledge. Further, this is a judgement-free zone. Too many create innuendo and guilt by association which are not supported by facts or evidence. Too many environmental and social justice texts use negative adjectives, such as "unfortunate" or "destructive." My view is that we need to dispassionately review where we are, use the facts and evidence at hand, consider alternatives and tradeoffs, and then select the best future we can have.

While I will not intentionally be confrontational or negative, the conclusions of this book are negative, so that if you require a trigger warning, consider yourself warned.

I will use a number of graphs to illustrate ideas. However, the key points from each graph will be explained in the text, so you can ignore the graphs, if you wish, and not lose track of any of the discussion and debate. There is very little math.

Finally, I would like to note that I am uncomfortable predicting gloom and doom, particularly following a lifetime of believing in continually-improving progress. I have lived an exceptionally wonderful life by being able to live in the United States at the pinnacle of capitalism. I want our son to be able to have all I have had and more.

Unfortunately, I cannot ignore the facts and data which have asserted themselves during my research and contemplation.

Here are those facts and data, together with some of my thoughts, for you to use in forming your opinion.

Join in the conversation on my website, http://www.pastsellbydate.com and on Twitter at @KitWebster. My email address is Kit@PastSellByDate.com .

I am writing a weekly newsletter on capitalism and the environment, *Green Growth is an Oxymoron*. Sign up for my newsletter here or access the QR code, below, and I will send you a free copy of my book, *The Only Ten Things You Need To Know About Global Warming*, in either pdf or eBook format.

Part I – Capitalism - From Incredible Success to Deterioration and Dysfunction

The future is in disorder. A door like this has cracked open five or six times since we got up on our hind legs. It is the best possible time to be alive, when almost everything you thought you knew is wrong. — *Tom Stoppard*[6]

Incredible Prosperity

There may not even be words to adequately describe the improvement in human well-being over the 300 years since the beginning of the Industrial Revolution.

One way to look at human history is that prosperity and economic growth are not normal, or at least have not been normal during essentially all of humans' existence. There has been meaningful economic growth only in 300 of the 300,000 years or so that modern humans have existed or the 10,000 years since humans began to become civilized.

Humanity's recent success in improving its own condition is nothing short of astonishing.

In the seventeenth century, philosopher Thomas Hobbes famously noted, "Life in an unregulated state of nature is solitary, poor, nasty, brutish, and short."[7] Life expectancy at birth in the Roman Empire and through the Middle Ages was 20-30 years, and world life expectancy averaged around 35 years until the 1800s.[8] This is a bit misleading, because of the large number of children who died at birth or in infancy, and the number of mothers who died in childbirth. Once a Roman attained the age of 5, s/he could expect to live to around 45 and occasionally into his or her 60s.

Until recently, there was no concept of disease other than an ill wind or the wrath of the gods. And no way to cure diseases. The germ theory of disease began its slow acceptance in the 1700s. Penicillin, essentially the first antibiotic, was not discovered until 1928, and anesthesia was not widely effective until the late 1800s. The slightest cut or abscess could be fatal, as could diseases, such as diphtheria, mumps and polio, which are dismissed out of hand today. As an example, U.S. President Calvin Coolidge's son died in 1924 from an infected blister, which he got while playing tennis. It has been estimated that until around the year 1900, doctors did more harm than good.[9]

Essentially everyone lived on farms, usually doing subsistence farming, producing food for their families and for paying taxes. There was little room for error, and changes in weather, insects or plant diseases could have life-or-death consequences. Famines were common.

Homo sapiens have struggled, battling nature, disease, and each other. Then the Enlightenment and the Industrial Revolution occurred, and (Western) humanity became the apparent master of all things.

Fast forward to the early 21st century. In the Developed World, life expectancies at birth are in the upper 70s (and the worldwide average is in the lower 60s). Most killer diseases have been conquered and there are medical treatments and medicines for ailments ranging from a toothache to menopause. Open-heart surgeries are commonplace. Even the poor have access to resources that kings and emperors could only have dreamed of: drinkable running water, indoor plumbing, salt, refrigeration, central heating and air conditioning. Even the poor command 200-300 horses of power when they drive their cars, far beyond the envy of the richest on Earth before the Industrial Revolution. And even the poor are generally literate, able to participate in the literature, science, and wisdom of the human legacy, when, 1,000 years ago, only an estimated 5% of Europeans could read and write.[10]

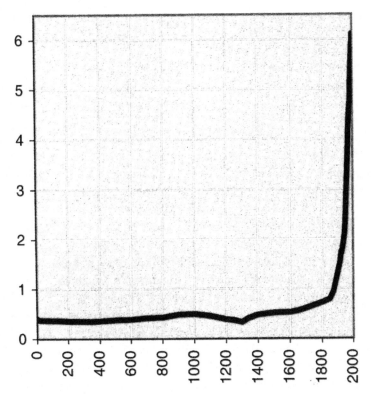

Figure 1 - World gross domestic product per capita in thousands of 1990 PPP U.S. dollars[11]

And it is not just the Developed World that has prospered. With the exception of Sub-Saharan Africa, which is now beginning to grow economically, essentially all humanity has shared in this progress, although the Developed World has shared disproportionately. Figure 1 shows the exponential curve, beginning during the Industrial Revolution, which reflects the average economic output per person from 0-2000 CE. It is more than a little amazing that while population has been increasing exponentially, so has economic activity per capita. Global economic output per person has increased more than 12-fold on average since the beginning of the Industrial Revolution through the use of energy to multiply and augment human efforts.

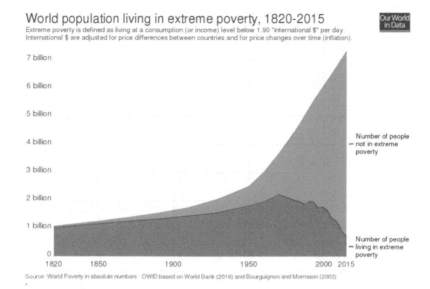

World population living in extreme poverty, 1820-2015

Extreme poverty is defined as living at a consumption (or income) level below 1.90 "international $" per day. International $ are adjusted for price differences between countries and for price changes over time (inflation).

7 billion

6 billion

5 billion

4 billion — Number of people not in extreme poverty

3 billion

2 billion

1 billion

Number of people living in extreme poverty

0

1820　1850　1900　1950　2000　2015

Source: World Poverty in absolute numbers - OWID based on World Bank (2016) and Bourguignon and Morrisson (2002)

Figure 2 – World population living in extreme poverty, 1820 - 2015[12]

As developing countries adopt variations of market economies and capitalism, enabling investments in education, social safety nets and infrastructure, extreme poverty has fallen to 9.6% of the world population in 2015, according to the World Bank - down from 37.1% in 1990,[13] and essentially the whole of humanity in 1820.

Fossil fuels have enabled environmental goodness. "As Alex Epstein points out in an unfashionable book, *The Moral Case for Fossil Fuels*, the use of coal halted and then reversed the deforestation of Europe and North America. The turn to oil halted the slaughter of the world's whales and seals for their blubber. Fertilizer manufactured with natural gas halved the amount of land needed to produce a given amount of food, thus feeding a growing population while sparing land for wild nature."[14]

The improvement in wealth, quality of life, and life expectancy of humans over the past 300 years has been nothing short of spectacular – there are no superlatives sufficient to describe it.

However, there is a fear, articulated well in *The Limits to Growth* and its 30-year update, that we are using up the Earth's resources and polluting the environment at the same time – including through man-made climate change. The fear is that, by capitalism's enabling humans to take growth beyond the limits of the Earth's ability to support it, we are leading to inevitable catastrophe, measured in terms of human suffering and environmental damage.

Four Things Have Been Critical to This Incredible Prosperity

The critical factors that have led to our incredible wealth, prosperity and longevity are

- the Enlightenment, which freed up our ability to read, innovate and think, leading to an explosion of knowledge, expressed in all aspects of life, particularly including technology, science and medicine; it introduced the concept of human progress, perhaps leading to perfection;
- the availability of natural resources to be deployed and re-formed according to our desires and needs;
- an economy based on some form of capitalism and some variation of free markets to productively discover prices and deploy savings; and
- inexpensive, plentiful energy to provide the means for enablement, transformation, communication and distribution.

The loss of any of these factors would lead to, at a minimum, significantly reduced levels of prosperity.

The Enlightenment is over and perhaps can be taken for granted, although significant portions of the population of Western countries are now calling its premises into question. In this book, I will take it for granted, remembering, however, how much human knowledge was lost in the Dark Ages and in the Greek Dark Ages before that. However, we seem to have entered a so-called "romantic" period in which emotions trump facts to an unusual degree, and knowledge may become endangered. Emotions have always trumped facts, but during romantic periods, which occur periodically throughout Western history, emotions become the legitimate measure of all things. Factual-based knowledge often suffers during such periods when literature, history and facts run counter to the dominant emotions, leading to their censure and, potentially, to their destruction.

Natural resources have been depleted to such an extent that we have reached the point that we are losing access to many critical natural resources.

Capitalism and free markets are under fire from several directions. Capitalism is now being gamed by its participants and is being inevitably influenced by the changing culture that it was a critical factor in enabling. Ironically, capitalism's success has contributed to the rise of the Information Age in which the requirements for both capital and labor have been dramatically reduced. This, in turn, reduces the effectiveness of capitalism, while leading to social unrest.

Capitalism is inevitably being taken to its illogical extreme, and is now contributing to a lack of sustainability.

The discussion, below, on Energy Returned on Energy Invested concludes that we are reaching the limits of our ability to generate sufficient energy of a sufficient quality to sustain a complex civilization.

Of the four critical factors to our prosperity, all four, are arguably beginning to decline.

Capitalism

Capitalism is "an economic system based on the private ownership of the means of production and their operation for profit. Characteristics central to capitalism include private property, capital accumulation, wage labor, voluntary exchange, a price system, and competitive markets."[15]

Other primary forms of economic systems today are socialism and communism, which will be considered on a limited basis, primarily with respect to capitalism. I will also briefly discuss fascism as an economic system.

Capitalism has existed in minor forms for centuries as traders traded and bankers lent money, but did not begin to take its modern form until the early stages of the Industrial Revolution. The first uses of the term in the modern sense included, ironically, by Karl Marx and Friedrich Engels in 1867 in their book, *Capital (Das Kapital* in German),[16] which was a foundational document for communism.

A foundational document for capitalism, *The Wealth of Nations,*[17] by British author Adam Smith, published in 1776, did not mention the term. Smith's thesis, as summarized by economist and Nobel laureate George Stigler, "is the most important substantive proposition in all of economics" and foundation of resource-allocation theory. The proposition is that, under competition, owners of resources (labour, land, and capital) will use them most profitably, resulting in an equal rate of return in equilibrium for all uses (adjusted for apparent differences arising from such factors as training, trust, hardship, and unemployment).[18] Stigler also describes Smith's theorem that "the division of labour is limited by the extent of the market" as the "core of a theory of the functions of firm and industry" and a "fundamental principle of economic organisation."[19]

As a simplified summary, the Industrial Revolution enabled the creation of wealth, and capitalism provided a basis for the productive deployment of that wealth in self-reinforcing cycles of increasing prosperity.

Capitalism evolved over time. In its beginnings, its treatment of labor was harsh. In an environment of smoke-filled, dangerous, crowded factories, people worked six days a week with no benefits - no vacation, no medical insurance, no pregnancy leave. If a worker did not work, s/he did not get paid. There was extensive use of child labor.

It is within this context that Marx wrote *Capital* (and Charles Dickens wrote some of his novels describing the working conditions of labor). In essence, much of Marx's critique of capitalism was valid at the time, and he predicted, among other things, that workers of the world would arise against their oppressors. In a sense, they did arise, forming labor unions and going on strikes. At the same time, governments were concerned about the concentrated power of the rising, big companies, and began to enact antitrust laws, which increased competition among these companies. The result was that capitalism evolved over time to include increasing benefits to laborers, which led to a radically-improved standard of living.

And to a future Marx did not envision.

Or, maybe, in one sense, he did.

It is important to separate communism, which is arguably a failed idea, with other topics on which Marx contemplated.

(Given that my primary thesis is that humans take all trends to their extreme, in the end, everything, including capitalism, is or will be a failed idea. Some ideas, potentially such as communism, are flawed to the degree that they cannot succeed. Others, such as capitalism, must either crumble underneath their own weight or be gamed to the point of absurdity.)

Marx thought about the interaction of technology, labor and wealth, and foresaw many of the issues we are discussing in this book, such as inequality and the competitive pressure on labor

Capitalism has continued to evolve since Marx's time in response to cultural pressures. For example, the U.S. has a less-constrained and less-regulated form of capitalism than Europe. China's development has exploded, based in part on capitalism "with Chinese characteristics," as the Chinese government describes it.

Economists have proposed that capitalism has experienced several stages, although they are not in agreement as to what those stages are. Most agree that our current stage is "late capitalism," although there are multiple definitions of exactly what late capitalism entails. One definition includes a mix of high-tech, concentration of financial capital, and a growing gap between rich and poor. Classical, industrial-based capitalism has evolved into this late stage.

Culture is changing in all countries, including the U.S. and Europe, placing additional pressures on capitalism, as society demands further evolution. Capitalism incorporates tradeoffs, some of which are implicit or hidden, that draw criticism and lead to attempts to change the existing system. Capitalism also includes inherent flaws and tradeoffs, which its participants game to its detriment and which draw sometimes stringent criticism.

A Quick Comparison of Socialism and Capitalism

Capitalism is not so much a philosophy or an ideology as it is the culmination of practical experience over the decades, modified by cultural demands. It is the embodiment of processes, procedures and ad hoc rules to be used in discovering prices, deploying savings, competing and accumulating wealth.

Simplistically, socialism is an attempt to address economic inequality and the plight of those who would otherwise be left behind by capitalism. It is more of an ideology based on various views of fairness.

In common usage, socialism is usually considered as the government's ownership of the means of production, with emphasis on workers' rights.

Socialism can work. It is the answer to a system having a different set of values than capitalism. Its set of values, its objective function, is workable, and comes with its own complement of strengths and weaknesses. It provides a response to our emotional instincts. Its Achilles' heel is that there is no limit to suffering and poverty, and there is a limit to resources, so that there are not enough resources to adequately address suffering and poverty at a high standard of living. Ever. And, socialism does not generate resources well. Socialism could work as long as it stayed within the limits of the resources it can generate. However, there is never enough, and socialism often implodes under its own ambitions. The irony is that, in order to even begin to adequately address suffering and poverty, socialism needs capitalism to increase the amount of resources available for redistribution.

Capitalism's fundamental problems include inequality and the business cycle (I will discuss additional issues, below). Inequality in and of itself is embedded in the way the world works. Lions and zebras are just not equal. However, too much inequality makes people angry and resentful – inequality leads to moral and political outrage.

The down parts of the business cycle create significant discomfort. The Great Depression in the U.S. was terrible for tens of millions of people for essentially an entire decade. However, if you look at a chart of the economy or the stock market today, you might have to work to find the blip caused by the Great Depression in the context of the incredible improvement in wealth and living standards since then. In general, the down cycles of recession and depression lead to much greater up cycles of prosperity – at least they have, so far.

Capitalism is also a process that can be gamed by the rich and the poor. The poor, through democracy, not necessarily capitalism, vote themselves some of the goodies that capitalism enables; the very rich use inequality to begin changing the system in their favor, creating a growing instability that results in political stress. The irony is that capitalism needs socialism to redistribute wealth to keep inequality within politically acceptable bounds.

Current-day China is trying its version of the best of all possible worlds. Lingling Wei, describing the philosophy of China's General Secretary Xi, states that, "Underpinning Mr. Xi's actions is an ideological preference rooted in Mao's development theories, which call state capitalism a tempo-rary phase that can help China's economy catch up to the West before being replaced by socialism," the senior China correspondent writes. "An ardent follower of Mao, Mr. Xi has preached to party members that the hybrid model has passed its use-by date. A 2018 article in the party's main theoretical journal, Qiushi, or Seeking Truth, laid bare his belief: 'China's practice shows that once the socialist transformation is completed, the basic socialist system with public ownership as the main body is established...[and] state capitalism, as a transitional economic form, will complete its historical mission and withdraw from the historical stage.'"[20]

Capitalism is also now running up against the limits of sustainability. However, that is also an issue for socialism, since the actual limits on the availability of resources for redistribution exist, irrespective of ideology.

Cultural Pressure on Capitalism

In addition to continual requirements to address its inherent weaknesses, demands are placed on capitalism by the culture in which it is embedded. Every institution and process must respond to the continually-changing culture within which it exists.

I have discussed, above, how capitalism has evolved in response to social and cultural pressures, sometimes exerted through the government. Capitalism today, because of its inherent weaknesses, and because culture is changing significantly and rapidly, is subject to increasing scrutiny and criticism.

Change is being demanded by most of the population, however the younger generations, perhaps sensing decreasing future opportunities, are among the most critical.

Viktor Shvets describes the dynamics driving demands for changes in capitalism by the current culture as follows:[21]

> Going forward, essentially, society is demanding that the government takes the excess capital that we have accumulated. And today we have at least 5- 10 times more capital than we need, and put it exactly where people want it, rather than sort of remaining in the cloud of finance the way it had been over the last 20 years. So the government will be more aggressive in fiscal policy, whether it's

universal basic income guarantees, whether it's going to be healthcare spending, whether it's going to be some infrastructure spending, whether it's going to be basic research and fundamental research. They're going to be spending money in a number of areas

He describes this as a shift from "freedom, choice and efficiency," which have dominated capitalism since the 1950s, to "fairness, equality and no waste," which are beginning to become powerful forces and will dominate the next era of capitalism.

This criticism often confuses capitalism, itself, with its primary mode of modern expression, the corporation. There is a significant difference between the two, to the point that many corporations are gaming the system and are, in many ways, anti-capitalist. However, the public generally does not see the distinction, so that for practical, cultural purposes, capitalism and the corporation are the same thing. Since capitalism is too abstract to address directly, change to capitalism will be primarily directed by social forces toward the corporation.

Broadly, society today is demanding more contribution to social goals by corporations and capitalists than it has in the past.

There has always been tension between the profit-making of capitalism and cultural demands that corporations become more "socially responsible." However, the culture has changed to the point that this tension has become extreme and change is being demanded. In addition to changes created by regulatory capture, the oligarchy of people at the top of the political power structure and compromise by the Federal Reserve, capitalism / corporations are being forced to change by a dramatic shift in cultural mores.

However, the corporation, itself, is evolving. Its structures, organizations and purposes are becoming more temporary and more contingent. "Within decades, the idea of a corporation (as an organizational unit) will change beyond recognition. Instead, we are likely to see business and commercial life dominated by "temporary" arrangements that would flare up in the sky and go dark in a matter of months or years rather than decades … This in turn will have a significant impact on how products or services are produced, delivered, marketed, or delivered."[22]

It will also create a profound change in the ways corporations are viewed by the culture and by regulators.

Before we discuss the current environment of capitalism's flaws and society's demand for change, I would like to take a brief detour.

What we Have Today Is Not Unfettered Capitalism

Apologists for any economic system, be it capitalism, communism or socialism, will tell you that it has never been correctly or fully implemented.

These apologists are correct.

And these systems never will be correctly or fully implemented.

Humans and human nature will get in the way. Culture and emotions will overwhelm any system. Every time.

Humans will always want to make the "pure" system "better." We will always want to mitigate their inherent flaws. We want to reflect the goals and values of our current culture.

The following is a version of an article I wrote in 2009, which has been edited and updated to fit into the context of this book and today's culture:

Is the U.S. Going to Become a Socialist State?

I am seeing a theme in my emails, my personal conversations, and in the news – the U.S. is becoming "socialistic," or there is the fear that it will. Democrats, particularly the young, are moving to the left under the influence of socialists such as Bernie Sanders and Alexandria Ocasio-Cortez.

So, is the U.S. going to become a socialist state?

Most likely.

Depending on your definition, we are already there or part of the way there.

This is not an either/or proposition, of capitalism or socialism. It is a matter of degree. Absent revolution, you don't wake up one day in a socialist country after having been capitalist the day before. This change takes decades and the preparation of a lot of ground.

We're boiling frogs, here. You know. If you throw a frog into boiling water, it will jump out. If you throw it into temperate water and slowly turn the temperature up, the frog will happily boil.

Cultural and political changes are the boiling of frogs in several dimensions. From self-reliance to welfare; from states' rights to a strong, centralized government; from only male property owners voting to universal suffrage; from Jim Crow to affirmative action; from virginity at marriage to friends with benefits.

Before we get too entangled in emotionally-charged words, it might be useful to step back and review some historical trends and human nature.

Capitalism has brought incredible, unimaginable wealth and well-being to the world, primarily the Western world, and now increasingly the rest of human kind. Capitalism's primary challenges have been how to deal with those unable to compete in a capitalist society and how to deal with inequality. Today, we are struggling with crony capitalism and the capture of regulatory bodies by the regulated. Increasingly it is becoming clear that the world cannot survive the continuing success of capitalism – capitalism has resulted in too many people consuming too many things – the other side of that unimaginable wealth and wellbeing.

Every good debate should begin with a definition of terms. I have provided one definition of capitalism and socialism, above.

I want to add a particularly emotionally-charged term, fascism. In the present context, I am discussing fascism strictly in its economic sense, explicitly excluding other attributes which have been associated with it.

"Where socialism sought totalitarian control of a society's economic processes through direct state operation of the means of production, fascism sought that control indirectly, through domination of nominally private owners. Where socialism nationalized property explicitly, fascism did so implicitly by requiring owners to use their property in the "national interest" – that is, as the autocratic authority conceived it. (Nevertheless, a few industries were operated by the state.) Where socialism abolished all market relations outright, fascism left the appearance of market relations while planning all economic activities. Where socialism abolished money and prices, fascism controlled the monetary system and set all prices and wages politically. In doing all this, fascism denatured the marketplace. Entrepreneurship was abolished. State ministries, rather than consumers, determined what was produced and under what conditions. Fascism is to be distinguished from interventionism, or the mixed economy. Interventionism seeks to guide the market process, not eliminate it, as fascism did."[23]

The primary differences among the three economic systems are, who owns the means of production and how are the results of that production distributed? As an over-simplification:

- Capitalism – private ownership of the means of production and the resulting production is returned to the owner for distribution.
- Socialism – public ownership of the means of production and the resulting production is distributed based on egalitarian principles.
- Fascism – private ownership of the means of production. The means of production are highly regulated by the government. The resulting production is distributed by the government or according to the government's directions.

Each system has its strengths and weaknesses, so that people attempt, over time, to create "mixed economies," which hopefully retain many of the strengths of one system while ameliorating its weaknesses by adding some strengths of another system. The U.S. has welfare, including Social Security and Medicare, in addition to its basically capitalistic system, while China has introduced some private ownership in addition to its quasi-communistic system. In addition, governments everywhere are introducing increasing amounts of regulation, adding a fascist component to the mix.

There is continuing, perhaps never-ending, debate as to the correct mix.

I assert without proof that capitalism is the economic system that will produce the greatest amount of economic wealth. Since it also has a significant amount of inequality in the distribution of that wealth and is associated with sometimes-wrenching business cycles, people want to make the system more "fair," with fairness being defined in many ways by many observers. The only problem is those pesky tradeoffs, one of which is that, in general, the greater the fairness in a system, the less total wealth it can generate.

But, let's keep this simple, with as little politics and ideology as possible. Each system has its strengths and weaknesses and each system is unfair to some groups of people. The question is not, which is the better system, but is the United States becoming a socialist country?

The answer is that the U.S. is and has been becoming both more socialistic and more (economically) fascist, but in its own, peculiar way. The culture and history of the U.S. assume private ownership of the means of production, but the government is taking up an ever-larger part of the economy for egalitarian reasons (there are many other motives at work, which will be ignored here). It is also regulating the economy ever more highly to dictate the conditions under which production is done and where the results of that production will go, including taxation and an increased emphasis on preserving the environment.

The Covid-19 pandemic has led to increasing reliance on government.

Our Founders envisioned a country with limited government, and with most governmental powers given to the states. We are not that country anymore. For better and for worse, the U.S. now has an extensive federal government, together with increasing governments at the state and local levels.

Perhaps one way to visualize how "socialistic" a country is would be to look at the size of the government, economically, compared with the size of the total economy.

Following is a chart that illustrates the increase in the relative size of the U.S. government and a comparison of that size with other Western countries.

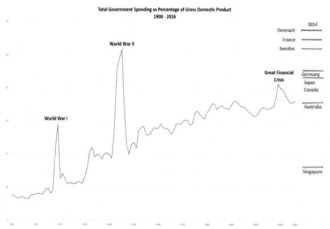

Figure 3 – Total government spending as a percentage of gross domestic product[24]

This chart shows the percentage of U.S. Gross Domestic Product accounted for by government spending. Since the time of Teddy Roosevelt in 1902, the government has become a larger and larger part of the economy – about 4% for our first 120 years or so, and 36% in 2016. This spending has increased through Democrat presidents and Republican presidents, through Presidents Johnson and Reagan (with a brief dip in the time of Clinton).

Why is that?

To do good, to be fair, to help the unfortunate and to fight wars.

You want Social Security? You want Medicare? You want an interstate highway system? You want an egalitarian medical system? You want public education? How about a space program? Support for the arts?

What's not to like?

However, along the way, the tradeoffs included in the various choices are never explicitly explained. You want a space program? As a (hypothetical) tradeoff, in return for the "goodness" of going into space, and five scientific advances and 10 technological breakthroughs generated by the space program, you lose ¼% of annual gross domestic product (GDP, roughly, a sum of all the goods and services produced by an economy) forever. You want Medicare? (Hypothetically) in return for a moderate level of health care, you pay a premium, probably add private health insurance, distort the workings of the medical care industry, and burden the future with a cost estimated to increase from 3.7% of GDP in 2017 to 6.2% of GDP in 2092 (these numbers are from the Trustees' Report[25]).

These tradeoffs may be "worth it," but they are not discussed in such a way that a citizen can make an informed decision.

So, the maximum, acceptable Western mixed-economy socialism these days is measured against Denmark's 58% of government spending to GDP. The minimum is Australia's 35%, with the U.S. at about the same level. The gold standard for Western-type economies is represented, ironically, by Hong Kong at 19% and Singapore at 17% (Hong Kong's position at the top of so many lists is threatened by recent changes imposed by China in violation of its agreement with Great Britain).

Due to regulation, the government's influence in the U.S. is greater than its 36% of the economy. The share of American employment accounted for by economic sectors that might be termed "highly regulated" - including education and health, finance, government and utilities - rose from 31.5 percent in March 2000 to 49 percent in March 2019[26].

Every country is trying to find the right combination of tradeoffs that fits its culture at any particular point in time. This is as much a cultural decision as it is an economic one.

I won't spend much time on the fascist bit. As government gets bigger, it accumulates more power to regulate and it exercises that power. As it takes over an increasing amount of the economy, government defines how those portions of the economy will behave, and how those who interact with the regulated portions of the economy will behave. In my nomenclature, increasing socialism begets increasing fascism, and therefore, discussing fascism is, in some sense, redundant. Although it is important not to lose sight of its implications.

Ignoring the agenda of the far left in providing free college education, etc., there are currently two primary issues under discussion that would significantly increase the government's regulation and control of the U.S. economy: renewable energy mandates, including a carbon tax; and a public option in the health insurance structure (or Medicare for All). The passage of either or both of these programs, regardless of their respective merit, would result in a significant increase in the government's share and regulation of the economy, moving the U.S. into the mainstream or perhaps the upper end of mixed economies in terms of governmental size and regulation.

It has been inevitable that Western societies in the twentieth and twenty-first centuries, having based their economies on private ownership of the means of production, have steadily evolved toward increased governmental participation in the economy and increased regulation of the privately-owned means of production. They have done this in order to achieve some degree of fairness, to redistribute some amount of goodies, including to the middle class, and to fight some wars (and in the future, to pay massive interest on debt). That trend may change, although the discomfort of those left behind in a globalized economy, combined with increased activism on the left indicate that increased government participation and regulation will be probably demanded in the foreseeable future.

In the 1970s, the United Kingdom decided that it had overdone the socialist thing and had become dysfunctional to the point that they elected Margaret Thatcher as Prime Minister – the socialist trend had been taken too far. The U.K., even after capitalistic reforms, is still more socialistic today than the U.S., with its government's share of spending of 49%, significantly greater than the U.S.' share of 36%.

During the last thirty years or so, many very-socialist and communist countries have been adding aspects of capitalism to their economies to provide for the economic growth that socialism stifles. They want economic goodies as well as government-supplied goodies.

The reason the U.S., or any country, is likely to become ever-more socialistic is that, once a level of governmental benefits is agreed to, it is then taken for granted and becomes the floor for the next round of discussions. Those who gain from the benefits, and all of the people gaining indirectly from the benefits, become a powerful lobby for their continuance. Again, we are boiling frogs. Once people get used to benefits, they rarely give them up. And there is an infinite demand for benefits, particularly those perceived as being "free."

Are these changes in the West and by socialistic economies good things or bad things?

Yes.

However, in the end, you cannot have your cake and eat it, too. At some point, after having increased debt far past the point of reason, hard choices must be made. At some point, benefits will have to be given up. A story for another day.

The Downsides of Capitalism

Democracy, which is based on egalitarian principles, and capitalism, which has inequality at its heart, make strange bedfellows, and also create perpetual tension.

In addition, capitalism has the following principal, inherent weaknesses:

- it will take itself to extremes and destroy itself;
- it leaves behind those who cannot keep up;
- it includes business cycles, which are not pleasant and at times can be extreme;
- the system can be gamed by its participants, including using cronyism, regulatory capture, administrative interference and monopoly power;
- it creates inequalities in income and wealth that can become sufficiently extreme that they destabilize the culture;
- because it demands and drives change, including creative destruction, and the creation of technologies, it is inherently destabilizing;
- it deemphasizes the future by analyzing it using a "discount rate;"
- it is being destroyed by its central bank; and
- it is creating environmental unsustainability.

Some of capitalism's biggest critics are the leaders of the world's major religions.

Pope Saint Paul II echoed many of today's concerns:

> If by 'capitalism' is meant an economic system which
> recognizes the fundamental and positive role of business,
> the market, private property and the resulting responsibility
> for the means of production, as well as free human creativity
> in the economic sector, then the answer is certainly in the

19

affirmative …. But if by 'capitalism' is meant a system in
which freedom in the economic sector is not circumscribed
within a strong juridical framework in its totality, and which
sees it as a particular aspect of that freedom, the core of
which is ethical and religious, then the reply is certainly
negative.[27]

An Islamist described the relationship between capitalism and Islam as
follows:

The first, and perhaps most important thing to note with
regards to Islam and economics is that Islam as a religion
covers every facet of our lives. The laws regarding business
and trade are very clearly defined within the religion – there
are clear boundaries and restrictions. So even to begin,
Islamically, pure capitalism is not an option because there
will never be an absolutely free market. …

Furthermore, this integration of spiritual and secular aspects
of life means there is no room for pure individualism. The
individual is trained to think of himself or herself not only
as their own entity but also in relation to God, religious
leaders, those who are less fortunate, etc. Thus, a moral
system is tied in with an economic system, forcing
entrepreneurs to think not only of bottom lines and profit
margins but also the good of society and maintaining a basic
level of quality of life for everyone.[28]

And, it has gotten to the point that the State of California in its new model
curriculum for "ethnic studies," approved in 2019, describes capitalism as a
"form of power and oppression."[29]

Part of the cultural pressure on capitalism can be attributed to the fact that
things have become so good that we are spoiled. What we want is more,
distributed more equitably. And we want more without tradeoffs – just more.
And corporations are one group that can potentially provide us with more.
(Actually, capitalism's productive use of labor, energy and resources is the
only source of more.)

This obsession with more has led to more debt at all levels to provide for goodies and to preserve and enhance unsustainable lifestyles. We incur student loans instead of parents' saving for their children's education or children working to fund their own education. Car loans are now commonly 5-7 years in length, as compared to the 3 years which was standard for decades. The government is incurring significant deficits to provide the benefits – from entitlements to military to roads to a space program – that we demand, while we are also demanding that we do not incur the direct cost of any of these things.

Another critical factor is a loss of history and perspective. We are spoiled today, but we do not understand what it took to get here or the implications of adopting other alternatives. Our education system has generally removed history and civics from its curriculum, leaving a vacuum. I believe that one of the most important questions when making a decision is, compared to what? Many people have nothing to compare the present with, except with perfection, and that comparison inevitably leads to dissatisfaction.

Many critics of capitalism want to tear it down. Others would like to change capitalism to be more responsive to today's culture's demands – to "fix" capitalism by fixing corporations.

They often assume that capitalists are bad and evil, and workers are innately good. However, capitalists are no more intrinsically bad or evil than are union members, communists or socialists. Some are good; some are bad; most are average (part good / part bad). Everyone is responding to the incentives provided by the rules of the game they are playing. And then, human nature kicks in, whether capitalist, socialist or communist, to game the system. Some of the literature criticizes capitalism as being corrupt, but it is humans who can be corrupt and who often corrupt systems that are inherently neither good nor bad nor initially corrupt.

These suggested changes to corporations / capitalism fall into two, broad categories: attempts to mitigate the fundamental flaws in capitalism, and attempts to address changing social and cultural values by changing corporations.

Capitalism's Inherent Flaws

Everything has "good" attributes and "bad" attributes; strengths and weaknesses. Everything.

I discussed the miraculous results of capitalism, above; following is a discussion of capitalism's inherent flaws.

Capitalism will take itself to extremes and destroy itself

A central theme of this book is that humans take all things to extremes. Capitalism is one of those things.

Capitalism will also suffer adverse effects of being a part of a culture that is also taking things too far and destroying itself.

Economist Joseph Schumpeter wrote in 1942 that capitalism would destroy itself in several ways, including those discussed in this chapter. However, Schumpeter made the key prediction which is currently unfolding. "Schumpeter believed that capitalism would be destroyed by its successes, that it would spawn a large intellectual class that made its living by attacking the very bourgeois system of private property and freedom so necessary for the intellectual class's existence."'[30]

Schumpeter believed that it was inevitable the capitalism would be succeeded by socialism.

Historian Niall Ferguson's thesis is that our demand for too much college education has produced generations trained in "worthless" subjects like humanities and gender studies who cannot now find a job. And who are laden with debt. This educated elite is part of Schumpeter's "intellectual class," described in the previous paragraph.[31]

More important than these trends is the inherent characteristic of capitalism, that it drives everything to zero.

Competition drives decreased cost and increased innovation through the use of technology.

As we progress to the Rise of the Robots, Viktor Shvets describes the dynamics that are "driving everything to zero,"[32] which he says is

> … one of the things technology does very successfully. And remember what we've done with financialization that we've met with that we embarked on in 1980s, and carried on to today and will continue to carry on. One of the things

financialization does is massively reduces cost of capital, and technology itself as a human spirit. But the pace, the speed with which technology propagates really depends on the cost of capital. So if one agrees with me, that cost of capital must fall forever, then it's like pouring a kerosene on a bonfire of technological age. And what technology does incredibly well is reducing marginal pricing power of both labor and capital, and corporates, and brands. And so what happens over time, those reduction in marginal pricing power converges into average pricing power, which also declines. And eventually, almost everything becomes free. There is no prices, just like information today is almost entirely free. Just like publications today, almost entirely free, just like trading on the New York Stock Exchange quite, not quite, but almost entirely free. Just like a lot of music is almost entirely free. So we already have massively reduced marginal pricing power in a lot of industries. We've already reduced marginal pricing power of labor. ..

In any event, capitalism's successes are resulting in the death of its golden goose.

Capitalism leaves behind those who cannot keep up

Societies and governments distribute power and goods on some basis. For most of human history, wealth and power were distributed, actually centralized, on the bases of strength and relationships to sources of strength. Alternatively, individuals and families achieved returns from their efforts at hunting and gathering. Socialism and communism attempt to distribute wealth equally, but in practice, devolve into dictatorships or oligarchies. Capitalism distributes wealth based on access to capital, and then generally devolves, as does democracy, into oligarchy.

When capitalism is functioning properly, its profits are returned to the providers of capital, who share with the providers of labor in a continually-fluctuating and continually-negotiated ratio. There are those, however, such as the elderly, sick or disabled, who cannot provide labor at all. There are also those who are willing to work, but either have no skills or do not have the appropriate skills, and therefore cannot work. There is no return for these people within capitalism.

Governments have imposed a layer of redistribution on top of capitalism in an attempt to assist those who are left behind, creating "social democracy." This creates a second level of negotiation and apportionment in addition to the labor / capital apportionment - a provision for those left behind. This provision for those left behind includes many programs under the general category of "welfare," including Social Security, Medicaid and Medicare.

Once again, there are tradeoffs. The distribution to those left behind reduces the ability of the economy to generate profits to be redistributed to anyone. However, morality and politics demand that the distribution be made.

During the past few decades, labor has increasingly required mental abilities and technical prowess that are only possessed by a decreasing minority of the population. This trend, combined with the loss of manufacturing jobs and a general increase in automation, is creating an ever-increasing number of people who are being left behind because they do not have appropriate skills or because their jobs have been automated or offshored.

This dynamic feeds increasing inequality.

Modern culture demands that this inherent flaw in capitalism be addressed. Various societies wrestle with the question of how to best do this without killing the capitalistic goose that lays the golden eggs.

There is no right answer, and different societies "solve," and then continually renegotiate, the question at different levels and with differing types of programs.

However, as increasing use of technology and automation continues to replace human jobs, an increasing number of humans will be left behind to the point that capitalism may be no longer politically viable. The election of former president Donald Trump may mark the tipping point at which a critical mass of Americans, both pro- and anti-Trump, believed that, for them, capitalism is no longer the answer and is past its sell-by date.

Business cycles, which at times can be extreme, are inherent within capitalism

Most people are aware of the Great Depression of the 1930s and the Great Recession of 2008-2009. Perhaps less well known are other economic depressions in the U.S.:

- The Great Depression of 1837 – ignited by the Panic of 1837, considered to be worse than the Great Depression of the 1930s. Ended in 1849.
- The Long Depression – 1873-1896

The Covid-19 pandemic accelerated an economic recession that intensified the economic and cultural flaws that were in place before the beginning of the pandemic.

In addition, less severe downturns, called economic recessions, have historically occurred in the U.S. every twelve years or so and have lasted an average of about 18 months, with significant variance in both numbers[33].

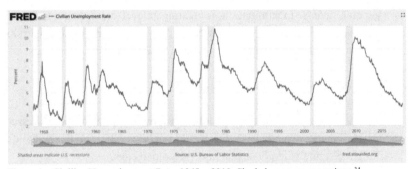

Figure 4 – Civilian Unemployment Rate, 1948 – 2018. Shaded areas are recessions.[34]

Recessions, and even-more-severe depressions, are associated with a decrease in economic activity and an increase in unemployment, and therefore an increase in stress and anxiety among workers and their families. The unemployment rate was estimated to be 24.9% in 1934 during the Great Depression of the 1930s, and did not decline below 10% until the beginning of World War II.[35] At its peak during the Great Recession, less severe in magnitude and duration than the Great Depression, unemployment did not quite make it as high as 10%.

The business cycle is inherent to capitalism and is the result of several factors, including optimism among all parts of the economy that leads to more plant, equipment and goods and credit than the economy can absorb, and also to efforts by the Federal Reserve (after its founding in 1913) to guide the economy.

Hyman Minsky, an American economist, proposed "The Financial Instability Hypothesis,"[36] which I think has significant merit. His theory is that stability causes instability in the economy. The details of his theory are beyond the scope of this book, but at a high level describe an economy that takes investment trends too far in his "Ponzi Phase." Investment goes beyond speculation, therefore setting up instability in the economy. Another example of humans taking trends too far.

Another of the trends we have taken too far is our attempt to control the business cycle for political reasons.

Voters tend to cast their ballots against incumbents during the bad times, motivating politicians to try to avoid economic downturns. As a lesson every politician learns, President George H.W. Bush lost his reelection campaign against Bill Clinton, primarily due to a slight economic downturn in 1992. This led to Clinton's advisor, James Carville's, stressing, "It's the economy, stupid," during the campaign. Since the 1970s, and accelerating since the 1990s, the Federal Reserve (Fed) has attempted to control the economy in such a way as to eliminate, or at least mitigate, the business cycle.

Since the purpose of the downward part of the business cycle is to eliminate the excesses and inefficiencies accumulated during the prior upswing, the downswing clears the economy and prepares the ground for the next upswing. If the Fed is successful in mitigating or eliminating the business cycle, excess accumulates, much like underbrush in a forest accumulates in the absence of periodic wildfires. The result for the economy is the same as for the forest – when a fire does occur, or when a downturn starts, it will be much bigger and much more devastating than it otherwise would have been.

Therefore, the Fed has to work harder and become increasingly creative to stave off an ever-increasing problem.

The next, eventual downturn will create distress that will generate ever-increasing criticism of capitalism. Again, people will try to find a better system that will provide growth without downturns. When the next surge of prosperity occurs, much of that criticism will become muted – until the next downturn, and assuming capitalism survives.

By attempting to mitigate the "flaw" of the business cycle, we have enhanced the probability of a pronounced downturn, which will have the capacity to undermine the civil and political foundations of capitalism, and of society.

Attempts to mitigate downturns, such as quantitative easing and unusually low, perhaps even negative, interest rates, have been used in the past. These actions distort the market signals on which capitalism is based, increase inequality and result in extremely low interest rates. These low interest rates, in turn, are creating a savings and pensions crisis that is beginning to impact the overall economy. The next downturn will prompt even more radical actions, such as those rationalized by Modern Monetary Theory, which will create money out of thin-air for distribution to the general population. It is likely that these actions, combined with the U.S.'s high level of debt, deficits and entitlements, will lead to a severe economic downturn as part of the crisis that ends our Fourth Turning.

The system can be gamed by its participants, including cronyism, regulation, regulatory capture, administrative interference and monopoly power.

The best way to influence any system to get the best outcome is to influence the referee / regulator. If you can get Congress or regulatory bodies or the Fed on your side, the game becomes unfair – to your benefit. Sometimes, this gaming erodes the very foundations of capitalism, and also of society.

Influence can come in many guises, from personal relationships to money, but money is usually the most effective.

Legislators are gamed in several ways. The most straightforward is by making campaign contributions. Although there is usually no blatant quid-pro-quo, there is often a wink-wink-nod-nod arrangement, where the legislator tacitly agrees to advance a significant contributor's agenda.

As the world becomes more interconnected and technologically complex, individual legislators cannot keep up with all of the subtleties of all of the proposed legislation. Legislators rely on lobbyists – paid representatives of various groups, such as labor unions, corporations, or interest groups, such as farmers – to explain the intricacies of various issues. There are now approximately 20 registered lobbyists for each Member of Congress, and those lobbyists are often instrumental in actually writing the laws. The willingness of organizations to incur the high costs of lobbyists is an indication of their effectiveness.

Regulators are also dependent on lobbyists and other representatives to assist them in understanding the complications and implications of various regulations. This has become increasingly important as Congress has enacted laws in the form of broad outlines, relying on regulators to create the regulatory details, in effect writing much of the law. For example, the Affordable Care Act ("ObamaCare") comprised approximately 2,300 pages. The length of the associated regulations is a matter of debate, but at least 10,000 pages is a reasonable estimate.[37] One result of this dynamic is the "capture" of the regulators by the group that they are regulating. Personal and professional ties become so significant that the regulated, in effect, write their own regulations.

When Members of Congress leave their posts, they often join lobbying and law firms and peddle their influence. This often leads to cronyism, where the same group meets to discuss and frame laws and regulations.

Large companies stifle competition with smaller rivals by inviting regulation that they can handle and afford, but which provides significant barriers to entry to companies which are smaller and have less political clout.

Monopolies and oligopolies (economic concentration among a few participants) are decidedly anti-capitalist in that they stifle competition. Competition under capitalism tends to drive profits toward zero, or at least to the cost of capital. If a business can only return the cost of capital, it would be much easier to just put money in a savings account instead of going through the effort and risk of investing it in a business. The upside of constant pressure on profits is that companies are driven to innovate to find new or enhanced sources of profit – remember, good and bad. Economic concentration is increasing today, in and of itself, and also with the rise of technology giants, such as Google and Facebook, which dominate industries through so-called network effects. These giants are warping the fabric of capitalism.

The following is from a review of Jonathan Tepper's book, *The Myth of Capitalism: Monopolies and the Death of Competition*:[38]

> "Capitalism without competition is not capitalism," Tepper writes. Four airlines shuttle most Americans around the country. Two corporations brew most of the country's beer. Three companies manage the lion's share of pesticide and

seed markets. Google and Apple host the entire mobile app market. You might think you have choices in the supermarket aisles, but a handful of companies produce all the varied brands. Every online travel booking site comes from one of two corporations.

This is made worse when monopolists cooperate to carve up the country; over 75 percent of all households have only one choice of internet provider. The concentration has spread to Wall Street, too. Tepper highlights Warren Buffett's zeal for monopoly companies with economic "moats." As investors copy Buffett's strategies, they allow big firms to suck up available capital. The same big shareholders own large stakes in the main players in entire sectors, removing the incentive to compete. (In this sense, Tepper does mirror Piketty's description of capital begetting capital, even if he would be uncomfortable with the comparison.)

If companies know they must create moats to attract investors, they will use political power to raise barriers to new entrants or acquire patent protections, building the walls ever higher. Failing that, they'll just buy out the competition. Tepper notes that Google, Facebook, Amazon, Apple, and Microsoft have purchased 436 companies and startups in the past ten years, without a single regulatory challenge to any acquisition.

The effects of all this are profound. Tepper started the book to decipher the wage puzzle: Why did leading indicators keep pointing to higher wages that never came? He found that workers with fewer choices to deploy their talents—a condition known as monopsony—cannot bargain for better pay. As the benefits of economic growth pool in corporate boardrooms instead of workers' pockets, inequality naturally follows.

Service quality suffers amid no alternatives to pressure monopolists. Fragility abounds in concentrated markets.

Monoculture crops planted in the farm belt are susceptible to wipeout from one fungus or disease; Hurricane Maria's devastation in Puerto Rico knocked out the manufacturing centers for the two companies that make nearly all intravenous saline solution bags for hospitals. That's right— last year we had a serious shortage of something so elemental as salt and water in a bag, thanks to the brittle supply chain of a duopoly.

Ben Hunt, a respected commenter on the financial community, notes that the U.S. economy is embracing financialization. Financialization is the improvement in profits through tax and balance sheet manipulation instead of increased productivity. Because its returns are to capital and not to labor, Hunt characterizes financialization as the "zombiefication of an economy and the oligarchification of a society. … Financialization wears the face of capitalism but is in fact the antithesis of risk-taking and competition."[39]

Corporations are gaming the system by producing profits through financialization when increases in labor productivity fail. Since financialization is, in a sense, unreal and occupies corporations in lieu of actually investing capital in the physical economy and taking risk, the overall economy and therefore employment and prosperity, suffer as a consequence.

Another primary example of gaming the system is corporations' buyback of their stock. This is somewhat complicated, because stock buybacks are not always a bad thing. However, corporations typically have two alternatives in the use of excess cash: they can invest it in plant, equipment and people for future growth, or they can return the cash to shareholders in the form of dividends. Increasingly, a third alternative arose, which was buying back stock. This had the effect of reducing the amount of stock available for purchase, thereby generally resulting in an increase in earnings per (a reduced number of) share and therefore an increase in the price of the company's stock. Stock buybacks became increasingly used in conjunction with stock compensation to executives, beginning in the 1990s when President Clinton signed a tax law that eliminated the deductibility for tax purposes of cash compensation to executives in excess of one million dollars. (This simple change in tax law is a wonderful example of an unintended consequence of a well-intentioned act that has distorted the fabric of the entire economy.)

<u>Capitalism creates inequalities in income and wealth that can become so
extreme that they destabilize the culture.</u>

Historically, there has not been that much income or wealth to distribute on
any basis; until the beginning of the capitalist revolution, there was very
little wealth in the world to be distributed. Such wealth as existed was owned
by the powerful few. Wealth and income were based on meager returns to
land and to power. Ironically, capitalism has contributed to incredible growth
in income and wealth such that its distribution has become an issue and a
perceived weakness of capitalism.

Let's go back to the definition of capitalism – capital is privately owned and
the returns from capital go back to the owner of the capital. The owner of
capital hires labor. According to the law of supply and demand, those in the
labor force having the skills most desired by the owners of capital, and
particularly those whose skills are relatively rare, receive the most
compensation. This creates an inherent inequality of income within the labor
force, based on the distribution of skills and the value of those skills. (I have
already discussed those left behind, so in this section, I will consider only
those who are participating in the labor force.)

The better your skills and the higher their need in the current market, the
more likely you are to be well employed. To capitalists, humans are a means
to accomplish a task, much like a tool. This view of humans as a means to an
end will become important when considering automation. But, unlike
machines, humans have many emotional responses when considering their
worth and employability. Humans want to be treated differently from a tool
and they become politically agitated when working conditions, fairness,
level of pay, comparative pay and other issues arise in the course of their
employment.

Therefore, the costs of employing humans expand beyond salary to include
benefits and respectful treatment and equity and fair play.

Most people broadly understand that their skills have a market value and that
other people may have skills that are more highly valued. However, most
people have a limit to acceptance of that variation that is based more on
perceived fairness than on the outcomes of Economics 101.

In 2019, this issue was illustrated by a continuing campaign by women
professional soccer ("football" to non-Americans) players to be paid the

same as men professional soccer players. The women had been among the best in the world for several years, won the World Cup of soccer in 2019 and asserted that they "deserved" equal pay. The problem was that women's professional soccer generated significantly less revenue than men's professional soccer – regardless of the women's successes. By one comparison, a recent Men's World Cup generated almost $4 billion, while a recent Women's World Cup generated almost $73 million.[40] This is a classic illustration of a variation in market value for many reasons, including a variation in skills and in perceived value. At the same time, there is an argument that this outcome is unfair. Perhaps other factors than skill level or revenue generation should be taken into account, particularly in a culture that is sensitive to gender issues. Perhaps the allocation of revenue within the women's soccer organization should be changed. Perhaps men's soccer should subsidize women's soccer.

In the extreme, people will pay to watch Tiger Woods play golf, and I would probably have to pay people to watch me play golf. Commercial endeavors must be profitable in order to continue in existence, therefore costs, including cost of labor, must include some relationship to revenue generation.

Once again, a cultural negotiation must take place that incorporates both financial reality and the culture's view of and demand for fairness.

A broad equilibrium is established within which bargaining for wages takes place and some amount of variation among groups is accepted. However, we live in an age which is violating perceived fairness in four, principal ways:

1. Labor is being hired offshore at lower rates, taking away "our" jobs, to "our" detriment.
2. Chief Executive Officers and high-level executives are receiving compensation at levels that are perceived as being both rapacious and unfair. These ratios are calculated in various ways, to include different components of compensation, but according to one computation, the CEO-to-employee ratio rose from around 10:1 in the mid-60s to a maximum of around 390:1 in 1978 to 271 in 2015.[41] According to another computation, these ratios vary internationally in 2012 from 67:1 in Japan to 147:1 in Germany to 84:1 in Great Britain (this study has the U.S. at 354).[42]
3. High returns to labor are associated with technical skills that are

beyond the education and capabilities of most people. This leads to a steady decline in the standard of living of those who do not have or cannot acquire technical skills.

4. Overall economic returns to labor are at historically low levels, while economic returns to capital are at historically high levels.

The increase in income of the select groups allows them to acquire wealth which they can use to deploy capital to acquire more wealth (and also game the system) in a spiral of increasing wealth inequality. Again, various studies come to differing specific results, but one study concludes that the share of wealth of the top 10% of Americans increased from approximately 30% in 1989 to approximately 76% in 2013.[43]

Inequality has been exacerbated by the Fed's inflation of asset prices through increased liquidity, which has primarily benefited the already-wealthy.

There have also been sources of inequality which cannot be directly attributed to capitalism. For example, before the rise in equal rights for women, high-status men would often marry, and elevate financially-lower-status women, decreasing average income inequality. Today, high-earning women tend to seek high-earning men, increasing average income inequality.

I would slightly modify (in italics and using strikethrough) pundit Jonah Goldberg's statement that, "Complexity is a subsidy. The more complex government *and society* becomes, the more ~~it~~ they rewards those with the resources to deal with that complexity, and the more it punishes those who do not.[44]"

These variations, particularly in times of economic stress, create political pressure for changes in the system, towards redistribution and increased "fairness."

As a result of this increased inequality, increased offshoring of jobs, increased demand for technical skills and decreasing economic returns to labor, many workers in the U.S. have literally despaired about their future. They have turned to suicide and opioids to the extent that life expectancy in the U.S. has actually decreased for several years. They contributed to the election of Donald Trump to change a system that they feel is destroying them. On the other side of the same coin, those who are strongly concerned about inequality are turning to socialists such as Bernie Sanders to deliver them a fairer system.

Although I am using examples from the United States, there is unrest throughout the capitalistic world, evidenced by the yellow vests in France, Brexit, and populist movements in various European countries, including increased authoritarianism in countries such as Hungary and Austria.

Walter Scheidel's thesis in *The Great Leveler*[45] is that during times of peace and prosperity, inequality always increases over time. He says that there are only four things which have reduced inequality throughout history: total war, total revolution, famines and plagues.

Because capitalism demands and drives change, including creative destruction, and the creation of technologies, it is inherently destabilizing

The economist Joseph Schumpeter (who derived the concept from Karl Marx) described a central characteristic of capitalism as creative destruction, the "process of industrial mutation that incessantly revolutionizes the economic structure from within, incessantly destroying the old one, incessantly creating a new one.[46]"

It is a cliché that humans do not handle change well. Today, we live in a time of relentless, accelerated, and accelerating, change that can be overwhelming and destabilizing.

- We love our cars without thinking about all the stable hands and buggy whip makers who lost their jobs when the automobile was invented.
- We love our cell phones without thinking about all the telephone operators who lost their jobs when calling, including international calling, became automatic.
- We drive through automated toll booths without thinking about all the toll-takers who lost their jobs.
- Most importantly, we do not think about all of the manufacturing and distribution jobs that have been lost, not to globalization, but to technology and to automation.

Figure 5 – A fully-automated factory[47]

The workers who lost their jobs, or could not get jobs, when this factory was built are experiencing the downside of the changes created by capitalism.

- Capitalists must reduce costs to meet and beat the competition.
- Labor is a significant cost to business.
- Technology can reduce the cost, including the hassle, associated with humans.
- Therefore, capitalism will embrace technology, often to the detriment of humans.

The other side of this dynamic is that the people who are displaced and cannot find jobs or who find lesser-paying jobs increasingly turn to political action to reduce their pain. This is a primary contributor to the rise of such politicians as Donald Trump and Bernie Sanders in the U.S.

People have always lost jobs to technology and to outsourcing. However, in the past, the number of jobs lost was relatively small, and over time, those who lost jobs could find new ones. The increasing rate of change today, combined with the high skill levels associated with a technology-driven society, means that larger numbers are being rapidly displaced, with nowhere to go.

<u>Capitalism deemphasizes the future by analyzing it using a "discount rate"</u>

Future prosperity critically depends on investments of capital in businesses, structures and equipment today. A primary approach used by corporations to decide which capital investments to make is to estimate future cash flows from those investments. In general, the investment with the greatest cash flows compared with the size of the investment, the greatest return-on-investment, wins.

This makes sense. If you have $1,000 to put in a savings account, all things being equal, you would choose the financial institution that gives you the highest interest rate – the greatest amount of cash back for your deposit.

Capitalists are looking for the same thing – the greatest amount of cash back for their investments.

However, corporations apply a discount rate to future cash flows. The concept is a little complex, but the idea is that a dollar a year from now is worth less than a dollar today. By waiting a year, I am losing the return I could have made on that dollar. I could have put it into a savings account and have received a year's worth of interest. A dollar in the future is worth less than a dollar today by the amount of interest a dollar today can earn.

Economists, bankers and corporations all use discount rates when evaluating future cash flows, and it is a sound approach to money flow analysis.

However, for our purposes, the practical effect of this discounting is that the farther in the future you go, the value of a dollar diminishes until it is worth close to nothing. A dollar in the far future is valued at around zero.

For example, assume a reasonable discount rate for a proposed investment is ten percent, which is actually low for most investment decisions (a lower discount rate results in greater future value). The discounted value for a dollar of cash flow ten years in the future is $0.35; at 25 years, it is $0.07; and at 50 years, it is $0.005.

In one sense, in the sense of the use of the discount rate for planning, past some point, the future does not matter to corporations. This distorts decision-making when the decision includes long-term effects, such as depletion or pollution or sustainability.

<u>We are in a strange time during which the Federal Reserve is destroying capitalism</u>

Perhaps the most profound undermining of capitalism has been by the Federal Reserve and other central banks.

Beginning in the 1970s, but accelerating in the 1990s, in response to various economic crises, the Fed took steps to manipulate liquidity and interest rates to avoid financial crises and to dampen or eliminate business cycles. In particular, it took extraordinary measures in response to the Great Financial Crisis of 2008-2009. These steps had four, significantly negative results:

1. Interest rates, particularly short-term interest rates, arguably the most important financial prices and signals, were manipulated in such a way that assets became misallocated. In particular, low interest rates supported business which otherwise would have struggled or failed. Pension funds could not generate sufficient returns to meet their obligations to retirees.

2. Business cycles, from the 90s forward, were unable to do their job of clearing out uneconomic activities to prepare the economy for new growth. As Nassim Taleb argues in his book, *Antifragile*[48], preventing small crises from happening on a regular basis eventually causes a very large crisis. In a tweet, financial writer Ben Hunt called the idea that the business cycle can be eliminated, "the idea that broke the world."

3. Returns to capital increased – businesses retained a greater share of profits - and returns to labor decreased – labor received a diminishing share of profits, increasing and exacerbating the growing economic inequality. This, in turn, contributed to increasing social and political divisions.

In effect and ironically, by seeking to manage or eliminate business cycles, the Fed became a political, anti-capitalist institution. (It should be noted that both the Congress and the Executive Branch avoided their duties and relegated the fight to the Fed.) Once the Fed began riding the tiger of economic interference, it could not get off because none of the underlying problems were actually being solved.

I described it this way in my book on the Great Financial Crisis:

The American consumer was like a drunk who has walked into a bar to get some alcohol. The alcohol that fuels economic bubbles is credit and the Federal Reserve provides the credit - or not. No matter how drunk you want to get; no matter how addicted you are to alcohol / consumption; no matter how many iPhones and granite counter tops you want, you cannot get them unless the Fed provides the alcohol / credit. The Fed can't supply it if the Sheriff, the Congress, will not allow it. So we have the Fed supplying the alcohol, the Sheriff just wanting everyone to be happy and vote for him in the next election and actually winding up buying several rounds, and your friends are rooting you on because they want to party, too. The whole town is in a mood to party. The longer the party goes on, the drunker everyone gets, and the more everyone wants to party.

By the way, there is another drunk in the corner, the investment banker, who also wants to party. And he has actually been told by the Sheriff that he can drink to his heart's content and will not be hassled by the Sheriff. In addition, the Sheriff would be grateful if the banker could help him with this problem of getting poor people into houses. So, the investment banker brings in all of his friends and begins buying the alcohol for much of the crowd.

Things began to get under way back in the 1930s and picked up some in the 70s, but the party really got rolling in the last half of the 1990s. It is important to understand that there would have been no 90s without the 70s and no 70s without the 30s. At the time of the dotcom bust and the attacks of 9/11, everyone began to sober up. But the Fed decided on its own that more alcohol was needed or else everyone would get a hangover, become surly, and vote the Sheriff out of office. The party continued and intensified. The whole town reached unprecedented levels of drunkenness. Meanwhile, through the internet and easily-accessible digital information, the whole world looked on and decided that they wanted to join the party, too.

(To be sure, the Fed's manipulation saved the world's financial systems from collapse in 2008. However, as a subject for another day, the Fed was largely responsible for both the existence of the crisis in the first place and its magnitude. Arguably, Fed actions since those directly responsive to the Great Financial Crisis have been counterproductive.)

As one wag on Twitter put it, "capitalism's 'invisible hand' has been replaced by the Fed's invisible hand." Even more poignantly, an anonymous Wall Street banker is referring to our age as the, "clown-car stage of capitalism."

By continually manipulating the economy to eliminate significant declines in the stock market, let alone actual, vital recessions, the Fed has created ever-larger crises to be dealt with. The government is incurring ever-larger deficits and the Fed is accommodating ever larger amounts of debt, creating a monstrously fragile and unstable economy.

By managing interest rates, the Fed has eliminated effective price discovery of arguably the most important price in the world.

By keeping interest rates low and by, in effect and probably illegally, buying junk (debt issued by companies which either cannot or can only marginally support debt service from their operations) debt, the Fed is keeping effectively insolvent, "zombie," companies alive. This not only significantly inhibits the creative destruction required for effective capitalism, it also allows subsidized companies to compete unfairly with unsubsidized companies, reducing the overall vigor of even healthy companies.

By enabling the creation of unprecedented amounts of debt, the Fed is hobbling future growth. Economists have established that, once past a threshold as a percentage of GDP, debt actually inhibits the economy's ability to grow.[49] We are now past that threshold.

The dot-com bubble lead to the larger real estate bubble, which led to the larger "everything" bubble. The Covid-19 epidemic accelerated and magnified the growth of the "everything" bubble.

The debt that is being created is not being used for productive purposes, and for all intents and purposes is being used to prop up consumers and businesses at unsustainable levels and standards of living.

As noted by investment manager, Louis Gave, "[2020's] debt buildup in the U.S. has funded zero new productive investments. No roads, no airports, railroads, nothing."

The combination of this debt build-up, continuing significant budget deficits and the increasing entitlements due retiring Baby Boomers is leading to another crisis.

The Fed has painted itself into a corner where the only politically-acceptable solution, at least in the short run, to manage the debt, deficits and entitlements is continual inflation of currency. These obligations have become so huge that the only way they will be met is through austerity – cutting spending so that the obligations can be paid; default – not pay the debt or entitlements; or inflation – debasing the currency to the point that the debt and entitlements will be paid in "cheaper" dollars.

Austerity is not politically acceptable and default would cripple the economy. Therefore, the Fed will attempt to solve the problem through inflation.

Although, as John Maynard Keynes noted, "The best way to destroy the capitalist system [is] to debauch the currency," and although one of the Fed's legally-defined objectives is to maintain "stable prices," the Fed has done an abysmal job of reining in inflation or maintaining stable prices. $0.04 in 1913, when the Fed was founded, would purchase in 1913 the equivalent goods and services that $1.00 would purchase in 2021.

The Fed will resort to ever-more novel and destructive tactics to hold things together. They will probably be aided by the Congress' enactment of novel measures, following the tenets of Modern Monetary Theory.

We are in totally uncharted waters and the end game, while not known, will likely not be pleasant, although there may be periods of relative calm and even growth as massive amounts of liquidity works its way through the economy.

There is another significant issue pertaining to the Fed that is too arcane for this book. However, the bottom line is that the Fed began to lose control of the number of dollars in the global economic system through the rapid growth of the Eurodollar system in the '70s. This has very important implications, including the requirement that the Fed supply the dollars to fund the system, which was estimated to be approximately $13.8 trillion in 2016.[50] (By comparison, a broad measure of the U.S. money supply, called M2, was $18.3 trillion in 2020.[51]) This adds pressure to existing debt, deficits and the Triffin Dilemma (see below) for the Fed to continue to issue dollars and apply downward pressure to the value of the dollar.

As a topic for another day, our economic policies are almost certainly leading to financial implosion. We have borrowed from the future to the extent that there is not much future left.

Capitalism raises issues of sustainability

Sustainability will be discussed in detail in Part II of this book. However, the conclusion of Part II is that capitalism has been too successful, together with the ideas of the Enlightenment, the availability of natural resources, and the availability of inexpensive energy, and has enabled an explosion in the creation of humans and things. Dramatic population growth and the natural human acquisitive desire (also motivated by a desire to have what our neighbors have and the things we see on television and on the internet) have created an addition to things – houses, cars, clothes, iPhones, video games, travel, granite counter tops, jewelry and more – that seems insatiable. The result is that the current consumption levels of the current population are unsustainable now, and it is only going to get worse in the future.

> The higher the level of economic development, the more money tends to become an abstraction rather than a counter for something concrete. Thus, the economy can boom as the ecology disintegrates. This is particularly true if the society resorts to currency debasement or loose credit as a way to evade the encroaching physical limits and foster an artificial prosperity, for then the economy becomes completely unhinged from concrete ecological reality. Overshoot and collapse is the inevitable result.[52]

We are at or past the peak of our ability to sustain ourselves at a high standard of living, and we will inexorably devolve into dystopia before a steady state is reached at a much lower standard of living, probably with fewer people.

Because this is such a strong statement, having profound implications, and because sustainability beyond climate change is not a general topic of discussion, I have included Part II of this book to primarily provide the discussion which validates this statement. In Part II I also discuss the implications of a loss of sustainability, one of which is that capitalism cannot be a part of our future.

We have an economic system that has inherent flaws and is being gamed on multiple fronts, much to the detriment and compromise of capitalism. And ultimately, to ourselves.

Dysfunctional systems can, in general, be modified and fixed.

Not those past their sell-by dates.

Not those that are fouling their own nests.

And, while capitalism is hamstrung by its own, inherent weaknesses, there are forces at work that compromise it further.

Headwinds

In addition to its inherent flaws, capitalism today faces headwinds that make the environment in which it is operating much more challenging. These headwinds hampers its return and in turn exacerbates its weaknesses and emboldens its critics.

These headwinds include:

- the law of diminishing returns;
- a changing cultural environment;
- attempts to implement social and political values through corporations;
- regulators have vacated the field;
- the Triffin Dilemma;
- the Fourth Turning;
- the rise of the robots;
- fighting climate change;
- mortgaging and hamstringing the future; and
- demographics.

Let's take a look at each headwind in greater detail.

The law of diminishing returns

At the beginnings of the Enlightenment and of the Industrial Revolution, there lay ahead what appeared to be an almost infinite horizon of possibilities for innovation. From horse-and-buggy to space travel; from pony express to wifi; from extensive pain, suffering and hunger to antibiotics, anesthetics and obesity.

Every trend exhausts itself for several reasons, including that the low-hanging fruit and the opportunities having the greatest returns are tackled first. As progress is made, the same effort / the same investment yields less progress than before – there are diminishing returns. After a while, most of the playing field has become occupied and the next step forward requires greater investment, more creativity, special materials, greater amounts of energy.

At the beginning of the exponential growth in human wealth and physical well-being, say around 1800, and as illustrated in Figure 1, progress was difficult. The tools were not developed, the capital was not available, there was no infrastructure to enable progress, the participants were untrained and there was little in the way of foundational knowledge. Slowly but surely, tools, capital, knowledge, infrastructure and training were accumulated and began to build on themselves to the point of take-off – the beginning of exponential growth.

Then came a wonderful period in which this accumulation process fed on itself.

At some point, the returns on innovation began to diminish as new, productive areas were more difficult to find and more expensive to explore and exploit.

Robert Gordon, in his book, *The Rise and Fall of American Growth*, argues that our most incredible, and unique, never-to-be-repeated, era was from 1870 – 1940.

He put it this way:

> The century of revolution in the United States after the Civil
> War was economic, not political, freeing households from
> an unremitting daily grind of painful manual labor,
> household drudgery, darkness, isolation, and early death.
> Only one hundred years later, daily life had changed beyond
> recognition. Manual outdoor jobs were replaced by work in
> air-conditioned environments, housework was increasingly
> performed by electric appliances, darkness was replaced by
> light, and isolation was replaced not just by travel, but also
> by color television images bringing the world into the living
> room. Most important, a newborn infant could expect to live
> not to age forty-five, but to age seventy-two. The economic
> revolution of 1870 to 1970 was unique in human history,
> unrepeatable because so many of its achievements could
> happen only once....
>
> This leads directly to the second big idea: that economic
> growth since 1970 has been simultaneously dazzling and
> disappointing. This paradox is resolved when we recognize
> that advances since 1970 have tended to be channeled into a
> narrow sphere of human activity having to do with
> entertainment, communications, and the collection and
> processing of information. For the rest of what humans care
> about—food, clothing, shelter, transportation, health, and
> working conditions both inside and outside the home—
> progress slowed down after 1970, both qualitatively and
> quantitatively. Our best measure of the pace of innovation
> and technical progress is total factor productivity (hereafter
> TFP), a measure of how quickly output is growing relative
> to the growth of labor and capital inputs. TFP grew after
> 1970 at barely a third the rate achieved between 1920 and
> 1970. The third big idea follows directly from the second.
> Our chronicle of the rise in the American standard of living
> over the past 150 years rests heavily on the history of
> innovations, great and small alike.[53]

That means that take-off began before 1870 and that the upward curve began
to follow a shallower climb after 1940. He believes that 1940-1970 provided

an acceptable amount of innovation, but that the modern era is innovationally mediocre. (He identifies a brief interruption in this mediocracy during the period of the development of the internet from 1995-2005.)

During the mediocre period, we were doing interesting things (e.g., Facebook, Twitter, Apple and Amazon) that basically changed nothing and did not add to productivity. (Google is an exception in that it provides the world of knowledge at your fingertips, enabling greater productivity.)

We are also financializing things instead of creating things.

The venture capitalist, Peter Thiel, summed it up by saying, "We wanted flying cars; we got 140 characters." Although to be fair, flying cars would not have been much of a step forward in either innovation or productivity.

Capitalism enabled the innovation of this age and benefitted from the material and physical gains made by people during this time. However, when capital has nothing better to do than to produce 140 characters or to increase financialization or create the robots that will make humans obsolete, it has arguably reached its sell-by date. Capitalism has, in effect, fulfilled its mission and is looking for something else to do.

Which, in turn, creates changes in the ways people think about and behave toward capitalism.

<u>A changing cultural environment</u>

Culture evolves over time and institutions and cultures engage in a mutual game of influencing the other. As culture changes, capitalism has to adapt, at times to the point of extinction.

The negotiations between capitalism and culture are continual. Because capitalism has the flaws discussed, above, there is constant pressure for it to change for the "better," to mitigate or eliminate its flaws.

The conversation at its essence is a discussion of trade-offs, and often the trade-offs are implicit and not discussed.

The United States is experiencing highly-emotional social divisions. For a number of reasons, including extreme individuality, comfort that comes with wealth and a lack of understanding of history, the United States' traditional values are being criticized and devalued.

Capitalism is being caught up in this process of deconstruction.

Younger generations do not value capitalism as highly as older generations and are becoming more sympathetic to what they view as socialism. A Gallup poll taken in 2019[54] indicates that 49% of Millennials and GenZers view socialism positively as compared with 39% of GenXers and 32% of Baby Boomers.

Racial divisions in the United States have become more pronounced and culture and institutions are increasingly being viewed through the lenses of race and racism. As a part of this trend, Ibram X. Kendi, an outspoken advocate for actively addressing racism, has said, "In order to truly be antiracist, you also have to truly be anti-capitalist." In a tweet, he said, "Historically capitalism + racism are interlinked, which is why I call them the conjoined twins + historians like me call them "racial capitalism" in the singular."

While there are always anti-capitalist parts of society, culture and institutions, the anti-capitalists are becoming increasingly vocal.

One result of increasing criticism of capitalism is an increase in the role of government. Part of this is related to a loss of faith that the capitalistic system can provide the benefits and growth citizens want. They are therefore increasingly turning to government at the expense of capitalists.

<u>Attempts to implement social and political values through corporations</u>

Corporations are creatures of the state. Governmental bodies (individual states in the U.S.) enable them, constrain them and regulate them. This makes them particularly sensitive and vulnerable to political and cultural pressures. To some extent, corporations reflect the values of the society within which they are embedded, and evolve as those values evolve.

Capitalism can exist without the corporation. However, the corporation can provide and has provided an efficient legal structure for undertaking capitalist transactions.

And the corporation is supported and enhanced by capitalism.

Corporations can be very anti-capitalist. One important characteristic of capitalism is competition, and competition is something that corporations do not want. Also, as discussed, above, as they gain size and amass power, corporations attempt to game the system by influencing regulators and legislators to tilt the rules in their favor.

It is a paradox that corporations are both important to the pursuit of capitalism and also one of capitalism's greatest nemeses.

But most people do not see the distinction, and equate capitalism and corporations.

As a culture evolves, its views of many things evolve, including its views of corporations. As the world seems to be increasingly - unfair, difficult, unsupportive – people look for and demand change. As capitalism passes its sell-by date and becomes more dysfunctional, dissatisfied people demand that corporations, as the tangible representatives of capitalism, change.

Reinforcing this dissatisfaction has been a steady decline in the portion of the economy that is returned to labor – essentially, paid to labor as compensation.

FIGURE 2:
COMPENSATION OF EMPLOYEES AS PERCENTAGE OF GDP

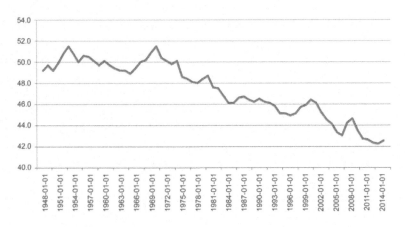

Source: US. Bureau of Economic Analysis, FRED, 01/01/48 to 01/01/14, as at 29/07/16

Figure 6 - Compensation of employees as percentage of GDP

Average hourly wages for production and non-supervisory employees on private, non-farm payrolls in 2018 dollars barely changed from $20.27 in 1964 to $22.65 in 2014.[55]

In the period from 1948 to 1975, employee compensation was approximately 50% of GDP. Since then, it has declined in almost a straight line to approximately 42% in 2014. (It has likely increased somewhat during the low unemployment period, which began in 2014, and then plummeted in response to the pandemic, and then increased with the opening up of the economy during the pandemic.)

The principal result is that cultural dissatisfaction is directed towards corporations, and include demands that corporations:

- eliminate short-term thinking and incentives, including the ending of quarterly reporting of financial results;
- provide a greater return (compensation and benefits) to labor;
- undertake greater environmental responsibility;
- provide for employee ownership of stock;
- give employees representation on boards of directors;
- be more ethical;
- actively address racism;
- include social goals along with financial goals;
- eliminate monopolies;
- restrict the pay of chief executive officers; and
- restrict stock buybacks.

Ironically, prior to, perhaps the 1970s, corporations, particularly major corporations, often took a paternalistic approach to many of their employees. The assumption was that an employee was an employee for life. Employees did not change jobs often – or at all. In an era when relatively few women had jobs, married men were paid more than single men for the same job. This difference attempted to pay for the expenses of a family.

Since the 1970s, corporations have increasingly considered returns to shareholders. When women entered the workforce, equal pay for married, single, women and men became culturally and legally important. Employees began changing jobs with ever-more rapidity.

Over the years, compensation has expanded to include increasing benefits to employees, such as increased vacation, parental leave and sick time. However, in general, corporations have been shielded from the cacophony of the many different social demands from the various parts of the political and social spectrum. Corporations are now encountering undefined requirements, such as being more ethical or including more social goals, together with straightforward requirements like restricting stock buybacks and having employees on corporate boards of directors.

In 2019, the Business Roundtable of Chief Executive Officers of major U.S. companies responded to these pressures by changing its statement on the purpose of the corporation, reflecting cultural and social pressures: "While each of our individual companies serves its own corporate purpose, we share a fundamental commitment to all of our stakeholders. ... (we will) protect the environment by embracing sustainable practices across our businesses, foster diversity and inclusion, dignity and respect."

More than 30 states, led by Maryland, have established a new form of corporation, the B corporation, where the B stands for "benefit." These corporations' goals are to help solve societal problems and also earn a profit.

The B corporation is not to be confused with the B Corp certification. This certification provides a measure of the "social and environmental performance" of any business. As of April 2020 there were over 3,300 certified B Corporations in 71 countries. Notable companies receiving certification include Ben & Jerry's; Natura & Co; Patagonia, Inc. and The Body Shop.[56]

There is an increasing emphasis around ESG (environmental, societal, governmental) practices in business. However, there is little guidance as to how to measure ESG effectiveness. A non-profit Sustainability Accounting Standards Board (SASB) has been created to create standards against which ESG-ness will be measured.

Areas of emphasis of the SASB are the environment (including greenhouse gas emissions), leadership and governance (ethics, behavior and risk management) business model and innovation (business model resilience, supply chain management, efficiency), social capital (human rights, privacy, data security, product quality and safety, selling practices, product labeling) and human capital (labor practices, employee health and safety, employee engagement, diversity and inclusion).

The answers to these social demands will be negotiated within society and between society and corporations. Little attention will be given to tradeoffs, and each change will be deemed to be "good" on its own terms.

There is much wisdom in declaring that the sole purpose of a corporation should be returns to shareholders. Shareholders can then use that money directly to, say, contribute to charities or environmental efforts. No debates about what constitutes fairness or equity need be held.

However, humans reasonably want to address unfairness and injustice and see only limited opportunities to do so in a significant way. Their first recourse is to governmental regulation and their second is to force change on corporations, some of which now exceed the size and power of some governments. Whether there is wisdom in the shareholder value approach to corporations, it, like capitalism, has reached its sell-by date.

With so many competing voices, there will inevitably be extended, contentious discussions of how best to define and implement the social goals of corporations. This controversy will likely result in a reduction of capitalism's economic returns. Ironically, this decrease in the effectiveness of capitalism will, in turn, increase the frustration of those who benefit from those returns – both capital and labor. This, in turn, will increase the level of criticism of capitalism.

One way to look at trends in attempts to change corporate objectives is to examine proposals made by corporate shareholders to be considered at meetings in which shareholders vote. A majority vote for any of these proposals at a shareholders' meeting would effectively create a mandate that corporate management implement the proposal.

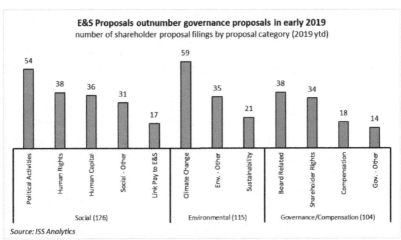

Source: ISS Analytics

Figure 7 – Shareholder proposals in early 2019[57]

One study of shareholder proposals in early 2019 found that social- and environmental-related proposals each outnumbered proposals relating to how the corporation was being run. Climate change was the largest category, and sustainability was on the list of considered proposals.

The study also found that a significant number of social and environmental proposals, 48% in 2018, were withdrawn following negotiations with companies prior to the holding of the related shareholders' meeting. In most cases, those making their proposals achieved most or all of their goals without having to put them to a vote of shareholders.

Significant changes to corporate governance in response to social pressures have begun.

The World Economic Forum's International Business Council created Stakeholder capitalism Metrics in September 2020[58]. The Metrics identify progress against the United Nations' 17 Sustainable Development Goals. The metrics are divided into four "pillars:" Principles of Governance, Planet, People and Prosperity.

The Planet pillar includes metrics pertaining to climate change, loss of land and biodiversity, and availability of fresh water.

Each of these objectives may be worthy, but each increases the overhead and regulation incurred by corporations and reduces profitability and returns to investors. Reducing returns to investors in turn reduces the attractiveness of the corporation for investment.

Prince Charles of the United Kingdom is sponsoring his Sustainable Markets Initiative. He indicates that, "To move forward, we must continue to show that sustainability and profitability are not mutually exclusive."[59]

In this, he is correct. The question is whether sufficient profitability or any profitability at all is achievable if effective sustainability is required. In section II, my answer is, no.

Regulators Have Vacated the Field

The cliché, which contains a great deal of truth, is that no one went to jail as a result of the Great Financial Crisis.

Since the Great Financial Crisis, there have been extraordinary events in the financial market for which the Securities and Exchange Commission took no action.

The credibility and reputation of capitalists, which are not elevated in the best of times, is being eroded, not only by misdeeds, but also by the system's inability to effectively police and cleanse itself.

Additional headwinds in the U.S. are fundamental part of the way in which the economy works.

The Triffin Dilemma

The U.S. has brought significant challenges (and "exorbitant privilege") on itself by supplying the world's reserve currency.

Recalling that everything is both good and bad, it can be very good to issue the world's reserve currency. Much of the world's trade is denominated in your currency, you have the economic power associated with having the reserve currency and you can incur levels of debt and trade deficits that other countries cannot incur without creating an economic crisis.

Without going into all the details, here is the problem, best described by Belgian-American economist Robert Triffin in the 1960s, and slightly restated for the current context. Foreign countries need to hold the reserve currency, in this case U.S. dollars, in order to transact international trade –

primarily the petrodollar (oil) trade. The U.S. must provide the world with dollars, so it must incur a trade deficit. As the world economy grows, there is an increasing demand for dollars, requiring that the U.S. incur ever-greater trade deficits. In general, this drives up inflation in the U.S. and makes its goods less competitive in world markets. However, the U.S. gains access to cheap capital through an effective interest-free loan associated with the issuance of its currency and the associated increased demand for its bonds.

The dilemma in the Triffin Dilemma is that sound economic management demands a current account surplus, while providing a reserve currency results in a current account deficit. Over time, the country issuing the reserve currency winds up with an unsupportable amount of debt, a hollowed-out manufacturing base and a net negative international investment position.

In effect, by supplying the world's reserve currency and gaining benefits from doing so, the U.S. is creating an economic crisis of major proportions.

Additionally, the U.S.'s share of world GDP has shrunk to the point that it cannot supply sufficient dollars to fund global energy markets and global trade.

Since humans take trends to their extreme, the U.S. has abused its reserve-currency status to incur previously-unimaginable levels of fiscal deficits and accumulated debts. The lack of a rival reserve currency enables this continuing abuse. However, the ultimate reckoning, perhaps when international faith in the dollar is compromised and foreigners cease buying U.S. government debt (which is already in progress), would likely lead to a massive decline in U.S. living standards and associated crises in both capitalism and political governance.

A number of countries have reacted to both the U.S.'s excessive debt and its use of the dollar as an economic weapon against those with which it disagrees, including Russia, Iran and China. There are increasing attempts globally, including by allies such as the European Union, to find ways to conduct international transactions by other means than by using the dollar and its associated international financial infrastructure. These include making transactions in other currencies, creating commodity markets based on other currencies and creating a competing international financial infrastructure, possibly based on central bank digital currencies. While the U.S. will win these skirmishes in the short term, in the longer term, by using its currency power arrogantly and irresponsibly, it is likely accelerating the date at which the dollar loses its status as sole reserve currency and the U.S. loses its exorbitant privilege. In the short term, there is no viable alternative to the U.S. dollar as the reserve currency and any change will likely occur in conjunction with a significant reset and restructuring of the world financial system.

There is another headwind that represents the effects of larger historical forces on the world, the U.S. and on capitalism.

The Fourth Turning

In the early 1990s, I began to formulate a view as to the U.S.'s position in a longer-term, economic cycle. I began to think that the U.S. would undergo significant crises in the early 21st century, based on my understanding of historical cycles and on the inability of the U.S. economy to fulfill commitments for Social Security, and particularly, Medicare. Specifically, I predicted a future in which domestic politics moved to the left, governance became increasingly authoritarian, there was increased and significant social unrest and instability in the financial system. I then read Strauss and Howe's *The Fourth Turning*, which incorporated my thoughts and expressed some of them better than I could. (Strauss and Howe include a framework of generations, which I did not contemplate.)

The U.S., and capitalism, are functioning within a longer-term cycle that is reaching a crisis. Following are some excerpts from *The Fourth Turning*:

> The next Fourth Turning is due to begin shortly after the new millennium, midway through the Oh-Oh decade. Around the year 2005, a sudden spark will catalyze a Crisis mood. Remnants of the old social order will disintegrate. Political and economic trust will implode. Real hardship will beset the land, with severe distress that could involve questions of class, race, nation and empire. The very survival of the nation will feel at stake. Sometime before the year 2025, America will pass through a great gate in history, commensurate with the American Revolution, Civil War, and twin emergencies of the Great Depression and World War II.
>
> An impasse over the federal budget reaches a stalemate. The

president and Congress both refuse to back down, triggering a near-total government shutdown. The president declares emergency powers. Congress rescinds his authority. Dollar and bond prices plummet. The president threatens to stop Social Security checks. Congress refuses to raise the debt ceiling. Default looms. Wall Street panics.

The book was written in 1996 – Howe (Strauss is deceased) placed the beginning of the Fourth Turning as 2008. The Great Financial Crisis marked the beginning of approximately 20 years of addressing the accumulated dysfunction in government and culture.

Beyond inherent flaws and self-inflected challenges such as the Triffin Dilemma, capitalism is embedded in a cycle that is leading to crisis – a social cycle instead of a business cycle. The accumulated excesses and dysfunction of the past 60-70 years have to be fixed or changed or eliminated to prepare the ground for future growth.

If the current Fourth Turning lasts an average amount of time for turnings, it will be over in about 2030. At that time, the various crises will have been resolved, for better and for worse. And the U.S. will be significantly and substantially changed.

Many of the indicators that I and Strauss and Howe anticipated have appeared as the Fourth Turning has begun. Government is becoming more authoritarian. There are a leftward swing in politics and a demand for increased governmental action. People, left and right, rich and poor, young and old, are increasingly dissatisfied with the culture and government they have created. We are in denial about our ability to sustain our lifestyles, governmental entitlements and our inability to achieve our dreams. There are demonstrations and riots in our streets.

The election of former president Donald Trump and the rise in popularity of Bernie Sanders are parts of the Fourth Turning. They are symptoms of the widespread dissatisfaction with current politics, economics and culture. The dissatisfaction is such that conservative, religious voters were willing to vote for an often-divorced, often vulgar, often promiscuous man. The dissatisfaction is such that many voters are discussing the radical change of the foundations of U.S. culture, including compromising freedom of speech and the adoption of socialism.

It is far from clear what the world will look like on the other side of this Fourth Turning. Looking at prior Fourth Turnings:

- In 1770, before the climax of the first Fourth Turning in the Revolutionary War, few in the colonies wanted independence from England, and many of those who pictured a new world imagined independent states and not a united nation. What they got were independence and the beginnings of a group of united states.

- At Lincoln's first inaugural, essentially no one thought that the second Fourth Turning would end in incredible bloodshed and destruction. And very few thought that the slaves would be freed. In the end, the slaves were freed, the country was divided and devastated, and had begun to become the United States.

- In the fall of 1929, there was no anticipation of two decades of economic suffering and world war that would mark the end of the third Fourth Turning. At the end of this turning, the United States was a different place, having a strong central government and the beginnings of the welfare state and unfunded entitlements. The (re)launching of the consumer society was at hand.

- In 2007, no one could have anticipated the incredible accumulation of debt and the extreme social and political division of the United States over the next decade and a half. And there is much change to come before the present Fourth Turning is over.

Hermann Hesse summed up our age in *Steppenwolf*:

Every age, every culture, every custom and tradition has its own character, its own weakness and its own strength, its beauties and cruelties; it accepts certain sufferings as matters of course, puts up patiently with certain evils. Human life is reduced to real suffering, to hell, only when two ages, two cultures and religions overlap ... Now there are times when a whole generation is caught in this way, between two ages, two modes of life, with the consequence that it loses all power to understand itself and has no standard, no security, no simple acquiescence.

Part of this hell is that technology is increasingly viewed as a threat, as well as a blessing.

The Rise of the Robots

One of the fundamental tensions within capitalism is the perpetual negotiation between capital and labor concerning who gets how much of the returns from capital.

Improved standards of living result from increased wages and benefits that are enabled by increasing productivity. Higher compensation means greater costs for businesses. In order to maximize shareholder return, costs must be minimized, therefore the costs associated with people, wages and benefits, must be minimized, or at least optimized.

Reductions in labor costs have historically been accomplished through layoffs during economic downturns, through improvements in technology and automation and through moving production to areas in which labor is less expensive, including globalization. Although globalization receives much of the criticism for the loss of jobs, particularly manufacturing jobs, in the U.S over time, technology and automation have been responsible for the loss of significantly more jobs than offshoring.[60] The combination has been devastating to manufacturing labor in the U.S.

In the past, the impacts of globalization and improvements in automation have occurred over relatively long periods of time. That slow rate of change generally allowed the workers that were affected to find another job in an increasingly-growing economy. This has led to isolated dissatisfaction, but a general, overall satisfaction with automation- and offshoring-related changes.

Three trends have occurred, which have upset this ability to absorb change:

1. Economic growth rates have slowed, perhaps for a decade or longer.
2. The rate of change in technology has increased to the point that resulting decreases in employment cannot be absorbed within a "reasonable" amount of time.
3. New jobs increasingly require technical skills and education, which most of the population cannot acquire.

These trends have led to a decrease in economic well-being and security for a significant portion of the population, and their dissatisfaction has led to far more widespread political dissention. As summarized by Viktor Shvets, "The only reason why productivity has been slowing is that technology has progressed far enough to erode marginal utility of labor, but not sufficiently to replace it altogether. However, over the next decade or two, labor inputs could become increasingly redundant."[61]

However, the larger crisis is what I call the Rise of the Robots. It is likely that automation will replace a significant proportion of jobs over the next few decades. Not only do robots not ask for raises, they also do not take sick days or vacation. They can work 24 hours a day, seven days a week. Estimates vary, but future job losses to automation over the next few decades in the 30-40% range do not seem unreasonable. One artificial-intelligence expert and venture capitalist forecasts the replacement of 40% of jobs in the next 15 years[62]. This job loss will lead to demands for substantial and significant changes to social and economic structures and institutions, including capitalism.

While workers fight to find a job or receive aid from the government, and while debt and entitlement obligations have grown to the point that they cannot be repaid, the physical environment in which we live is under existential threat.

Fighting Climate Change

A discussion of climate change is beyond the scope of this book. However, organizing a "fight" against it has become a primary focus of the agenda of many political parties, particularly in the West, and particularly parties of liberal (left of center) persuasion. Green parties have been created, principally in Europe, which have environmentalism and climate change as their primary focus. U.S. President Joe Biden made addressing climate change a centerpiece of his legislative strategy.

The current discussion on climate change involves a great deal of misinformation or one-sided information. Those fighting for action against climate change do not seem to grasp the true cost of an effective campaign against this challenge in terms of a reduction in economic activity and profits.

Although different groups provide different specific recommendations, in general an effective fight against climate change is defined as a reduction in carbon dioxide emissions of some 80-90% below various measurement dates.

That is an astounding objective.

To reduce carbon emissions to that degree, the entire world – Europe, Australia, Japan, China, the U.S., Canada, emerging markets – must overhaul their energy sources, upgrade their infrastructures and change their economic incentives within a period of (again, differing sources differ), say, 30 years. If your reaction is, it can't be done, then I would agree with you. However, if climate change is the threat that many say it is, there is no alternative.

To the extent that the threat of climate change is literally one of life-or-death, capital and labor, a significant portion of all available capital and labor, must be devoted to the campaign against climate change. Some of this investment will be productive, but most will not, since it will be replacing existing systems. The results will include a decrease in growth and in potential living standards, and a significant change in the way economies and jobs are organized.

Keith Farnish summed all of this up in his book, *Time's Up*[63]: "The only way to prevent global ecological collapse and thus ensure the survival of humanity is to rid the world of Industrial Civilization." Dr. James Hansen, a preeminent scientist in the field of climate change, agrees: "Keith Farnish has it right: time has practically run out, and the 'system' is the problem."[64]

Polls indicate that Americans are becoming increasingly concerned about climate change, albeit from a low level of concern and a low amount of willingness to pay small amounts of money to address it. While it is in the forefront in the minds of Europeans and increasingly showing up in the American conscience, not much has practically been achieved. To date, the fight against climate change has been incorporated into the largely-symbolic Paris Accord among the world's nations. Efforts to take concrete steps, such increasing the tax on diesel fuels in France in 2019, have met with (in this case, violent) resistance. Germany's ambitious program to phase out fossil fuels has encountered a number of negative, unintended consequences. These consequences include increased prices for electricity and an increasing need for fossil-fuel-based electric generation to provide backup when the sun does not shine or the wind does not blow.

Other countries, principally China and India, continue to add to their rapid-economic-growth electricity-generation capacities by using coal.

Each step in the fight against climate change will redeploy capital to often unproductive uses and will result in less-efficient processes than those using fossil fuels. Economies and employment will be challenged during these processes.

Capitalism will struggle and likely become irrelevant in this environment.

Climate change is not the only time bomb ticking in the U.S. and global economies. The level of debt in the world has reached unsustainable levels.

Mortgaging and Hamstringing the Future

One way that its participants have gamed the capitalist system is by incurring extreme levels of individual, corporate and governmental debt. Another way the system is being gamed is by promising unaffordable future goodies (entitlements and pensions) without paying for them.

Debt can be both good and bad. Let's talk about business debt. If debt provides money that is invested in such a way that the business generates greater returns than the cost of the debt, then that is a good thing for the economy. That debt increases the overall level of economic activity.

However, if debt is used for unproductive purposes, such as consumption or stock buy-backs, then there is no future revenue stream to pay off the debt. Future income from existing sources or savings must be used to pay back the debt, reducing the amount of future income for other economic purposes, thereby diminishing future economic activity.

We have mortgaged our future by using debt for consumption and to maintain unsustainable standards of living (individuals), stock buy-backs (corporations), welfare and war (government) beyond the point that any reasonable future economic growth rate will result in reducing debt. We have severely mortgaged our future.

Governments and corporations have promised massive entitlements and pensions for which there are no funds. Either these promises will not be kept, or payment will have to be made out of the economy at the time payments are made, negatively impacting the economy. Or high inflation must be used to effectively decrease the obligations. We have severely mortgaged our future.

Academic studies have shown that debt beyond certain levels actually reduces the growth of overall economic activity. The U.S. is at or beyond those levels, as illustrated in Figure 12, which indicates that the turning point at which growth was negatively affected by increases in debt was in 1999.

The implications for capitalism are that this mortgaged future will yield diminished prospects for its participants and therefore increased dissatisfaction with the current system.

Ironically, instead of addressing our inability to service debt, pension and entitlement obligations, many on the left are proposing significantly increased government benefits, such as free college tuition and Medicare for all, without proposing practical, effective alternatives for paying for those benefits. Those on the right and left, including President Biden, are supporting continuing budget deficits, which will result in increasing debt in amounts measured in trillions of dollars a year. The U.S. is at the point at which increased debt is a detriment to the economy, in turn increasing the deficit. We are in a cycle of increasing the dysfunction that must be resolved in this Fourth Turning.

And, while debts and deficits were beyond all reason before the Covid-19 pandemic, the debt and deficits incurred during and after the pandemic have taken us into the realm of the absurd.

As David Hume, known as the father of the Enlightenment, noted in his paper on the relationship of extreme debt to economies, "When a state has mortgaged all of its future revenues, the state lapses into tranquility, languor, and impotence."[65]

The worse the problem becomes, ironically, the more it is ignored. Social Security is running out of money (actually, it already has, given the fiction of the "Trust Fund"), Medicare is already incurring a deficit, debt is at record peace-time levels and the country was incurring pre-pandemic deficits in excess of $1 trillion dollars every year.

The reaction in the U.S. has largely been one of denial. In an article published in June 2019, *The Wall Street Journal* noted, "Political support for taming deficits has melted away, with Republicans accepting bigger deficits in exchange for tax cuts and Democrats making big spending promises around 2020 election campaigns. ... The new bottom line: The U.S., despite a record-long economic expansion, is on course to test just how much it can borrow."[66]

The U.S. and much of the Western world have become economically unsustainable through abuses of the capitalistic system.

In the midst of all of these challenges, societies throughout the world are having fewer children, which, in turn, decreases the economy's ability to generate economic growth to address the problems of debt and deficits.

Demographics

Growth in gross domestic product, GDP, by definition depends on two things: growth in population and growth in the productivity of that population.

The story of the U.S. economic growth since World War II is complex, but one of the critical factors in that story is the unusual growth rate in the population of the Baby Boomers. That growth is now in reverse, as Baby Boomers retire from the workforce.

This trend is exacerbated by the fact that U.S. citizens are not having enough babies to replace the existing population.

This chart illustrates the projected decline in working age population in the U.S. and other selected countries.

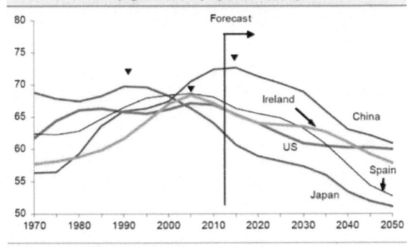

Figure 8 – Working age population as a percentage of total population[67]

The decade-long "Super-Trough" that we are now in, triggered by Baby Boomers leaving the workforce, has enormous implications for consumption and for the growth of GDP. Retirees are reducing their consumption, are moving into smaller living spaces and need fewer cars.

The combination of these two trends, lower population growth and the movement of the Baby Boomers into retirement, means that obtaining growth in GDP over the next few decades will be challenging, and dependent on an increase in productivity. Although capitalism will not be the culprit, it will bear much of the blame for the coming economic malaise.

Capitalism has created miracles, but has weaknesses and is incurring headwinds. How do we reinvigorate capitalism? What goals do we set; what decisions do we make? The answers to these questions turn out to be complicated.

Tradeoffs

There are no solutions. There are only trade-offs. - Thomas Sowell

When deciding what goals to set, it is once again imperative to understand the tradeoffs inherent in any decision. Only, humans don't do that much, if at all.

Everything has good attributes and bad attributes. Whether something is worthwhile depends on two crucial questions: what are the things you value most highly, and how does one system provide those things compared with alternative systems? What are the tradeoffs of choosing an item, a lifestyle or a culture, and what might the unintended consequences be? (When I ask, what do you value, I am talking about the answers you would give under a lie detector test, and not socially-acceptable or conscience-pleasing answers.)

For example, the automobile has provided mobility and freedom to generations, worldwide. It also pollutes the atmosphere, generates greenhouse gasses and in 2016, 37,461 people were killed in automobile accidents in the U.S. (A much more stark statistic is that over 3.6 million people have been killed in automobile accidents in the U.S. from 1899 to 2013.) The implicit tradeoff is that people consider the pollution and deaths arising from riding in automobiles to be "worth it."

Actually, it is more complicated than that. We drive automobiles because that is the accepted way to get around. We ignore or deny the deaths until they happen to someone we know. The odds that any one particular person will die in a car crash are very low. The air pollution problem rarely even enters our thoughts. And then only for a moment while reading an article or listening to a segment on TV.

The tradeoffs inherent in decision making are often implicit. We frequently try to mitigate the downsides by doing such things legislating seat belts and unleaded gasoline. Mitigation helps, but the central problems remain.

Implicit in the discussions about capitalism's tradeoffs are questions like, if ten people can be well off at the expense of two who barely get by, is that better than having twelve people live a mediocre life? This refers to lifestyle, but the question also applies to quality of life, health and life expectancy, because in the first scenario, the ten people are able to leverage greater wealth to invest in greater future prosperity, including, partially, for those "left behind." Since these effects compound over time, the differences between the two scenarios become significant.

Trade-offs matter, and compounding makes them matter even more.

Compounding – A Digression

A little math, but I will use words and not formulas and will keep it short. However, the idea of compounding is extraordinarily important when considering tradeoffs, to the point that author William Poundstone said that "the most powerful force in the universe is compound interest." (This quote has been inaccurately attributed to the great physicist, Albert Einstein, who actually said, "Compound interest is the eighth wonder of the world.")

Given a particular rate of growth, the time for the growing thing to double in size can be determined by dividing 72 by the growth rate. So, if inflation is increasing at the Federal Reserve's old target rate of 2% per year, prices will double in 72-divided-by-2 or 36 years. Therefore, prices would more than quadruple during your expected lifetime, even under what is currently thought to be "mild" or "reasonable" inflation. If inflation is increasing at a rate of 4% per year, then prices would double in 18 years, and would increase eight-fold during your expected lifetime. If inflation is increasing at the rate of 11.3% as it was in 1979, then prices would double in about 6.5 years, and would increase eleven-fold during your expected lifetime.

If the economy can grow at 4% per year, everyone will become twice as prosperous (on average) in 72-divided-by-4 or 18 years. If that rate of growth slows to the 2% per year many economists believe will be a more likely outcome for the near future, then the time to become twice as prosperous extends out to 36 years.

As a practical example, Dr. Lacy Hunt, a well-known economist, notes that between 1790 and 1999, the U.S. economy grew at an average rate of 1.9% per year. Dr. Hunt said in an interview that 1999 is the date that many academic studies indicate that debt levels became a drag on the economy. Since 1999 the U.S. economy has grown at an average rate of 1.2% per year, 63% as fast as the period from 1790 until 1999. If the U.S. economy had grown at its historically average rate, GDP per person today would have been $8,000 higher, or $64,500 as compared to the actual GDP per person of $56,700.[68]

Compounding makes a big difference. A small change can have big consequences.

Back to Tradeoffs

"Pure" capitalism provides the highest rate of growth of any economic system over the long term. However, it results in, among other things, a potentially high inequality in the sharing of the resulting wealth and well-being. You can't have one without the other. So, how would you answer my two, key questions?

1. What is it you (really) value? Material goods, lifestyle, health, longevity vs. equality?
2. Given your values, how much of one would you tradeoff for the other? In the extreme, would you give up ten years of your life to be a millionaire? Would you give up half of your income so that the poor can minimally flourish? Would you consume things and incur associated debt now in exchange for a diminished future? Would you consume things, knowing that consumption is not sustainable in the long run?

We seldom explicitly assess these valuations and tradeoffs, because we often assume we can have it all.

We can't.

Very often, we incur debt and defer having to face the tradeoffs into the future. We also seldom discuss the opportunity cost of making a trade-off.

Earlier, I reviewed hypothetical tradeoffs when making economic decisions. It is probably obvious, but seldom understood, that when you decide to do something, you decide not to do other things. If you spend money in one place, you cannot spend money in another place.

More importantly, if you decide to spend money on consumption (or welfare, etc.) instead of investing it in growth, potential future growth will be lower. And that growth will be lower, essentially forever, compounding the effective (but invisible) loss, year after year.

However, tradeoffs are more complicated than that. We have discussed how cultures try to find the "right" mix between capitalism and socialism - effectively the "right" mix between economic growth and fairness. As an oversimplification, we give up growth to be fair.

But, it is even more complicated than that.

Humans are behaviorally complex. Some tradeoffs go beyond economics.

Swedish culture is an interesting example. For decades, the Nordic cultures have been used as examples of the best tradeoffs yielding both economic growth and fairness. They are not as unequal as many other Western cultures, such as the U.S., and they have not collapsed economically, which seems to be the fate of primarily-socialist cultures.

A reasonable portion of Sweden's success can be attributed to its being a small, ethnically homogenous country. Being small and being ethnically homogeneous make decision-making and problem-resolution much easier.

Under the covers, things are not so simple, as Sweden has encountered several issues. At times, lower economic growth has led to increasing unemployment. Although inequality is relatively low, it has been expanding. As the economy ebbs and flows, welfare becomes less and then more affordable. If Sweden wants to be part of the global community, it must have a currency value and products that are competitive on the world stage. That, in turn, means that the welfare state cannot overly burden corporations with taxes – one of many tradeoffs. In the end, or at least for now, it has decided on a combination of relatively reasonable corporate and personal income taxes and a value-added tax (essentially what those in the U.S. would call a sales tax) of 25%. Although Sweden has no minimum wage, its workforce is relatively highly unionized. Although healthcare is nationalized, co-pays and deductibles are high.

One effect of lower inequality is that there is not as much of a return on a college education (free in Sweden but it does cost time), so there is less incentive to get a tertiary education.

However, there are behavioral issues that are inherent in a welfare state that must be understood as tradeoffs. There is a disincentive to work, there is incentive to cheat on benefits, wages are less flexible and competition is less vibrant.

Economies and their human participants are large, interconnected, nonlinear complex systems. You cannot change just one thing. Making any change requires the understanding of tradeoffs both in terms of the secondary effects of the change, and also in the opportunity costs of change.

We do not do that well, if at all.

All Trends Exhaust Themselves

I met a traveler from an antique land,
Who said—"Two vast and trunkless legs of stone
Stand in the desert. . . . Near them, on the sand,
Half sunk a shattered visage lies, whose frown,
And wrinkled lip, and sneer of cold command,
Tell that its sculptor well those passions read
Which yet survive, stamped on these lifeless things,
The hand that mocked them, and the heart that fed;
And on the pedestal, these words appear:
My name is Ozymandias, King of Kings;
Look on my Works, ye Mighty, and despair!
Nothing beside remains. Round the decay
Of that colossal Wreck, boundless and bare
The lone and level sands stretch far away."
Ozymandias – Percy Bysshe Shelley

There seems to be a deep human need to hang on to things that are perceived to be constant and everlasting when the world is actually in a state of continual change and disruption. While we understand that the Roman Empire is no more and that their gods are no longer worshiped, we believe that our country and our religion will endure.

At some point, however, our country and our religion will end, as will capitalism, consumerism and the human race and the Earth, itself.

Capitalism and consumerism have brought an incredible increase in the standard of living of humans across the globe, primarily in the West, and now increasingly throughout the world. I believe that both capitalism and consumerism have run their courses and are now or will soon be counterproductive. They will end because they must end – ironically, because they have been too successful in converting the Earth's material wealth into people and things.

Everyone believes their time is special. The Ancient Greeks did, the Romans did, the Ancient Chinese did, the Incas did, the British did, the U.S. in the '20s did. And each special time, in retrospect, while having its glories, ultimately faded away. Countless mighty empires are now only memories.

Every several hundred million years, essentially all of life on Earth is extinguished by some catastrophe or other. We are exposed to existential consequences from meteors, viruses, super volcanoes and ourselves. Earth, itself, will be destroyed in some 1 billion years as the sun goes through a traumatic transformation. Assuming that the human lifespan is 80 years, the Earth has passed its 64th birthday in human years. The universe will ultimately expand into distance and cold.

The U.S. is not immune to these forces any more than were Rome or Byzantium or the Inca Empire or the British Empire. Nor is capitalism more immune to extinction than feudalism or mercantilism. The fact that the U.S. and capitalism are institutions that exist today does not make them any different with regard to their evolutionary dynamics than those of other days, either in the past or in the future. Capitalism and consumerism are particularly important to us because they exist when we do.

The development and decay of many human processes and organizations can be described by the s-curve.

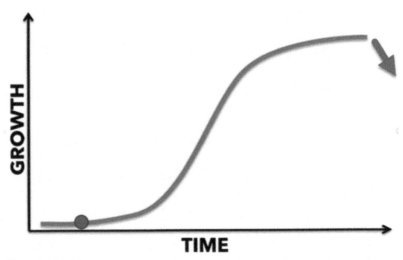

Figure 9 – the S-Curve

Human processes, including humans themselves, organizations, product adoption within organizations and empires, begin without promise. At the beginning, many fail. Those that succeed struggle at first, but soon achieve a period of rapid growth. The rate of growth slows to zero, and the process goes into decline.

There are many reasons that growth slows and ultimately stops, including:

- inherent flaws in the process;
- saturation of markets;
- exhaustion of resources;
- a loss of motivation;
- a corruption of the process from too much success;
- inherent flaws in human nature, principally greed, lust and the desire for power; and
- external forces, such as climate, technology, war, competition and natural disaster.

Examples of trend exhaustion include, for the U.S., life, liberty and the pursuit of happiness:

- Decline of life expectancy – the U.S. ranked 53rd in the world for life expectancy in 2019.[69]
- Erosion in happiness – the U.S. ranked 19th in the world in happiness in 2019. The associated report included a chapter titled, "The sad state of happiness in the United States and the role of digital media."[70]
- Erosion in individual freedom – the U.S. ranked 12th in the world in individual freedom in 2019.[71]
- Erosion in press freedom – the U.S. ranked 48th in the world in press freedom in 2019.[72]

Trend exhaustion also includes decreased U.S. dominance of many sports, decreases in U.S. rate of growth of GDP, increased air pollution, decreased U.S. dominance of many areas of science and technology, the failure of the U.S. education system, the value of the dollar is $0.04, compared with the value of the dollar in 1913, when the Fed was founded, in spite of the Fed's mandate to maintain stable prices; friends with benefits exist several decades after chastity at marriage was accepted as the norm.

We have devalued many words, such as friend, awesome, hero, news alert. States' rights, one of the founding principles of the U.S. Constitution, are now all but gone, undermined by political expediency. Student debt, once essentially unknown, is now a plague.

Venezuela exists, Chicago exists, unfunded pensions exist, entitlement underfunding exists, student loans exist ... we do these things to ourselves, over and over again.

Because we humans are creative, and because we have some fairly impressive flaws, we tend to take things to excess, revealing the fatal flaws inherent in all processes and things. We continually push boundaries, moving them inch by inch over years, decades and centuries, until we cannot see the place where we began. Boiling frogs, again, over and over and over.

In the Western world today, we are in the midst of a series of trends that began with the Enlightenment and the Industrial Revolution. People began to use reason to solve problems and as a basis for inquiry into the nature and workings of things. That thinking, combined with the availability of cheap, fossil-fuel-based energy, and the rise of capitalism to make the world's savings productive, resulted in an incredible explosion of knowledge, technology, well-being and population.

That trend – the trend of extraordinary prosperity based on technology, cheap energy and capitalism – is exhausting itself because of its own success – running up against the inherent limits and flaws that have only recently become apparent and which will be the subject of Part II of this book.

All trends exhaust themselves, and the way of life that began with the Enlightenment and the Industrial Revolution is running on borrowed time as we have reached the limits to consumerism, the latest stage of this process.

Big changes are coming, and they are coming soon to an economy near you. Inequality, debt, entitlements, system gaming and the creation of an oligarchy are exhausting capitalism.

It bears repeating that, by far, the most important consequence of capitalism for the future is that it has been too successful in converting resources and energy into humans and things. This success has led us to the point that our path is not only unsustainable, it is highly likely we have already passed the point of sustainability and are borrowing from the future, in turn, reducing the prospects for the future.

Many of the faults of capitalism can be mitigated through regulation or cultural change. The fact that we are creating an unsustainable economy in a rapidly-declining environment is an existential issue.

My point is not about making capitalism more or less socialistic or about reducing inequality. My point is that we are facing an impending and significant decline in our quality of life and standard of living. The Earth simply cannot support a large number of humans who are consuming at a high level.

So, What Is The Best Way to Organize an Economy?

Everything has good points and bad points. Every decision requires tradeoffs. Humans will mess up whatever system there is and take everything to an extreme. There is not a perfect answer.

But, there may be a best answer in the short term before humans start screwing it up. What might that be?

The first step for humans who want to find a best answer is for each of them – each of us - to define their values – what objectives do we want to attain?

Clarifying objectives is the vital first step because it allows people's differences to begin to emerge and proliferate.

Many people value things that are not possible. My biases are that impossible-to-attain values include world peace, equality and uniform prosperity. World peace and equality are not possible because they are contrary to my understanding of human nature. Human beings are a violent species. Within our species are numerous variations in both genetics and experience that lead to a sorting based on a number of factors, such as strength or intelligence or economic power, leading to inequality.

The third issue, uniform prosperity, is related to the first two, but also to the limits of resources and limited access to resources, such that if there was a uniform economic condition, it would not be prosperity. Today, we have incredible prosperity in much of the West, and the poor in the West live at much higher standards of living than much of the rest of the Earth's population. Median global per capita income in 2013 was $2,920, varying from $19,308 in Norway to $287 in Zambia (the U.S. was $15,480)[73]. If we were to have uniform global prosperity today, each U.S. citizen's standard of living would decrease by about 81%, from $15,480 to $2,920. Americans would be shocked to the core, but the citizens of Zambia would be ecstatic.

So, within reasonable expectations, what is the best way to structure an economy?

A presentation by Dr. Woody Brock, President and founder of Strategic Economic Decisions, Inc., began with what seems to be the reasonable objectives held by most people about structuring an economy:[74]

- Efficiency
- Increasing living standards
- Stability
- Fairness 1 (providing for the needy)
- Fairness 2 (rewards in proportion to relative contribution)
- Rule of law

Brock believes that the best system which can deliver those objectives would include the following:

- Competitive capitalism
- Redistributive tax system
- Rule of law

This seems to be a reasonable start, and approximates what Western democracies have attempted to achieve over the last century.

However, Western democracies have taken the system to extremes to the point that competitive capitalism either does not exist or is disappearing for all the reasons outlined, above.

In addition, Brock's logic ignores the critical sustainability issue. It is ironic that the best economic system to deliver what most people want creates mountains of waste and is running out of resources.

All of this has led to capitalism's being past its sell-by date.

When Was the Actual Sell-By Date?

The sell-by date for a perfectly good item of food comes from its steady compromise by bacteria, beginning on the date that food is created or sterilized. It is the end-point past which the food is no longer viable. It is the culmination of a number of trends taken to their extremes.

Capitalism's sell-by date is the result of a long process of events, each creating a chain of future events. The sell-by date is the end product of relentless frog-boiling in the erosion of boundaries of gaming the system. It is the result of a steady demand for benefits without funding those benefits. It is the result of increasing hubris on the part of the Federal Reserve.

There are several quotes regarding the decline of civilization which fit the decline of capitalism well. Particularly since the decline of the United States and the decline of capitalism are happening simultaneously and reinforcing each other.

William Ophuls, in a book I highly recommend, *Immoderate Greatness – Why Civilizations Fail*,[75] says

> Reducing the process to its essence, a civilization declines when it has exhausted its physical and moral capital. A civilization begins with abundant resources, inspiring ideals, strong morals, solvable problems and high morale. "Green and fresh," it accumulates wealth and power. However, its rise to dominance also prepares its downfall, for although greatness brings "bustle and abundance," it also entails scarce resources, faded ideals, loose morals, intractable problems, and, in consequence, low morale. In addition, because, "the general tendency of wealth and power is to enervate a people, to make them proud and indolent," they succumb to hubris and become the authors of their own demise. ...
> In other words, the populace does not yet understand that the civilization has reached an impasse. As Tainter notes, "It takes protracted hardship to convince people that the world to which they have been accustomed has changed irrevocably."

Of course, there is no precise date at which a complex system such as capitalism peaked or began causing more harm than good. It is more likely that different components of the system peaked at different dates. However, there are several prominent candidates for capitalism's sell-by date in the U.S.

While not the sell-by date, perhaps the first date of note was the enactment of Social Security in 1935. It was limited (1% of the first $3,000 in salary ($55,870 in 2019 dollars); beneficiaries were over age 65 at a time when life expectancy was 61), and much of its implementation was deferred as not being productive during a depression. But Social Security marked the beginning of unfunded liabilities – an unwillingness to pay for future promises (or denial that this bill would ever come due).

The U.S. is now taking this trend and its denial to their extremes. According to the OASDI Trustees, Social Security had, in 2019, a 75-year present value unfunded liability of approximately $13.2 trillion (and Medicare had a 75-year present value unfunded liability of approximately $34.3 trillion).[76] That means that, in addition to anticipated collection of Social Security taxes over the next 75 years, we need $13.2 trillion in the bank today to pay anticipated claims (and, similarly, $34.3 trillion for Medicare).

The next date of note was 1944, when the Bretton Woods Agreement was enacted. The Agreement established the relationship between the U. S. dollar and other currencies, and between the U. S. dollar and gold. This pact institutionalized the U.S. monetary and economic dominance of the world, but also set the Triffin Dilemma, requiring the U.S. to ultimately incur unsustainable debt, into motion.

In 1970, Robert Gordon's period of incredible innovation came to an end.

In 1971, President Nixon took the U.S. off the last vestige of the gold standard, because there was not enough gold to guarantee our currency, and countries were demanding payment in gold. This imbalance was a result of the U.S. creating too much money, primarily as the result of deficits associated with President Johnson's "guns and butter" policy. Johnson needed to wage the Vietnam War without raising taxes, which would upset voters, so he incurred debt. The result of taking the dollar off the gold standard was that the U.S. had a fiat currency, a currency based no longer on gold, but on nothing other than faith in the U.S. government and its economy. Extraordinarily importantly, it also removed the last restriction for Congress to be able to create unrestrained deficits and debt, so that Johnson's deficits look today like chump change.

With gold no longer available to back the dollar, the U.S. entered the petrodollar era. The U.S. guaranteed the national security of Saudi Arabia, the primary source of oil at the time, in exchange for Saudi Arabia's agreement to price and transact its oil sales in U. S. dollars. This arrangement helped perpetuate the dollar's place as the world's reserve currency.

In 1975 at the end of the Vietnam War, the U.S. national debt was approximately $533 billion (approximately $2.5 trillion in 2019 dollars) and in 2020 it was approximately $27 trillion (excluding off-balance-sheet obligations and entitlement obligations) and rapidly increasing due to deficits and programs to compensate for the economic damages to the economy due to the Covid-19 pandemic and to pay for President Biden's social agenda. A dollar in 2019 was worth $0.16, compared with the value of a dollar in 1971. We took those trends to extremes, also.

In 1984 the federal government rescued Continental Illinois Bank because it was "too big to fail." This set the precedent of saving too-big-to-fail banks that culminated in acts taken during the Great Financial Crisis of 2007-2008 to bail out banks and other financial institutions. (Another trend extreme.) In the meantime, the issue of having vital institutions too big to fail was not addressed.

Many authors trace the beginnings of the "Greenspan put" or the "Fed put," whereby the Federal Reserve took ever-more-significant actions to support the stock market in general or individual sectors or companies from its rescue/bailout of hedge fund, Long-Term Capital Management in 1998. I would suggest that it began in 1984 with the rescue of Continental Illinois Bank.

These rescues increasingly interfered with market mechanisms and market expectations, eroding the dynamics of capitalism.

(Many financial institutions around the world have become larger than countries or are large enough that the host country does not have enough assets to rescue them in the event they fail.

The U.S. set up the Federal Deposit Insurance Corporation in 1933 to insure bank deposits. The FDIC increased faith in banks when banks had historically failed during times of economic stress. An estimated 4,000 banks failed in the U.S. in the year 1930. Even in the U.S., the largest economy in the world, many of its financial institutions have become so large that the

Fed is required to take extraordinary actions in order to rescue a failing bank – the FDIC is too small to help. A failure of one of these "too-big-to-fail" banks would have a significant, negative effect on the economy as well as those who had deposits in the bank. This problem continues today and may not be resolvable, short of breaking up large banks into several smaller banks.)

Increasingly, over time (the trend-to-extreme thing), the Fed gained confidence that it could control, minimize or abolish the business cycle by manipulating short term interest rates and injecting liquidity into the financial system. The result has been an extraordinary accumulation of debt, inflation of asset prices and an increase in political instability, including increased wage and wealth inequality.

The petrodollar era is drawing to a close as a result of the U. S.'s shrinking share of the global economy; the U. S.'s weaponization of the dollar against its foes; the increasing use of other currencies in international transactions, including those for oil; the increasing use of other currencies, including the European Union's euro and the Chinese yuan; the introduction of Central Bank Crypto Currencies; and the fear by holders of dollars and of U.S. Treasury obligations that the significant increase of U. S. debt and deficits will ultimately lead to a devalued dollar.

If I were to pick a date when it became clear that we were at or past the sell-by date, it would be one of the following:

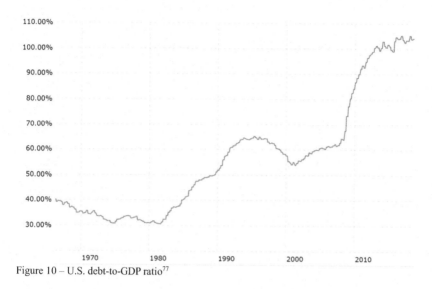

Figure 10 – U.S. debt-to-GDP ratio[77]

1982, when the debt-to-GDP ratio began to accelerate, and ultimately reach counterproductive, unsustainable levels. Simplistically, think of GDP as national income. Increasing debt-to-GDP means that debt is increasing compared to the nation's income.

1985, when the value of the U.S. dollar peaked. In a time of fiat money, when paper money is not backed by anything physical, but is backed only by the promises of the government, the value of a country's currency basically represents the market's views of that country's existing assets and its future prospects, much as you would value the price of a share of stock. To value a currency, the market would look at the way a country is run by its management - its political leaders; it would look at its profitability – its surplus or deficit; it would look at the amount of leverage it is using – the debt on its balance sheet; and it would look at its underlying assets – its minerals, the fertility of its land, the productivity of its population, its use of technology – to estimate how the country will fare economically in the future.

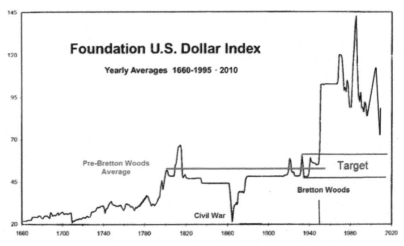

Figure 11 - The Foundation U.S. Dollar Index, 1660 – 1995. I have added price data through 2010, the purple line and the red Target.[78]

This chart tracks one measure of the value of the dollar from 1660 – 2010, and tells the broad story of the United States. The country grew in wealth and importance until reaching a plateau from roughly 1820 – 1945, the end of World War II, with a temporary loss of faith during the Civil War along the way, indicated by the severe decline in value after 1860. America's superpower status and the use of the dollar as the world's reserve currency are reflected by the steep increase in the price of the dollar until 1985, with a general decline since that time.

(It is my view that the dollar, following an initial increase in value after the period depicted on this chart, will likely significantly decline in value. That decline will take the dollar at least back to its value during its long plateau, which is before the time that the dollar became the world's reserve currency.)

Many economists have argued that, past some point, increasing debt leads to diminishing returns. That is, debt becomes a net drag on the economy.

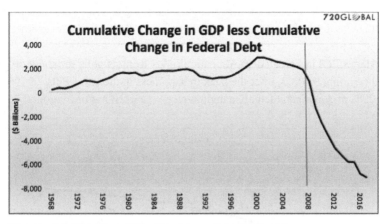

Data Courtesy: St. Louis Federal Reserve (FRED) and Baker & Company Advisory Group/Zero Hedge

Figure 12 – Cumulative Change in GDP less Cumulative Change in Federal Debt[79]

Figure 12 indicates that debt became a net drag on the economy, leading to negative changes in GDP beginning in 2009. According to Figure 12, additional debt incurred after 1999 has actually resulted in an associated decrease in GDP.

Perhaps we are looking at the question from the wrong perspective. Perhaps the sell-by-date can best be measured by the diminishing returns of capitalism to its constituents.

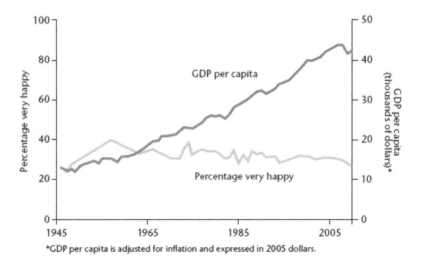

*GDP per capita is adjusted for inflation and expressed in 2005 dollars.

Figure 13 – Happiness as a function of GDP per capita in the U.S.[80]

Happiness is difficult to measure, but, according to some studies, it peaked in the U.S. in the late 1950s, and has been generally declining, ever since.

Harris Poll has created an Alienation Index from its polls for about 50 years, beginning in 1963, after the peak in happiness in the late 1950s. In 1963, 29% of Americans felt alienated; in recent years, it has been around 70%.[81]

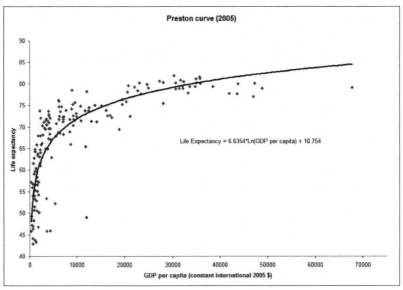

Figure 14 – Life expectancy as a function of GDP per capita[82]

Life expectancy has been measured as a function of GDP. Life expectancy seems to peak at a GDP per person of around $20-30,000 – U.S. average GDP per person in 2017 was approximately $60,000.

Several researchers have tried to bring together a calculation of the "good" things in society and the "bad" things, such as pollution and crime. This is a difficult and perhaps impossible task, but one approach is reflected in the Genuine Progress Indicator, or GPI.

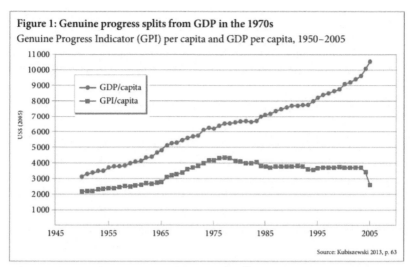

Figure 15 – GPI per capita; GDP per capita, 2005 dollars[83]

Measuring nations using the GPI and other such indicators leads to the conclusion that there is a maximum level of economic development beyond which growth is actually detrimental to society and to the environment. In other words, at some point the costs of growth, such as congestion and pollution, exceed its benefits.

Genuine Progress Indicator includes 26 sub-indicators, which can be divided into three main categories: economic, environmental, and social. A GPI analysis of existing economies indicates that when the GDP of a country exceeds approximately $20,000 per capita, GPI begins to decline. This means that increasing GDP past this point yields social and environmental costs that increase more rapidly than associated economic benefits. Some of those costs include resource depletion, crime, ozone depletion, family breakdown, pollution, loss of farmland and loss of wetlands.

However, the per capita GPI of both China and Thailand have already begun to fall even though their per capita GDPs are much less than the $20,000 per person threshold experienced by high-GDP countries[84].The reason for this is that the marginal cost of growth for these later-developers is much higher than it was for high-GDP nations in the 1950s and 1960s. This is because the world is now "full" and the best and the most accessible of the world's material and energy resources have been depleted by high-GDP countries, which has left poorer grade resources for low-GDP countries to fuel their current and future growth.

Given that current U.S. GDP per capita is approximately $60,000, the U.S. is overconsuming on a GPI basis by about 3 times. The U.S. reached maximum quality of life as measured by the GPI around 1977. GPI has been declining ever since and GPI for the U.S. was, in 2005, at levels achieved in the mid-1950s.

There is an entire website, http://www.wtfhappendin1971.com which provides multiple graphs illustrating changes in the U.S. economy in 1971. Not coincidentally, 1971 was the year it became apparent that the U.S. was living beyond its means, primarily due to President Johnson's policy of "guns and butter" during the Vietnam War, and when President Nixon took the U.S. dollar off the gold standard. This opened the way for undisciplined spending, promises of entitlements and debt, creating waves of ever-increasing instability in the U.S. economy.

The following graph illustrates the disconnect between real GDP and real wages after 1971.

Real GDP, Real Wages and Trade Policies in the U.S. (1947-2014)
Index (1947=100)

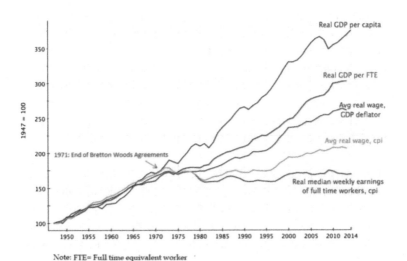

Note: FTE= Full time equivalent worker

Sources: Bureau of Economic Analysis (BEA), Bureau of Labor Statistics (BLS)

Figure 16 – Economic trends changed significantly in 1971

Even prior to the Covid-19 pandemic, in the midst of extraordinary prosperity, there was an increasing sense of diminution, coarseness and degradation.

Figure 17 – Public Trust in Government: 1958-2021, Pew Research Center[85]

This graph illustrates trust in government over time. It depicts the decline of trust from 75% during the Eisenhower and Kennedy years to 15% during the Obama administration. This is simply an astounding loss of faith in government, institutions and values. Capitalism has been caught up in this decline. The assassination of President Kennedy, the Vietnam War and the social upheaval of the Civil Rights and Feminist movements began the decay.

Although it is difficult to establish, precisely, it is likely that the sell-by date for U.S. Capitalism was a process, beginning with Johnson's guns and butter and the Great Society in the late 1960s, and the end of the period of incredible innovation.

The beginnings of the decline were made apparent by the taking of the dollar off the gold standard in 1971 and progressed into the mid-1980s, with confirmation in the late 1990s. The actions of the Federal Reserve in response to the multiple financial crises since the mid-1990's both confirmed its existence and sealed its fate.

Negative interest rates, negative oil prices, social unrest and unsustainable debt and deficits are symptoms of a system that is in decline, is dysfunctional and is past its sell-by date.

All because humans take all trends to their extremes.

In the sustainability section below, we will conclude that consumption probably became unsustainable under the dynamics of capitalism during the same general period.

What to Do?

Capitalism faces a crisis, ironically due to its own success and also to humans' need to fiddle with the existing system to make it "better." In the past, it has endured in spite of its weaknesses primarily because it has been able to change and adapt and provide extraordinary economic rewards to those who live according to its rules.

However, today, it not only faces its usual flaws and usual critics, it also faces headwinds, such as the Fourth Turning, a mortgaged future, the Rise of the Robots, the Triffin Dilemma, investments in the fight against climate change, changing demographics and limits to sustainability.

Capitalism is in a position much like that of Gulliver in Lilliput.

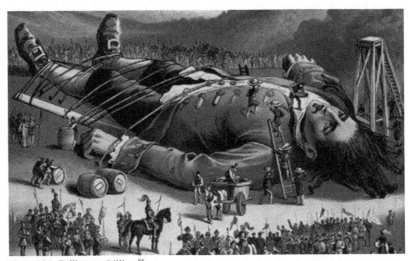

Figure 18 – Gulliver on Lilliput[86]

According to author Jonathan Swift in his novel, *Gulliver's Travels*, Gulliver is washed ashore, unconscious, in the land of Lilliput, inhabited by tiny people. These people, fearing the giant, tie him down with hundreds of inconsequential strings, the combined effect of which prevent any movement, in a land which he should easily be able to dominate and rule.

Similarly, capitalism today is bound by hundreds of strings – regulations, special interests, inequality, etc., layered on in a boiling-frogs process – any one of which would be inconsequential, but the combined effect of which makes the giant of capitalism unable to move.

There is a reasonable argument that I am ignoring my own framework. History rhymes, so that capitalism may yet flourish again, just as beards from the late 1800s recently reappeared on Millennials.

Of course I do not know. However, I believe that too many trends have been taken too far. Too many people and organizations benefit from the way things are now, regardless of whether they lead to dysfunction. There are too many strings holding Gulliver down.

Reform may sever one or ten strings, but in the end will be insufficient to free the giant.

I have noticed utopian strains in the literature on changing capitalism, which parallel literature on sustainability and on climate change. They assume that humans will not behave like humans. In essence, many works on sustainability assume we will all come together and fight the adversary together.

One example of this idealistic human behavior can be found in an article in the *Harvard Business Review* on reimagining capitalism[87]. What the author actually reimagines is human nature by

- "focus(ing) the entire organization on a higher purpose and embed such virtues as generosity and selflessness into everyday interactions, evaluations, and reward systems ...
- act(ing) as wise stewards of organizational values, resources, and stakeholder well-being ..."

Ray Dalio, a very successful hedge fund manager, wrote a thoughtful essay, "Why and How Capitalism Needs to be Reformed."[88] In it, he covers many of the same topics discussed in this book and includes others, such as education in the U.S., that are significant cultural issues. However, in the end, his recommendations, although all valid, tend toward the aspirational and are probably not achievable in the real world, particularly absent a crisis.

Dalio's thoughts are in quotes and my thoughts follow his for each bullet point.

- "Leadership from the top." [Kit - In my view, this will have to come from an entirely new group of leaders. Our current leaders are not up to the task. There is hope that in a time of crisis a great leader such as George Washington or Abraham Lincoln or Franklin Roosevelt will arise. However, there is no evidence of great leadership in either political party in the U.S. or in any countries around the world.]

- "Bipartisan and skilled shapers of policy working together to redesign the system so it works better." [Kit - There may come a day when the politics of the U.S. is bipartisan, but not any time soon. Current politics seem to be dominated by each side taking the opposite position in a knee-jerk reaction to the other side's position.]
- "Clear metrics that can be used to judge success and hold the people in charge accountable for achieving it."
- "Redistribution of resources that will improve both the well-beings and the productivities of the vast majority of people." [Kit - Even if possible, the devil will be in the details.]
- "Coordination of monetary and fiscal policies." [Kit - As long as politics are divided, this will be difficult. The primary scenario under which this would likely be accomplished would be violating the "independence" of the Federal Reserve Bank. That independence has been fundamentally compromised in response to the Covid-19 pandemic.]

Whatever the cure for capitalism's ills, utopia is a low-probability outcome. Humans have repeatedly shown that we do not do utopia well. "Kumbaya" is a great camp song, but not a practical basis for planning the future.

It may take a revolution to clear the dysfunction and provide a clean slate to do it "right" all over again. The problem with revolutions is that they have pronounced unintended consequences. The French Revolution led to the Terror and mass killings. The Russian Revolution led to communism. The fall of the Soviet Union led to a dictatorship by oligarchy.

A revolution based on restoring some sustainability to the economic world might begin with a debt jubilee. The concept of a debt jubilee goes back thousands of years, when debts were declared forgiven by the ruler, and it was a matter of Mosaic Law in the Old Testament. Since our debt is arguably unpayable in any event, a jubilee covering part or all of the debt might be considered. The consequences would be severe – bankruptcies, economic recession or depression. However, after some period of time, the system would stabilize and be able to flourish.

There is no easy way out of our current situation. We have simply gone too far so that all the easy answers no longer apply.

Since entitlements in the U.S. are also likely to be unpayable, an entitlement jubilee could also provide the basis for creating a system that would actually work – a system within which newly-considered promised benefits could actually be paid.

Jubilees will most likely occur only under extreme circumstances, but extreme circumstances are likely in our future. These extreme circumstances include the inability to financially deal with student debt, Social Security, Medicare and private and governmental pensions. The culmination of these programs in a time of low growth will likely lead to extreme actions.

The trust-busting of the early 1900s, together with laws addressing such things as working hours and working conditions, had a significant impact on the capitalism of the day. Perhaps another major effort could address financialization and the natural, winner-take-all-from-network-effects of technical monopolies. However, those are the symptoms and not the underlying diseases of debt, demographics and entitlements, which will not be easily addressed. Nor would they address sustainability.

Some have proposed that capitalism is in the process of evolving into another process, such as "world-system theory." It is highly likely that capitalism is evolving, but it is far from clear that the direction or the outcome is known.

Economic growth would cure most of the ills currently causing social unrest, or if not exactly cure them, address much of the current angst and anxiety.

It would also make unsustainability even worse.

We have become accustomed to economic growth. We not only expect it, we demand it. We want ever-more goodies and better lives, and we also want even better lives for our children.

However, for the foreseeable future, the prospects for economic growth are limited, at best.

And, sustainable growth is an oxymoron.

Limited prospects will change economics from yielding an increasing cornucopia to becoming a zero-sum game. Contention for the limited resources of the zero-sum game – a fixed amount of pie instead of an ever-growing pie – will lead to conflict and crises. This conflict could be among countries, races, classes and generations, and perhaps genders.

Historian Niall Ferguson describes the future I envision: ... "the key to thinking about history is to recognize you're not studying a bunch of living organisms with a natural life cycle. You're studying complex systems. And complex systems behave differently from individual organisms. ... What happens in a complex system is that you are on the edge of chaos for really, quite a long time. And then a phase transition happens. And quite suddenly, what has appeared stable falls apart. That's what you have to worry about."[89]

There is not a good alternative for this new world, although I will explore one likely alternative in the sustainability section.

In any event, capitalism has gone beyond its sell-by date and it is not clear what will take its place.

I will argue in Part II that unsustainability necessarily leads to a no-growth economy.

Part II – Unsustainability – The End Game

We can tinker with capitalism – make it, and/or make corporations, fairer and more equitable. We can enforce redistribution of income and wealth. We can provide support for those left behind, including those caught in the Rise of the Robots. We can legislate against increased automation.

However, there is no group of actions, short of a drastic decrease in living standards and/or population, which can effectively address the fact that, largely as a result of capitalism's success, our economic activities are no longer sustainable, no matter how distributed. We have been too successful.

Seen from one perspective, capitalism is an enabler of the creation of a vast amount of goods and services, from technology to science to medical advancements to consumerism. Seen from another perspective, capitalism is a devouring monster, requiring ever-greater resources in order to create ever more goods and services to meet the demands of an ever-higher, ever-safer and ever-longer standard of living to an increasing number of people.

The goods that are created must be maintained, repaired and replaced while new goods are created.

At some point, billions of people's creation and consumption of goods and services crossed a threshold, beyond which the materials and energy which are used up in the process are not sustainable. The waste which is created becomes overwhelming. Humans begin to eat their metaphorical seed corn and set themselves up for a future somewhere between dystopia and disaster.

That point was arguably passed in the 1980s, although there are other estimates for the date at which the threshold was passed, which we will explore, below. Of course, there is probably not one date. There is likely a date for water and a date for fish and a date for petroleum. And, differing parts of the world will face limits before other parts. They can mitigate their decline by importing resources, to the detriment of the part of the world that is exporting those resources.

In the end, it is not surprising that a finite, although very large, world could reach its limits in its ability to provide resources to what will almost inevitably be in excess of ten billion people by the end of this century.

Capitalism enables exponential growth in population and therefore the demand for an exponential increase in the creation and consumption of goods and services.

We have reached our limits. Which means that capitalism can no longer drive humans' economies. Capitalism has reached its sell-by date.

Worse, to the extent that we are eating our seed corn, some combination of population and consumption must be reduced to a level consistent with sustainability of the creation, maintenance and replacement of goods and services.

The subject of sustainability is unfamiliar and controversial. This analysis of population and resource unsustainability enabled by capitalism will reaffirm that capitalism and other forces have driven human consumption beyond sustainable levels. Humans must learn to live within a no-growth framework.

The Environmentalists Are Right (Sort Of)

My perspective has been that environmentalists are mostly well-intentioned and concerned people, some of whom regularly predict catastrophes, including the end of the world. When the end of the world does not come, there is a new prediction of Armageddon, which doesn't come, and then another.

The conclusions of this book are that many of the environmentalists have actually gotten it right, and I have often been too glib about their concerns. The end of the world is not literally coming any time soon, but we have put ourselves into one hell of a mess, and on a path which is only going to get worse and worse. The quality of our lives will likely be significantly eroded as competition for resources increases – as the Earth's human population increases by approximately 50% by 2100, and as available resources decline. Once the sensationalism is stripped out of environmental rhetoric, there is an insightful truth about an awkward, challenging and dangerous future.

One consequence of loss of sustainability is that free-market capitalism is past its sell-by date. More fundamentally, consumerism is past its sell-by date. Socialists and Communists want to consume goodies, just as capitalists do. Their economic systems just don't generate goodies at the same level as capitalism does. That desire for goodies will create ever-increasing stress and misery.

This is a difficult book for a lifelong, died-in-the-wool, free market capitalist to write. This is not so much a subject that I chose as a subject that chose me. Over time, it took up residence in my consciousness and conscience and would not go away until I dealt with it. Once I began to deal with it, I began to understand that the challenge of consumption is profound and existential. It would not go away, and I could not let go of it.

I Really Did Not Want To Be Here

After a deep-dive into researching climate change, I came to the end of a journey of more than a decade and I did not like where I had wound up or the conclusions that were forcing themselves on me. I was determined to go where my research into the data and facts about climate change led me. The data and facts that emerged from my research forced me face practical and ideological conclusions which were contrary to my prior conclusions about capitalism and the environment.

At the same time, I was excited that my thoughts and research had led me to critically important insights, no matter how awkward.

While thinking about how to end my book on climate change, I continually returned to one of my principal conclusions, which is that there are many environmentally-related challenges, only one of which is climate change. While writing the book on climate change, I had continued to ignore these challenges, but they would not go away. I then had an important, although not unique, insight that climate change is not the problem; it is a major symptom of a deeper, underlying disease.

This underlying disease began to enter my mind when I read the 1972 book, *The Limits to Growth*. *Limits* in effect, also said that climate change is a symptom of this deeper problem. But *The Limits to Growth* can be difficult to understand and does not relate directly to real-world cases. Its concepts are sound, but I would need to understand how the world in 2021 and going forward is actually impacted – what is really going on underneath *The Limits to Growth's* equations as applied to the future?

My conclusion is that the fundamental disease we must address is the combination of human population and human consumption. A large number of humans using energy and natural resources to create and consume a large number of things has a number of profound consequences. One, but only one, of these consequences may be an increase in the rate of climate change.

If all energy were renewable tomorrow and the problem of climate change were solved tomorrow, we would still face the existential problem of the limits to human population and to the consumption and depletion of global resources. The associated crises will likely begin within the next 40 years, however, it has probably already begun.

The critical issue is the combination of both population and consumption. A relatively few humans who intensively consume can have a much greater effect than a larger number of humans who consume sparingly.

It had become time for me to think about the limits to consumption using the same approach I had taken with climate change: letting the facts and data take me wherever they would take me.

I had not come to the end of my journey, but was in the middle of it, and I had a great deal more research and thinking to do. Worse, that journey would put me in the company of Thomas Malthus and Dr. Paul Ehrlich - famous people who incorrectly predicted population-driven catastrophes – another place I definitely did not want to be.

Worse still, I had to face the possibility that the consumer society and perhaps capitalism itself were coming to their logical conclusions.

There is a long tradition of predicting doom when it comes to overpopulation, and, so far, all of those predictions have been wrong. It would be critical for me to avoid the traps and logical fallacies of previous predictors.

And, as part of avoiding those traps, I needed to consider that things might turn out well, after all.

Technology and Abundance

We humans are in the midst of an existential crisis of our own making. The evidence will strongly support a future in which there are too many humans consuming an unsustainable portion of the Earth's resources. Essentially, the only possible positive outcomes will be created by extraordinary technological achievements.

One of the best summaries of the other outcome, of a positive technological future, is the 2012 book, *Abundance, The Future is Better Than You Think*, by Peter H. Diamandis and Steven Kotler, which forecasts a great future:

> Humanity is now entering a period of radical transformation in which technology has the potential to significantly raise the basic standards of living for every man, woman, and child on the planet. Within a generation, we will be able to provide goods and services, once reserved for the wealthy few, to any and all who need them. Or desire them. Abundance for all is actually within our grasp.
>
> Imagine a world of nine billion people with clean water, nutritious food, affordable housing, personalized education, top-tier medical care, and nonpolluting, ubiquitous energy. Building this better world is humanity's grandest challenge.[90]

Enlightenment Now: The Case for Reason, Science, Humanism and Progress by Steven Pinker, and published in 2018, details the incredible progress made by humans, beginning with the Western Enlightenment, and concludes that human rationality and creativity will successfully solve any challenges ahead.[91]

While such a future is possible, it is highly unlikely, primarily because the challenges we face are significant, and that effectively solving those challenges will require not only extensive improvements in technology, but also a change in values by most, if not all, of Earth's human population.

Conceptually, it is important to grasp that today's technology is very resource and energy intensive. In essence, we are finding innovative ways to combine and redeploy ever-more exotic materials and to refine energy into ever-more controllable forms in order to create what are essentially miracles. Technology is a double-edged sword: it leads to more efficient use of energy and materials, and it requires the use of ever-more sophisticated processes, exotic materials and increasingly-refined energy to create the special materials that enable technological transformation.

Take the iPhone as one example. The iPhone is not the pinnacle of technological achievement, however, in order for it to provide a touch screen and the many sensors it employs, it uses novel materials and processes. Discussing the iPhone 6, today a very dated piece of equipment, the Visual Capitalist said, "Of the 83 stable and non-radioactive elements in the periodic table, a total of 62 different types of metals go into the average mobile handset."[92] Materials used include aluminosilicate glass, lithium cobalt oxide, silicon, copper, gold, silver, tungsten, tantalum, tin, neodymium, iron, boron, aluminum and sapphire glass.

If technology is to save the day, it will use a significant amount of materials and energy.

As we discuss the challenges ahead, I will review the improvements that technology is making in each area.

Climate Change Will Affect, but is not Critical to, the Discussion About Overpopulation and Consumption

If all energy were renewable tomorrow and the problem of climate change were solved tomorrow, we would still face the existential problem of the limits to human population and to the consumption and depletion of global resources.

Human-caused (anthropogenic) climate change is principally the result of burning fossil fuels for the creation and consumption of goods and services.

The atmosphere's temperature is increasing. In fact, it has been increasing, more or less, for some 11,600 years, since the end of the last ice age. There is a consensus among scientists that one of the principal causes of recent increasing temperature is the emission of greenhouse gasses, such as carbon dioxide (CO_2), as a by-product of burning fossil fuels, such as oil, coal and natural gas, for energy. Consumption of energy and natural resources, enabled by capitalism, creates today's extraordinary goods and services.

Addressing climate change without dealing with overpopulation and overconsumption is like putting a Band-Aid on a broken arm.

As sociobiologist E. O. Wilson says in *The Future of Life*, "The race is now on between the technoscientific forces that are destroying the living environment and those that can be harnessed to save it. We are inside a bottleneck of overpopulation and wasteful consumption."[93]

However, climate change contributes to and complicates the sustainability story.

The following graph provides an overview of the probable timelines for climate change and for humans exceeding the maximum population the Earth can effectively sustain, which is probably between 7 and 10 billion.

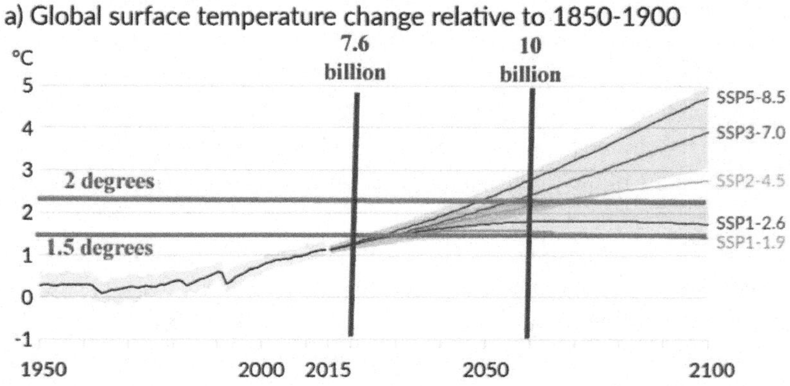

Figure 19 – IPCC's forecast of future temperature under five scenarios for the future (SSPs). I have added the 1.5 and 2° red lines and the two purple population lines.[94]

The United Nations' Intergovernmental Panel on Climate Change (IPCC) publishes a summary of current scientific consensus on climate change approximately every five years. Figure 19 illustrates its most recent forecast of the change in future atmospheric temperatures under different scenarios (SSPs). The climate change community shares a goal of keeping the change in temperature below 2° C (3.6° F), compared to temperatures in pre-industrial times, and, hopefully, below a 1.5° C (2.7° F) change.

Under all scenarios, atmospheric temperature exceeds the 1.5° C maximum increase around 2030; only slightly above under SSP1-1.9. Under two scenarios, temperature never exceeds a 2° C increase; under three scenarios, it is exceeded around 2062, 2056 and 2049, respectively.

Addressing sustainability will include addressing climate change. Addressing climate change does not necessarily solve the challenge of sustainability.

In order to be able to get our minds around population and consumption, we need to first discuss a few foundational concepts.

Before We Get Started

I would like to outline some key concepts which we will use to lay a foundation for our analyses and to provide a better framework within which to understand our sustainability.

Data

Much of the data underlying the concepts in this book require the measurement of things that are difficult, or impossible, to measure – at all, much less measuring them to multiple decimal places. How much water is there in the world? How much of this water is used for agriculture? How much has the temperature changed around the entire globe? What was the temperature of the Earth's atmosphere's a thousand or a million years ago – or yesterday?

All data that I use can be criticized and contested due to the strong opinions associated with the topics we will discuss and to the difficulty of measurement.

This book uses data from mainstream sources, but it is still important not to get caught up in the data. Whether we have 10 or 12 years of a particular resource remaining is not important, and probably not measurable to that level of accuracy. What is important is whether we are running out of that resource and what actions we need to take to prevent running out. Or what the implications are of running out, if running out is unavoidable.

All calculations, including predictions, whether made by me or someone else, should be associated with the word, approximately.

An additional challenge is that many of the statistics that will be included in this book are averages, and averages can be misleading. For example, global averages regarding water include consumption near the Great Lakes in the U.S. and in the Sahara Desert. Averages are important in that they simplify the discussion and provide a yardstick for comparison. Variations from averages will be included, and it is important to keep in mind that averages may be misleading.

Finally, there is inherent error in any measurement, arising from measurement methodology, restrictions on the amount of data and from limitations of the measuring tools and instruments. For example, when discussing global warming, these errors, or this uncertainty, is seldom discussed. However, errors may be significant. One study found that the increase in atmospheric temperature from 1880 to 2000 was 0.7^0 C $\pm$ 0.46^0 C (1.3^0 F $\pm$ 0.8^0 F), which the author characterize as "statistically indistinguishable from 0 C." [95]

It is important to associate the word, approximately, or the words, more or less, to any measurement quoted in this book. There is a general inference of precision in the literature that should be viewed with some skepticism.

Complexity

Population and consumption are large, non-linear, complex systems that have a significant number of inputs, outputs and feedback loops. Unfortunately, because of the dynamic, living nature of these systems, there are no simple approaches to describing them or analyzing them. Because of incomplete data and uncertainty about the future, conclusions will be subject to significant revision as culture, technology, the economy and other factors go through profound changes. The answers of a devout believer (or non-believer) in climate change or of a population doomsayer (or optimist) provide simple visions of our complex world, and are generally wrong or materially incomplete.

When discussing population and consumption, there is not one number that can be used as a benchmark, since differing levels of consumption are possible at differing levels of population. For example, in the United States, today, there are globe-trotting billionaires who own multiple houses, private jets and eat at expensive restaurants – extremely outsized consumption, enabled by capitalism. There are many people who are just getting by in a rented apartment and subsidized by food stamps. There are also people who are homeless.

As we continue these discussions, I will point out things that are known, things that are guesses, and things that are not known. Things that are not known and are guesses will lead to disagreement as to appropriate actions and solutions.

Contentiousness

Because much-needed data are missing or are subject to dispute, both data and conclusions may create vocal, and perhaps emotional, opposition. My intention is not to be precisely correct – probably an impossible objective in any event – but to be broadly correct, to capture the contours and the implications of the crisis. And most importantly, not to mislead. This subject is important, and we need to get it as right as we can, while understanding the limitations of our analyses and thoughts.

Prediction

> *"Prediction is very difficult, especially*
> *if it's about the future." – Niels Bohr*[96]

Essentially all predictions about the future are wrong.

Any prediction that uses a recent trend and projects the future in a straight line for any extended length of time will almost certainly be wrong. There are too many variables to consider, particularly those involving human behavior – humans will react and cleverly attempt to solve any problems that arise. And they also have a tendency to make matters worse.

As examples of extending trends into the future, the number of women with computer science degrees has declined steadily since around 1983. Therefore, "if this trend continues, there will be no women with computer science degrees in 2033." "The rate of autism is increasing at a rate such that in 2035 a majority of boys will have autism." "Given the rate of increase in the horse population in 1894, if this trend continues, by 1934, every street in London would be buried under nine feet of manure." (These quotes are paraphrases of articles found on the internet.)

This silliness of extending data trends is repeated in the popular press. In reality, life proceeds in cycles or is interrupted by technology or cataclysm or a change in cultural mores. Even more importantly, as Herbert Stein famously said, "If something cannot go on forever, it will stop." London would not have experienced one foot of manure, much less nine. The manure trend in London would have stopped because it had to stop.

Looking back over my life, I think about how culture and society have changed for better and for worse, just in that relatively short period of time. I also think about all the predictions about the future that were made along the way and how wrong they were.

Who could have even imagined, much less predicted, the amount of debt in our society or that negative interest rates or negative prices for oil would even be possible? When could people first imagine that China would quickly rise from third-world status to become a major contender and that it would compete with the U.S. for power and wealth? What will human culture become when robots perform the majority of jobs? What do the forces underlying the rise of Donald Trump and Bernie Sanders in the U.S. and "far right" parties in many other countries portend for the future? What would the U.S.'s Founding Fathers think about such changes as the all-but-annihilation of states' rights and the finding of a right to privacy? What would Adam Smith think about the modern role of central banks and shadow banks? In the same vein, what does the current trend of decreasing attention spans and increasing visual inputs portend for thoughtfulness and analysis, and therefore such things as self-governance, in the future? Who knew in the 50s, when oral sex, even between heterosexual or married people, was often illegal, that there would be friends with benefits just 60 years later and that homosexuality would be legitimatized? Or that I would mention oral sex in a book?

Several of these kinds of predictions will show up in this book. They may contain a kernel of truth worth contemplating, but it is highly unlikely that they will be precisely correct.

The following review of the history of oil prices and the implications for future oil prices provide a glimpse into the dynamics of prediction and of peak resources. Looking at oil price history also provides insight into the cultural, economic and technological changes that dramatically affect the supply and the price of resources. They also provide insights into the limits of prediction, as humans, technology and regulation interact.

We have not been able to even come close to predicting the price of oil, arguably, after water, the most important commodity on the planet.

Peak Resources

Peak oil, or peak anything (water, phosphorus), is the date when production of oil is at its highest and then begins to decline. It is not the date of exhaustion of all of the Earth's oil reserves, but the date when it is no longer economically and / or technically practical to produce more oil from new wells. Old wells may be pumped to their economic or physical exhaustion long after peak oil is reached.

The concept of peak oil was first introduced in the 1950s by American geologist and geophysicist, King Hubbert. Hubbert basically started with several truisms and then tried to predict the date for peak oil. Hubbert's truisms include:

- The amount of oil in the Earth is finite.
- We will produce the easiest to get to and cheapest to produce oil first. As time goes by, oil will become more expensive and more difficult to obtain.
- At some point, the combination of exhaustion of resources and increase in price will make the production of oil uneconomical and peak oil will occur, even though the Earth will contain a significant amount of hard- and expensive-to-get oil.

Hubbert predicted peak oil for the U.S. would be in the early 1970s.[97]

And, he was right ... for a while. U.S. oil production did peak in the early 1970s.

Then, technology, and the availability of huge amounts of cheap financing, happened to Hubbert. In the case of oil, fracking was invented and low interest rates enabled the production of fracked oil. As a result, around 2015, the U.S. began producing about the same amount of oil as it did at its peak in the 1970s.

U.S. Field Production of Crude Oil

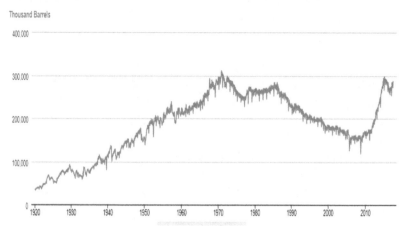

Thousand Barrels

Figure 20 – U.S. field production of crude oil (thousands of barrels)[98]

Figure 21 – Price of crude oil ($/barrel) in 2018 dollars.[99]

And then price happened. In 2016 the price of oil fell into the $26 / barrel range, affected by the combination of increasing supply from the U.S. and decreasing demand in China, among other factors, which made the production of much oil uneconomical. (The price necessary for oil to be economical depends on several factors, including ease of access and technology required. Although the following numbers will change from year to year, they are representative. For new production, fracking breakeven in the U.S. can vary from $25-60 / barrel[100]. Saudi Arabia's breakeven production cost is estimated to be around $3 / barrel[101]; Russia's around $18 ($120 in the Arctic)[102]; China's around $30[103]. However, these numbers relate only to production cost.

Countries which have economies that rely on oil for revenue thrive or struggle depending on the market price for oil. In 2018, it was estimated that Saudi Arabia, which has an economy based on oil, needed an oil price of around $85 / barrel to balance its budget[104], while Russia required more than $100 / barrel[105], although both countries are implementing projects to reduce those numbers.) As these countries' populations increase, the budgetary breakeven price of oil would also increase.

During the oil crises in the 1970s, no one predicted that the price of oil would decline into the $20s several times over the next few decades. Everyone believed the price of oil would continue climbing. In 2008, no one predicted that the price of oil would decline into the $30s in less than a decade. In 2020, for a day or two, the spot market price of oil was actually, and absurdly, negative.

Basic economics tells us that supply and demand of anything are equal at a price. Simplistically, if price is stable and demand goes up, price will go up, causing demand to go down, so that supply and demand again balance. If supply goes up, price will go down until supply and demand again balance.

Here's a thought experiment.

Assume that the oil price is stable, and supply and demand are in balance, when China's economy begins growing and demanding more oil. The price goes up. As price goes up, it becomes profitable for oil companies to look for oil in increasingly difficult areas (e.g., in the Arctic; deep under oceans – we are looking in difficult places because essentially all of the easy-to-find oil has been found), creating, after a period of time for discovery and production, an increase in supply. When demand continues to increase more rapidly than supply, price continues to increase and new technology, such as fracking, becomes profitable. Again, after some period of time, additional supply is created from fracking.

While all of this is going on, the West is going through financial difficulty and is implementing regulations and technology to reduce reliance on fossil fuels to address climate change. China's economic growth begins to slow.

Demand for oil goes down or remains roughly stable, however, all of the wells created when the price was higher and as a result of new technology continue to produce oil. Supply exceeds demand and the price of oil declines.

Because of the low price of oil, the amount of activity around discovery rapidly declines; existing oil wells continue to deplete their supply; and some uneconomic oil wells have to be shut down. The result is that the supply of oil will, over time, decline, ultimately triggering an increase in the price of oil.

And so the cycle continues.

The point of this thought process is to reinforce the difficulty of prediction. In order to make an accurate forecast of the price of oil at some time in the future, you have to predict changes in technology, changes in culture, changes in regulation and changes in the growth rates of multiple economies. More importantly for the larger issues of population and consumption, this interaction of supply, demand and technology will ensure that humans will apply their boundless creativity to support more population at a higher level of consumption than we can imagine today.

However, there will be limits to growth, no matter how much ingenuity is applied. Humans simply consume an almost-unimaginable amount of oil. Peak oil is still out there, even if delayed by fracking.

To provide an idea of scale, in 2015, the world consumed a little more than 35 billion barrels (1.47 trillion gallons) of oil[106]. In 2016, what may be the largest oil discovery in history in the U.S., of approximately 20 billion barrels (840 billion gallons) of oil, was found in West Texas[107]. Simplistically, that gargantuan oil field will supply the world for a little less than seven months at the rate of oil consumption in 2015, assuming that the estimated volume of oil is correct and that all of that oil is economically accessible.

Peak oil is still out there.

However, it may never be reached.

At some point, a factor other than supply and demand and technology becomes dominant in the supply of oil, or any natural resource. This restriction is Energy Return On Energy Invested (EROI or EROEI), which is fundamentally important when considering sustainability. EROI boils down to the fact that at some point, as oil becomes more difficult to find and produce, it will take more than the energy in a barrel of oil to produce a barrel of oil. That means that, at any price, producing the next barrel of oil does not make any sense – you would be using more energy to produce the oil than that new oil can produce when burned.

Worse, civilization requires that the investment of one barrel of oil must return fourteen barrels or more to fuel our everyday lives. One barrel of oil must return enough energy to support all of the activities of an advanced civilization, from food to defense to entertainment to healthcare.

Every increase in the complexity of a society demands that there must be an increase in the surplus of energy to accommodate that complexity.

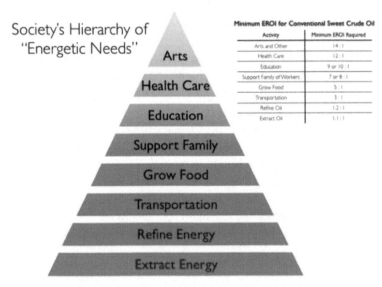

Figure 22 – Society's Hierarchy of "Energetic Needs"[108]

The lower the EROI, the simpler we have to live. An EROI of 3 is probably required just to get the oil out of the ground, refine it, and to provide the infrastructure for transportation and delivery. That is, the energy from one barrel of oil must provide three times the energy required to get it out of the ground just to make refined oil available for use. Basic survival may require an EROI of 5; a complex society with sufficient energy for arts and music may require an EROI of 14.

As with most things, estimates of EROI from different fuels vary. An article from *ScienceDirect* states that, "The EROI for discovering oil and gas in the U.S. has decreased from more than 1000:1 in 1919 to 5:1 in the 2010s, and for production from about 25:1 in the 1970s to approximately 10:1 in 2007 (Guilford et al., 2011). Alternatives to traditional fossil fuels such as tar sands and oil shale (Lambert et al., 2012) deliver a lower EROI, having a mean EROI of 4:1."[109] Wind energy is currently around 18:1; solar photovoltaic currently is around 6.8:1[110] (although a study in Spain came up with 2.45:1[111], asserting that conventional calculations of EROI systematically overstate the level of EROI). Intermittency and other issues are not usually included in the calculation of EROI, but drastically reduce the actual, effective EROI of wind and solar energy.

Because most of the high EROI fuels have either been found or are limited by regulation, the world will increasingly find itself constrained in its energy use by EROI. It will be more and more difficult to find the quality of energy to sustain a modern, Western lifestyle.

EROI is an important consideration in our discussion of sustainability, because EROI is in steady decline. However, it is critical to understand that order and complexity, in an open system such as our economy, can only arise if energy is consumed. The availability of relatively cheap energy enables and is the basis for the complexity of our civilization and culture.

The Future – A New Definition of Peak Oil

"Historically, people have talked about peak oil but now disruptive trends are leading energy experts to consider the implications of peak demand," Ged Davis, executive chair of scenarios at the World Energy Council[112]

There were some 7.8 billion humans in the world in 2020, driving more than 1.2 billion vehicles, increasing to a projected 2 billion vehicles by 2035.[113]

The average gasoline mileage of cars sold in January 2015 in the U.S. was approximately 25.4 miles per gallon[114], about the same as the estimated 25 miles per gallon of the Ford Model T in 1908[115]. In between these two dates, car mileage decreased significantly as cars became bigger and heavier and contained more features and equipment, and then increased in response to regulations. Cars became smaller and lighter and technology improved engine and transmission efficiency.

Doing some very approximate math, in order for overall gasoline consumption to be the same in 2035, when there will be more cars on the road, as it was in 2013, cars in 2035 would have to average approximately 46 miles per gallon. Cars will have to continue to become smaller and lighter, and improvements in technology will be crucial in meeting that objective.

There is increasing conversation around the question of whether peak oil is occurring now. Not because of resource exhaustion or decreasing EROI, but because of disruptive changes in technology and behavior limiting the demand for oil, not its supply. The new definition of peak oil is not a peak in production caused by economics or from EROI, but a peak in demand, caused by technology, changes in the way transportation is provided and by regulations, relating primarily to climate change. The Covid-19 pandemic has had a dramatic effect on the demand for oil. It is not clear what that effect over time will be, but it is likely that it will result in some net reduction in demand for oil.

The world is now rapidly moving toward ride sharing, electric vehicles, reduction of emissions and driverless cars. California has outlawed the sale of new, gasoline-powered cars after 2035; France and the United Kingdom have decreed that there will be no new gasoline engines in cars after 2024. One result of these trends will be a significant reduction in the number of gasoline-burning cars in garages as many people purchase electric vehicles and give up their cars for transportation on demand. In this new world, even an increasing population may require fewer cars than exist today. This effect will be compounded by continued increasing mileage efficiency required by regulation.

The net effect of these trends could be that the date when the maximum amount of annual oil production is reached, peak oil demand, regardless of price, resource availability or EROI, could be right around the corner.

As always, experts differ as to how far away that corner is.

Simon Henry, Chief Financial Officer of Shell Oil, put it this way in 2016: "We've long been of the opinion that demand will peak before supply. And that peak may be somewhere between 5 and 15 years hence, and it will be driven by efficiency and substitution, more than offsetting the new demand for transport."[116]

In 2016 the International Energy Agency examined this new definition of peak oil limited by demand and indicated that it would not occur before 2040.[117]

We are close to or past peak coal due, again, not only to economics or resource limitations, but also to regulation. Burning coal yields a large amount of CO_2 (and other pollutants), and the fear of climate change has led to regulations that effectively make the production of coal uneconomical.

As China increases its demand, we may also be near peak uranium, both because resources are limited and also because of the political and cultural disinclination to use nuclear fission. (However, nuclear energy will likely be an important tool to address climate change, so that the disinclination to use nuclear energy may change over time.)

Yet Another Twist

This gets a little complicated, but it turns out that even with peak demand and the increased supply from fracking, the price of oil will likely skyrocket.

In summary, fracked wells deplete (run out of oil) quickly – perhaps a reduction of 70% in the first year of operation. Given the enormous amount of oil we use, even at peak demand, within a number of years, the amount of fracked oil will begin to decline. In addition, very little "regular" oil has been found in the last few decades. Peak oil-discovery, on which we are still living, was the 1960s. Since that time, relatively little oil has been discovered. We are not discovering enough oil to replace the oil we are pumping out of the ground. The result will likely be a supply crunch in the 2020s which will send the price of oil to new, record highs, even at peak demand.

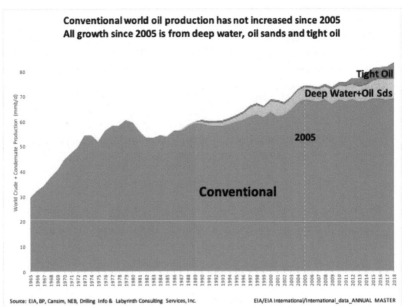

Source: EIA, BP, Cansim, NEB, Drilling Info & Labyrinth Consulting Services, Inc.   EIA/EIA International/International_data_ANNUAL MASTER

Figure 23– Sources of increases in oil production since 1965 ("tight oil" is essentially that recovered through fracking)

Additionally, since it takes years, perhaps decades, to recover investment in discovery, production and refining, as providers of energy anticipate peak oil demand and increased regulation associated with climate change, they will decrease investment. This, in turn, will create a self-fulfilling prophesy, leading to a shortage of oil, leading to high prices. To the extent that the anticipated peak demand for oil is optimistic due to constraints on the capacity of the electric grid and other factors, the oil shortage could become acute and prices for oil-based energy could skyrocket.

As a part of this trend, the International Energy Agency has said that, in order to reach the goal of net zero emissions by 2050, development of new oil and gas fields must stop in 2021. In addition, there can be no new coal-fired power stations, and the agency recommended that no new gasoline- and diesel-powered cars be sold after 2035.

It is very difficult to forecast multiple outcomes, decades in advance. The odds of getting it right are small, and the associated challenges and investments are large.

In yet another twist, any high price of oil would motivate intensive investment in the electric infrastructure.

And, The Final Twist

The world's major economies are sufficiently fragile and highly indebted to the point that they cannot stand high oil prices. High oil prices will cripple those economies.

Producers require higher prices in order to profit from producing oil.

There is an ever-decreasing band within which both producers and the economy can flourish.

The irony is that the demand for green energy will lead to peak demand for oil, which will lead to high oil prices, which cannot be sustained by the world economy.

Back to Prediction

It is not possible to simply conclude that, "the world will come to an end on October 22, 2075." The most likely outcome will be a series of changes and reactions to those changes. These changes and reactions will occur within a general framework of increasing scarcity. Humanity will attempt to alleviate or compensate for that scarcity through technology.

Technology can change the rules of the game.

Let's take a look at how nature is holding up amidst all of this change.

The U.N. Intergovernmental Science-Policy Platform on Biodiversity and Ecosystem Services (IPBES)

In 2019, the IPBES issued its first report, which was summarized in an article by Marlowe Hood of AFP.[118] The sustainability cousin to the IPCC, the U.N.'s climate change body, essentially examines how nature is holding up during what some call the Anthropocene – a geologic era dominated by humans. In the Anthropocene, humans are having a measurable effect on the planet. Robert Watson, chair of the committee, said, "The way we produce our food and energy is undermining the regulating services that we get from Nature," adding that only "transformative change" can stem the damage.

"If we're going to have a sustainable planet that provides services to communities around the world, we need to change this trajectory in the next ten years, just as we need to do that with climate," noted WWF chief scientist Rebecca Shaw, formerly a member of the U.N. scientific bodies for both climate and biodiversity.

Among the report's findings are

- Up to one million species face extinction due to human influence.
- The accelerating loss of clean air, drinkable water, CO2-absorbing forests, pollinating insects, protein-rich fish and storm-blocking mangroves - to name but a few of the dwindling services rendered by Nature - poses no less of a threat than climate change.
- Deforestation and agriculture, including livestock production, account for about a quarter of greenhouse gas emissions, and have wreaked havoc on natural ecosystems as well.
- Three-quarters of land surfaces, 40 percent of the marine environment, and 50 percent of inland waterways across the globe have been "severely altered".
- Nearly half of land and marine ecosystems have been profoundly compromised by human interference in the last 50 years.

We will explore the effects humans are having on fish, insects and other species, below. The following graph provides striking evidence of humans' effects on mammals.

This chart shows an 85% decrease in wild mammalian biomass in the last 100,000 years.

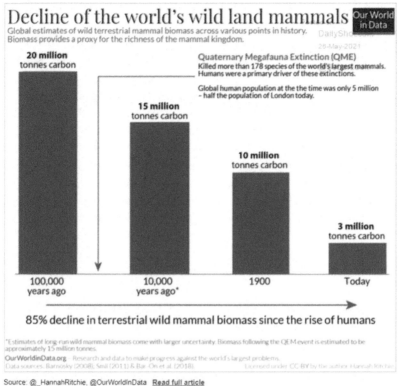

Figure 24 – Decline of the world's wild land mammals[119]

Mammalian biomass associated with humans and the livestock we raise for food now thoroughly dominate the planet. "Humans account for about 36 percent of the biomass of all mammals. Domesticated livestock, mostly cows and pigs, account for 60 percent, and wild mammals for only 4 percent."[120]

Which raises the question, how many people can our planet support?

Carrying Capacity

As Malthus and Darwin showed, every biological population expands right to the limit of its starvation –
Kevin Kelly[121]

Carrying capacity, as used in this book, means the number of humans that the Earth can sustain in the long run. It is the number that can be supported at a given level of consumption without harming the environment to the point that the number of sustainable humans decreases due to environmental and resource degradation.

As an analogy, consider the capacity of a field to support rabbits. Rabbits happily procreate and increase their numbers, so long as their field can supply adequate food and water. Simplistically, ignoring predators and disease, the carrying capacity of rabbits is determined by the number of rabbits that can be sustained by the food available from the field.

In a year with unusually good weather, as the food supply increases, the number of rabbits increases beyond normal, sustainable carrying capacity. If the next year is a drought, or even an average year, the food supply decreases from that available in the good year, there are too many rabbits for the field, the rabbits' health declines and rabbits die. The excess of rabbits over the long-term, sustainable carrying capacity is called Overshoot. Overshoot is not sustainable and can be damaging to the field.

Carrying capacity depends on consumption as well as population. There is not one level of carrying capacity, but various levels within a range, corresponding to various levels of "quality of life" for the rabbits. Rabbits can live near starvation in a field at one population level, live optimally at another and temporarily overconsume in Overshoot, denuding the field, at another.

We humans have faced the constraint of carrying capacity continually during our history. Primitive hunters moved from place to place in search of sufficient game. Tribes would settle in a valley and live or die based on the amount of food and game they could access in that valley. If they consumed all the firewood, they had to move. City states depended on good weather to stave off the constant threat of famine.

Modern humans have used capitalism-enabled technology to dramatically improve carrying capacity. "It took six times as much farmland to feed a single person 9,000 years ago, at the dawn of the Neolithic revolution, than it does today, even as almost all of us eat much richer diets.[122]"

As transportation improved and trade increased, humans could make up for shortages in one field, on one farm, in one village or in one area by trading for surpluses in other fields, farms, villages and areas. Ultimately, worldwide trade means that shortages can be mitigated anywhere on Earth, and that we, in the 21st century, can enjoy luxuries, such as strawberries in December.

This increase in available food and materials has increased the carrying capacity of the Earth and made the entire Earth humans' field. Having access to the resources of the entire Earth enables more than 600,000 people to live in the desert of Las Vegas, more than 1.6 million in the desert of Phoenix, and more than 4 million in the desert of Riyadh. It also enables some 325 million people, even the poor, to have an extraordinary standard of living in the United States, compared with the standard of living of the vast majority of humans who have ever lived.

(There is a downside to this interconnection, unintended consequences, summarized by Taleb, et. al. as follows: "The greatest impact of human beings on this natural system connectivity [the natural connectivity of different parts of the Earth via oceans and atmosphere] is through dramatic increases in global transportation. The impact of invasive species and rapid global transmission of diseases demonstrates the role of human activity in connecting previously much more isolated natural systems. The role of transportation and communication in connecting civilization itself is apparent in economic interdependence manifest in cascading financial crises that were not possible even a hundred years ago. The danger we are facing today is that we as a civilization are globally connected, and the fat tail of the distribution of shocks extends globally, to our peril."[123])

Determining the human carrying capacity of Earth has been a subject of intense debate ever since the Reverend Thomas Malthus published his first edition of *An Essay on the Principle of Population* in 1798[124]. His basic thesis was, since unchecked population growth is exponential (growing ever faster) and growth in the food supply is linear (straight line, at a constant rate), the results of unchecked population growth are suffering, poverty and famines as populations out-strip food supplies. Malthus said, "The power of population is so superior to the power of the Earth to produce subsistence for man that premature death must in some shape or other visit the human race."

From the conditions during his time and the knowledge available to him, Malthus' logic and conclusions were perfectly reasonable.

Then technology happened to Malthus. He did not foresee (and could not have foreseen) the agricultural revolution brought on by using fertilizer, applying science to planting crops and modifying plant genes. These factors have led to an exponential growth in the availability of food, supporting an exponential growth in human population. We have now gotten to the point that obesity is arguably as significant a problem as malnutrition.

Malthus would be astounded.

However, we are running out of land, running out of water, running out of phosphorus, running out of topsoil and running out of fish. We may be at a Malthusian point in the early 21st century, similar to the Malthusian point in the late 18th century. We could be on the verge of overrunning our field, of running out of things, while still producing more people. And we are producing unimaginable amounts of waste.

We need to be humble and cautious when predicting doom and gloom, remembering not only Malthus, but also Paul Ehrlich. Dr. Ehrlich wrote *The Population Bomb* in 1968[125], which predicted widespread starvation and the depletion of many natural resources. He said, "The battle to feed all of humanity is over. In the 1970s hundreds of millions of people will starve to death in spite of any crash programs embarked upon now. At this late date nothing can prevent a substantial increase in the world death rate." Ehrlich still believes that he was right, just early, as was Malthus.

Either there will be another technology transformation similar to the one brought on by the Industrial Revolution, or we will overshoot (or may have already overshot) the capacity of the Earth to carry humans.

While agreeing that technological miracles are entirely possible, let's explore the current state of play regarding carrying capacity.

Carrying capacity depends on several things: land, water, groundwater, topsoil, the ability to handle waste, energy, etc. In any given geographic area, the first limit reached will determine the carrying capacity for that area. For example, in one area, there may be sufficient water, but not enough arable land to produce adequate food.

Computations are complicated, because carrying capacity includes two primary variables: the number of humans and the amount consumed by each human. Human consumption varies dramatically, from the starvation of subsistence farming to the luxuries of billionaires.

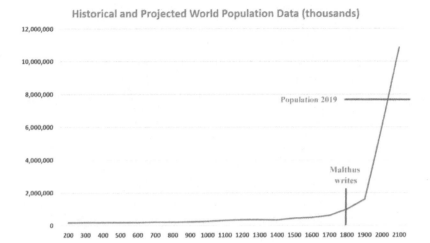

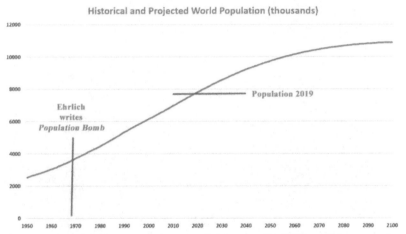

Figure 25 – Growth in human population. Historical data from WorldOMeter.[126] Forecast and historical data by the United Nations Department of Economic and Social Affairs[127] "medium" case. I prepared these charts.

Malthus made his projections just as the Industrial Revolution was beginning, when the Earth's human population was approximately 1 billion. Human population began its exponential increase and in 2020 was approximately 7.8 billion. Because of improvements in medicine, hygiene and medical care, life expectancies increased dramatically. Ironically, increasing quality of life, the cost of children in an urban setting and, particularly, reasonable assurance that children will survive childhood, seem to contribute to a decreased desire for offspring. This decrease in the relative number of children, combined with a one-time increase in population from longer average lifespans, which is ending, leads to a forecast that the rate of increase of the population of humans will decrease significantly between 2050 and 2100 (most of the projected increase in population will be in Africa). Population is forecasted to increase more slowly above 10 billion. However, even though the rate of growth will decrease, population is projected to increase by approximately 50% by 2100 - within about one human lifetime.

(When the U.N. made its population projections, it assumed that lifespans would generally increase over time. However, there is a potentially significant increase in longevity that is predicted by those involved with the science of aging. Some of these scientists are predicting healthy living to 120 or 150 years of age, a trend which may begin as early as 2029[128]. If these predictions are correct, fewer people will die at any one time, increasing future population levels above these estimates. The economic good news is that people may live significantly longer; the sustainability bad news is that they will also be consumers for much longer.)

Figure 26 – Billions and billions of people, some of whom consume conspicuously

Various individuals and groups have attempted to calculate the Earth's carrying capacity for humans.

The Limits to Growth

The Limits to Growth and its 30-year update anticipated the later modeling of climate change, and its models are subject to the same criticisms and limitations. These books reported on a complicated, dynamic mathematical model, which factored in population, pollution, food and other resources interacting with one another. The result was the ability to look at projected population under various scenarios.

One such projection is that, under a "business-as-usual" scenario (BAU), population would peak at around 8.1 billion in 2030, more or less, and then would collapse to below 4 billion by the end of the century. Carrying capacity under these assumptions is below 4 billion, following an Overshoot of 8.1 billion.

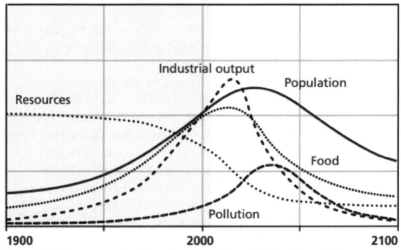

Figure 27 - Business-as-usual model results, *The Limits to Growth – 30-year Update*

This more-nuanced look at human population predicts a collapse in human population, following a point when resources begin to become exhausted. The analogy might be that the rabbits denude the field during Overshoot to the point that the field cannot fully recover, which in turn significantly reduces the number of rabbits that can be carried sustainably in the future.

This population collapse does not occur because the Earth runs out of resources, but because the quality of key resources decreases as it costs more and more to extract usable resources from raw materials.

Although *The Limits to Growth* was criticized and subject to a good deal of mischaracterization, the assumptions used in *The Limits to Growth* were reviewed by Graham Turner in 2008 and updated in 2014. Turner concluded that the predictions in the books remain valid, and that "we have squandered the past decades, and that preparing for a collapsing global system could be even more important than trying to avoid collapse."[129]

In a podcast in 2019, Dennis Meadows, one of the co-authors of *The Limits to Growth*, discussed its conclusions, looking back over 47 years. His conclusions were much the same as Graham Turner's. He also said that he was not going to create an additional update to *Limits*. He said that previous updates had included recommendations of actions to be taken which could lead to sustainability. He now believes that it is too late – that we have too many people consuming too many resources so that decline is now inevitable.[130]

In 2021, Gaya Herrington recreated the *Limits to Growth* calculations for all scenarios which were considered in the original study. She concluded[131]

> The data comparison, which used the latest World3 version, included four scenarios: BAU, BAU2, CT, and SW. Empirical data showed a relatively close fit for most of the variables. This was true to some extent for all scenarios, because in several cases the scenarios do not significantly diverge until 2020. When scenarios had started to diverge, the ones that aligned closest with empirical data most often were BAU2 and CT. This result is different to previous comparisons that used the earlierWorld3 version, and which indicated BAU as the most closely followed scenario. The scenario that depicts the smallest declines in economic output, SW, is also the one that aligned least closely with observed data. Furthermore, the two closest aligning scenarios BAU2 and CT, respectively, predict a collapse pattern and moderate decline in output. At this point therefore, the data most aligns with the CT and BAU2 scenarios which indicate a slowdown and eventual halt in growth within the next decade or so, but World3 leaves open whether the subsequent decline will constitute a collapse.

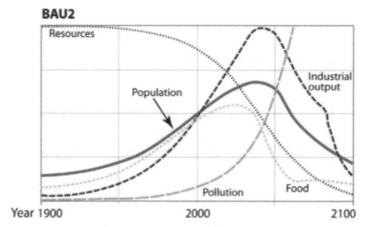

BAU2

Resources

Population

Industrial output

Pollution

Food

Year 1900   2000   2100

Figure 28 – Limits to Growth's scenario BAU2 as illustrated in the Herrington article

BAU2 includes essentially the same assumptions as scenario BAU (business as usual, i.e., assume that historical trends will continue), except that it assumes double the natural resources of BAU. Population peaks at somewhat higher levels and perhaps a decade later, around 2040, in BAU2 than BAU.

Scenarios other than BAU and BAU2 assume that substantial actions are taken to prevent the predicted collapse.

Eco-Footprint

Another approach to determining carrying capacity comes from calculating the eco-footprint per person. An eco-footprint is a measure of the amount of resources consumed by an average person. There are various calculations and disagreements, so the following numbers are not unanimously agreed upon. However, they do indicate the magnitude of the problem. According to the Global Footprint Network[132], the Earth is currently overpopulated by some 60%, or approximately 2.9 billion people. Carrying capacity is, therefore, on the order of a little less than 5 billion people. (Of course, one solution to this problem is to lower the average amount of resources consumed by each person by about 40% and produce no more people.) On this scale, each person is using the resources equivalent to 2.7 hectares (6.7 acres), while the Earth is supplying 1.7 hectares (4.2 acres) of resources (all data are from 2016 – as population increases the available resources per person decreases).

On average, according to the ecological footprint approach, the world transitioned from sustainability to unsustainability in 1970.

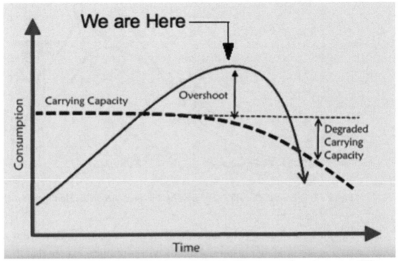

Figure 29 – Illustration of current overshoot as calculated by the eco-footprint approach[133]

When considering eco-footprints, it is important to look beyond averages. Data from 2012 by country[134] provides some perspective. For example the U.S. is blessed with above-average resources of 3.87, but, at 8.2 is consuming more than twice the amount of resources it has. Canada is also blessed with 16.01 in resources and is consuming only 8.17. In comparison, Luxembourg has biocapacity of only 1.68 and is consuming 15.82 global hectares per person.

Simplistically, by these calculations, the U.S. is consuming almost five times the average resources available, worldwide. Another way to look at it is that the U.S. would have to reduce its consumption by approximately 80% in order to equal world average resources available.

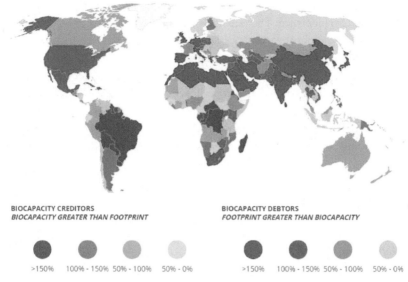

BIOCAPACITY CREDITORS
BIOCAPACITY GREATER THAN FOOTPRINT

BIOCAPACITY DEBTORS
FOOTPRINT GREATER THAN BIOCAPACITY

>150%   100% - 150% 50% - 100%   50% - 0%   >150%   100% - 150% 50% - 100%   50% - 0%

Figure 30 – Biocapacity creditors and debtors.[135]

Figure 30 shows that the nations of the northern hemisphere are exceeding their biocapacity, while the nations of the southern hemisphere are generally within their sustainability limits.

Any country that is living beyond its biocapacity is either denuding its field or importing someone else's biocapacity or both.

An excellent example of the importation of biocapacity is various countries importing wheat from the U.S. Topsoil, water, fertilizer, pesticides, seeds, labor, energy, equipment, transportation and infrastructure are combined in the U.S. to grow wheat (and many other grains, fruits and vegetables) to be exported to other countries. One way of looking at this process is that the U.S. is exporting (or using up) its biocapacity - topsoil, water, fertilizer, pesticides, seed, labor, energy, machines, transportation and infrastructure - and sending the resulting wheat to other countries. A kernel of wheat is effectively a tiny package consisting of topsoil, water, fertilizer, pesticides, a seed, labor, energy, machinery, transportation and infrastructure. The U.S. exports a huge amount of wheat. According to the U.S. Department of Agriculture, the U.S. exported 27.89 million metric tons (30.74 tons) of wheat in the 2016 / 2017 season[136]. Since 1,500 liters (396 gallons) of water are required to produce one kilogram (2.2 pounds) of wheat[137], 19 million liters (5 million gallons) of water are required to produce one year's volume of wheat exports. Much of that water is being drawn from aquifers that are not being replenished. The U.S. is using up its biocapacity and incurring pollution from fertilizer and pesticides to provide other countries with wheat. From an economic perspective, as currently viewed, this is a good deal. From a sustainability perspective, and economically, if water usage, resource depletion and pollution were properly accounted for, this is a bad deal.

On a global basis, according to the eco-footprint measure, we are rapidly denuding our field, in agreement with *The Limits to Growth's* forecast.

Rigorous Analysis

In a paper published in *Nature Sustainability*, O'Neill, et. al. attempted to compute carrying capacity based on Planetary Boundaries, discussed below. Their conclusion is that the Earth's carrying capacity at a low, but survivable, standard of living is around 7 billion.[138]

In a paper published in *Nature*,[139] Bologna and Aquino modeled population and resource consumption and generally concluded that population would peak around 10 billion and then begin a "catastrophic decline," to a low number (approximately 2 billion by the year 2500).

> In conclusion our model shows that a catastrophic collapse in human population, due to resource consumption, is the most likely scenario of the dynamical evolution based on current parameters. Adopting a combined deterministic and stochastic model we conclude from a statistical point of view that the probability that our civilisation survives itself is less than 10% in the most optimistic scenario. Calculations show that, maintaining the actual rate of population growth and resource consumption, in particular forest consumption, we have a few decades left ["on the order of 2-4 decades] before an irreversible collapse of our civilisation. Making the situation even worse, we stress once again that it is unrealistic to think that the decline of the population in a situation of strong environmental degradation would be a non-chaotic and well-ordered decline. This consideration leads to an even shorter remaining time.

Edward O. Wilson calculated a carrying capacity of 10 billion, assuming everyone became a vegetarian. (Others have examined the effect of diet on carrying capacity in greater detail and have concluded that, given the requirement for protein in the human diet and that cows and other meat producers can be raised on land unsuitable for raising crops, there would be little effect from a switch to vegetarianism.)

A study by the Potsdam Institute for Climate Impact Research in 2020[140], concluded that, "adopting radically different ways of farming, reduction of food waste, and dietary changes," the world could support 10 billion people and remain within the planetary boundaries, discussed below, preserving the environment. The study concludes that the present food system could provide a balanced diet of 2,355 kilocalories per person per day within the planetary boundaries for only 3.4 billion people. Radical changes are required in spatially redistributed cropland, improved water-nutrient management, food waste reduction and dietary changes to achieve this outcome.

Therefore, one, simplistic upper limit of carrying capacity, ignoring other constraints and challenges, and ignoring the march of technology, is 10 billion, the forecasted human population of Earth around 2060.

Pimentel, et.al. produced estimates for "adequate food supply and assuming that soil conservation programs were implemented to counteract erosion," that carrying capacity would be approximately 3 billion.[141] (Under other assumptions, the result was that, "a population of 1-2 billion could be supported in relative prosperity."[142])

Ken Small, professor of Anthropology at Kenyon College, is pessimistic, saying that we need a shrinkage in global population from a peak of 9-10 billion to a "population optimum" of "not more than 2 to 3 billion."[143]

Paul Ehrlich was asked to sum up his view of the best intersection of consumption and population in an interview with *New Scientist* magazine in 2020.[144] His response was

> ...we (he, his wife, Anne and Stanford biologist, Gretchen Daily) decided that what you'd want is a world where

people could make choices about their lifestyles, where there were few enough people so that you could actually have wilderness, but enough people so you could have big cities and operas and nice restaurants and so on. And we figured about 1 or 2 billion people, because that would be about the number between the 19th and 20th centuries, around 1900 when there were big cities and there was still wilderness. And we have better technologies today, so we could do a better job of it.

William Rees, in a paper in *Ecological Economics*, "Ecological economics for humanity's plague phase,"[145] describes homo sapiens as a "plague species."

> The human enterprise is in potentially disastrous 'overshoot', exploiting the ecosphere beyond ecosystems' regenerative capacity and filling natural waste sinks to overflowing. Economic behavior that was once 'rational' has become maladaptive. This situation is the inevitable outcome of humanity's natural expansionist tendencies reinforced by ecologically vacuous growth-oriented 'neoliberal' economic theory.

> … human society has exceeded regenerative limits of ecosystems and become parasitic on the ecosphere. An economy that grows and maintains itself by depleting the biophysical basis of its own existence is inherently unsustainable

> … accept that rational short-term economic behavior at the individual or small group level has become maladaptive at the long-term global level

> … conceive and implement a global fertility strategy to reduce the human population to the two billion (±) people that might be able to live in material comfort on this already much-damaged single planet Earth.

Most of the predictions in this book are subject to so many assumptions, and future possibilities are so great in number, that exact amounts or even approximate estimations are impossible to compute (either here or by other authors). What we will be looking for are broad approximations, trends and change dynamics.

For example, potential limits for sustainable human population under various assumptions considered so far are 10 billion, 7 billion, 5 billion, less than 4 billion (following a collapse from 8.1 billion), between 2 and 3 billion (also following a collapse, in this case from 9-10 billion), 2 billion (following a collapse from 10 billion), 3 billion, 1-2 billion, 1.6 billion and (in calculations later in this book) 7.5 billion and 7 billion, in a world currently populated by more than 7.7 billion people, inevitably headed for more than 10 billion. These estimates lead to the conclusion that human population is probably, in 2021, already in Overshoot.

However, most of these calculations of carrying capacity are based on a kind of best-case scenario. The question they tend to address is, "What is the carrying capacity based on current consumption?" In order to calculate a more accurate carrying capacity, we have to take into consideration that resources have to be available for maintenance of existing assets (roads, clothing, tools, etc.), for use in providing common goods and services (water, sewer, garbage collection, etc.) and for the use of future generations.

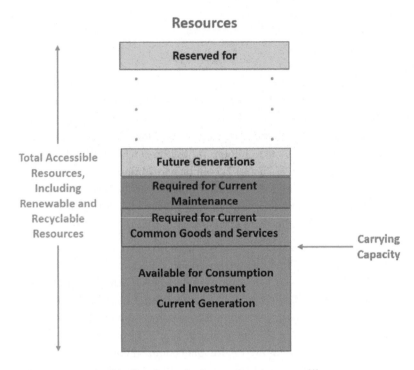

Figure 31 – Simple allocation of resources in a steady-state economy[146]

Figure 31 is a graphic description of the fact that resources must be reserved from current consumption to supply common goods and services, to maintain existing assets and for the use of future generations. These resource allocations must be considered in the calculation of carrying capacity, making the 7 – 10 billion range of "reasonable" estimates significantly higher than the likely, actual, effective range. This idea will be explored further in the section on the steady-state economy, below.

We will be looking for evidence and not certainty, however, the trend is clearly heading in the wrong direction. It is all but certain that some portion of the human population in some locations is in Overshoot now. And all indications are that the human population as a whole is either in Overshoot now or soon will be.

However, paradoxically and counter-intuitively, it turns out that population does not matter, in the sense that there is little we can do about it over the timeframe between now and the greatest projected time for Overshoot. Although population is one of the two principal causes of the consumption crisis, it is essentially uncontrollable during the timeframe we will be discussing. *The Limits to Growth's* theoretical population peak-before-collapse of around 8.1 billion people less than approximately 9 years from now means that, unless there is some unusual catastrophe, population will inevitably reach that limit, and we may be exposed to the projected collapse. As Paul and Anne Ehrlich put it, "… only dramatic changes, on the scale of World War 2 mobilisations, hold out … hope."[147]

And if such a collapse does not happen, then a population of 10 billion will occur in approximately 40 years. Within less than one half of one human lifetime, we will reach what appears to be an upper limit to carrying capacity.

Population may be critically important, but it does not matter in the sense that there is nothing that can practically be done about it in the Overshoot timeframe. There is not enough time for education or even to develop the consensus required for worldwide regulation to result in a reduction in population. If the critical level of population is less than 10 billion, we will inevitably reach that level when a baby born in 2021 is in middle age.

By the time overpopulation and shortages of resources are obvious to most people, the carrying capacity will have been exceeded. It will then be time to focus on survival, which will, in turn, force sustainability under any alternative.

The opposing view – the technological cavalry

(I will use the metaphor of the technological cavalry to indicate that the "good guys" can win in the end by the unexpected arrival of sufficient technological progress to turn the tide to sustainability. It is a reference to many old western movies in which, just as all seemed lost, a cavalry of soldiers arrived to save the day. As a resident of Texas, where the story of the Alamo is ingrained into every citizen, I am aware that sometimes, in real life, the cavalry does not arrive.)

Erle C. Ellis, writing an op-ed in the *New York Times*, argues that we have always met the challenge of carrying capacity in the past, primarily through the use of technology, and we should assume that we will meet it in the future. "The idea that humans must live within the natural environmental limits of our planet denies the realities of our entire history, and most likely the future. Humans are niche creators. We transform ecosystems to sustain ourselves. This is what we do and have always done. Our planet's human-carrying capacity emerges from the capabilities of our social systems and our technologies more than from any environmental limits."[148]

I believe this view is wrong, due to the turkey fallacy. A turkey, in early-November, can look back on a very pleasant life. However, as they say in investing circles, "past performance is not a predictor of future results." On the next day, the turkey experiences a severe change in trend. (Turkey is the primary component of Thanksgiving dinner in the U.S., a celebration held in November of each year.)

Without significant technological improvements, the future will be increasingly crowded and constrained. The way to bet is that there will be continued technological improvement, which will, in effect, increase carrying capacity. Whether there will be sufficient technological change requires a leap of faith, which Mr. Ellis has made.

We will need a lot of technology in a short amount of time.

My View on Carrying Capacity

It appears that we humans, on average, are currently exceeding our carrying capacity and are in Overshoot, denuding our field. The average combines the Overshoot in the U.S. and the Western world with countries living within their ecological footprints. While the eco-footprint approach to calculating carrying capacity is flawed, it does indicate of the magnitudes of the problems. Humans, at current population levels, must decrease our consumption materially and immediately. The average human must cut their consumption by something on the order of one-fourth to one-half. As population increases, the amount of reduction in consumption must increase, proportionally, effectively reversing consumer capitalism.

The good news is that we have always been able to find a way out of problems with our creativity expressed in new technology. Technology can help by making the use of natural resources more efficient, however, any finite, non-renewable resource can ultimately be depleted (economically and practically). Any renewable resource will be able to support a given population level, and that sustainable population level will change in direct proportion to changes in the efficiency of use of those resources. The future becomes a race between population control and consumption control on one hand and increased efficiency, including the use of technology, on the other hand.

What are these limitations on resources?

Planetary Boundaries

The scientific community is in the early days of creating a concept called planetary boundaries. This idea provides a structured framework for discussing and defining the limits beyond which "the Earth system will no longer be in a resilient and accommodating state." In essence, these are measures of the degree to which the creation of goods and services is reaching its limits. While this concept and the associated data are evolving, following is a summary of the boundaries and their status:

- Climate Change – The proposed boundaries have already been surpassed. The proposed boundary for atmospheric concentration of CO_2, 350 parts per million (ppm), exceeded 400 ppm in 2017. The proposed boundary for radiative forcing (the increased energy in the atmosphere due to greenhouse gasses) of 1 watt / square meter, was 1.5 in 2016.
- Stratospheric Ozone Depletion – Ozone is a variation of the oxygen molecule that, among other things, has formed a layer in the upper atmosphere, protecting the Earth's inhabitants from destructive ultraviolet rays. A proposed planetary boundary is no more than a 5% decrease in ozone levels for a particular latitude with respect to 1964-1980 values. Actions taken by the world to reduce the emissions of fluorocarbons have resulted in an increase in the level of stratospheric ozone and the beginning of closure of an "ozone hole" that formed over Antarctica so that there is confidence that this boundary can be maintained.
- Interference with the Global Phosphorus and Nitrogen Cycles – Primarily due to the heavy use of fertilizers, ecosystems are being degraded and disrupted, and climate change potentially increased. The first planetary boundary is a limitation on the extraction of nitrogen from the atmosphere, thereby limiting the use of nitrogen in fertilizers. A proposed preliminary boundary is 25% of its current value, so that the boundary has been significantly exceeded. A boundary on the use of phosphorus is required to prevent severe

oxygen depletion in the oceans due to runoff of fertilizer containing phosphates. No boundary has yet been proposed, and it is unlikely that phosphorus will exceed any proposed boundary in the near future.

- Atmospheric Aerosol Loading – Aerosols are fine particles introduced into the atmosphere by humans and through natural and manufacturing processes, and include particles, atmospheric ozone, sulphur oxide and nitrogen oxide. Aerosols have a role in climate change, ecosystem degradation and in adversely affecting human health. Although aerosol loading is considered important, there are currently no proposed planetary boundaries for the different aerosols.

- Ocean Acidification – Basically, some of the increased atmospheric CO_2 from human activity is absorbed by the ocean, making the water more acidic (actually, less alkaline). This decreased alkalinity dissolves the shells of some ocean creatures, disrupting the ecosystem and food chains. There is discussion around a planetary boundary of 2.75 for a measurement of a form of calcium carbonate. The current value is around 2.99, so that this boundary remains intact. (This issue is complicated, since some tiny unicellular shellfish (foraminifera) make better shells in a less-alkaline environment.)

- Chemical Pollution – "Primary types of chemical pollution include radioactive compounds, heavy metals, and a wide range of organic compounds of human origin." No boundaries have yet been established for the thousands of potential chemical pollutants.

- Freshwater Use –Humans are, in effect, using up stores of freshwater, severely disrupting ecosystems. The boundary for human consumption of water is 4,000 cubic kilometers per year. Current consumption is 2,600 cubic kilometers per year, so that this boundary has not been exceeded on average. However, this boundary average has been exceeded in many parts of the world.

- Land-System Change – Land-system change primarily results from the conversion of forest and other ecosystems to agricultural land, disrupting the original ecosystems. If this trend continues, it will threaten biodiversity and compromise some of the Earth system's functioning, such as the hydrological (water) cycle. The proposed planetary boundary is 15% of the global, ice-free land surface as a maximum devoted to cropland. The current level is approximately 12%. This boundary remains intact.

- Biosphere Integrity (biodiversity loss) – A large number of species is becoming extinct due to the direct and indirect actions of humans, to the point that the current period is being referred to as the sixth great extinction. (Previous large-scale extinctions have been caused by meteors and volcanoes.) "Humans have increased the rate of species extinction by 100-1000 times the background rates that were typical over Earth's history." An initial boundary is proposed to be 10 times the background rate (the historical rate prior to significant human intervention), which is already significantly exceeded.[149]

Four of the eight proposed and quantified planetary boundaries have already been exceeded - atmospheric concentration of CO_2, radiative forcing, extraction of nitrogen from the atmosphere and biodiversity loss. In addition, water use boundaries are being exceeded in many parts of the world, indicating stress in the resiliency of Earth's systems.

Several of these boundary areas will be discussed in this book as they pertain to consumption, including ground freshwater use, the nitrogen and phosphorus cycles, ocean acidification, land-system change and climate change.

Consumption

Consumption and its effects on the use of resources can be summarized by the consideration of three categories: food, energy and materials, such as iron, aluminum and rare earths. An analysis of food leads to a deeper look at soil, water, fish, and fertilizer.

The Magnitude of the Consumption Challenge

The amount of things currently consumed in one year around the world is astounding to the point of being difficult to comprehend. Following are some examples:

Oil	34 billion barrels (1.4 trillion gallons) (2015)
Natural gas	3.6 million cubic meters (127 million cubic feet (2016)
Coal	6.9 billion tonnes (7.6 billion tons) (2017)
Uranium	86 million kilograms (190 million pounds) (2016)

Steel	1.7 billion tonnes (1.9 billion tons) (2017)
Aluminum	60 million tonnes (66 million tons) (2017)
Beef	59 billion kilograms (130 billion pounds) (2015)
Chickens	20 billion (2012)
Concrete	25 billion tonnes (28 billion tons) (2009)
Silicon wafers	7.6 million square meters (9.1 million square yards) (2018)
Automobiles	70.5 million (2018)

And, it gets worse. Population is forecasted to increase from 7.8 billion in 2020 to around 10 billion in 2060. Most of this increase will be in third-world countries, whose occupants will want to strive for a better life and therefore consume more than those countries' inhabitants are consuming today.

Humans are trying to understand the impact of this level of consumption on the environment and on the Earth's sustainability.

Food

Not only will there be more people in the future, but those people will want to consume more. Humans seem to have a natural desire for more, and capitalism provides the mechanism by which one can get more. One projection by the United Nations Food and Agriculture Organization is that by 2050, we will need 70% more food to feed an ever-increasing population, which will demand greater quantities and a greater variety of food, including meat.[150]

The U.N. has estimated that, "Globally, the current yields of wheat, maize [corn] and rice have been estimated at 64, 50 and 64 per cent of their potential respectively, but the size of the yield gap varies greatly from region to region under the influence of different factors." These estimates are based on applying state-of-the-art farming to all available land. "Extending conventional agriculture into uncultivated lands requires mechanization to modify the surface, and supplements in the form of fertilizers, herbicides, pesticides and irrigation water. Excessive use of machinery and chemical supplements, however, breaks up soil structure, increases erosion, chemically pollutes soil, contaminates groundwater and surface water, changes greenhouse gas fluxes, destroys habitat and builds genetic resistance to chemical supplements."[151]

Simplistically, since essentially all arable land is now being farmed, existing land must produce 70% more in 33 years' time. Since this is unlikely to happen, something will have to give. If the trend cannot continue, it will stop. Technology can help, but a 70% increase is more than a significant challenge.

Those additional people in the future will also demand the material possessions associated with the good life, e.g., cars, cell phones, entertainment. These require natural resources to produce.

Even though the Earth is very large, there are now enough people consuming enough things to begin to infringe on and violate the Earth's planetary boundaries.

Perhaps the most precious contributor to our wellbeing is one we take for granted.

Water

"When the well is dry, we know the worth of water" - Benjamin Franklin[152]

Humans have, to a great extent, taken capitalism out of the equation for water. Because of culture, politics and resulting regulations, water is not being priced properly and is therefore being wasted.

Although about 71% of Earth's surface is covered with water, only approximately 3% of that is fresh water. Worse, much of the fresh water, over 68%, is all but inaccessible, in icecaps and glaciers. Only about 0.3% of fresh water is found in the surface water of lakes, rivers, and swamps.

Where is Earth's Water?

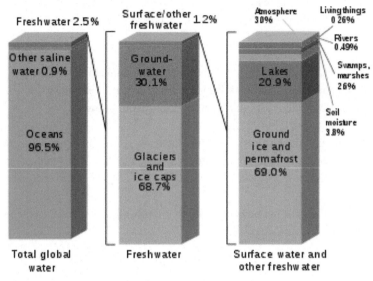

Figure 32 – Where is Earth's Water?[153]

Much of the surface water circulates in the Water Cycle, as water evaporates from surface water, rains from clouds and runs off into surface water again.

Of course, it is more complicated than that.

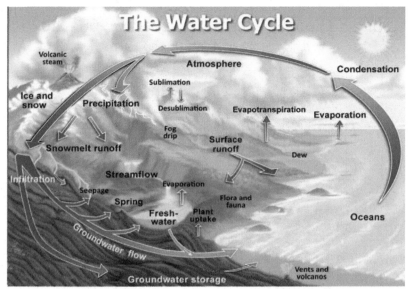

Figure 33 – The Water Cycle[154]

There are glaring indications that all is not right with respect to water:

- rivers, including the Colorado in the U.S., are totally depleted before they reach the ocean;
- aquifers, including the Ogallala in the U.S., containing millennia of accumulated water, are being depleted and in some instances have been exhausted;
- lakes around the world are shrinking; and
- much of the water that is available for use is polluted to the point of being toxic.

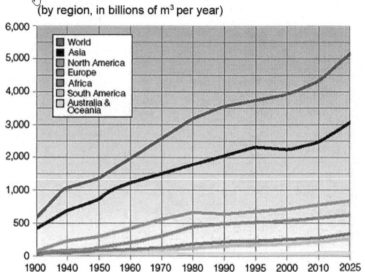

Global Water Consumption 1900 – 2025
(by region, in billions of m³ per year)

Legend:
- World
- Asia
- North America
- Europe
- Africa
- South America
- Australia & Oceania

Figure 34 – Historical water consumption by region, billions of cubic meters (one cubic meter = 264 gallons)[155]

We use gargantuan amounts of water, and not just for showers, watering the grass, flushing and drinking. We may not fully understand the amount of water required to produce food and materials. Grace Communications Foundation calculated the water required for a simple lunch and concluded that a loaf of bread requires about 240 gallons of water, a pound of cheese takes about 56 gallons of water, a small bag of potato chips uses 12 gallons, turkey comes in at 160 gallons, and soda needs 46. If you decide on beef instead of turkey, a single pound of beef takes approximately 1,800 gallons of water. Altogether, our simple lunch requires over 200 gallons of water; a hamburger requires more than 800 gallons.[156]

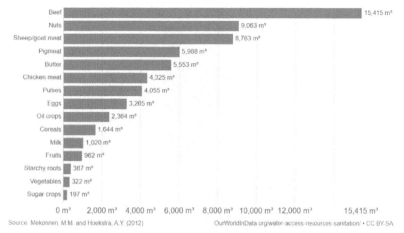

Water requirement per tonne of food product

Global average water footprint of food production, which includes water requirements across its full supply chain and the quantity of freshwater pollution as a result of production.

Beef	15,415 m³
Nuts	9,063 m³
Sheep/goat meat	8,763 m³
Pigmeat	5,988 m³
Butter	5,553 m³
Chicken meat	4,325 m³
Pulses	4,055 m³
Eggs	3,265 m³
Oil crops	2,364 m³
Cereals	1,644 m³
Milk	1,020 m³
Fruits	962 m³
Starchy roots	387 m³
Vegetables	322 m³
Sugar crops	197 m³

0 m³   2,000 m³   4,000 m³   6,000 m³   8,000 m³   10,000 m³   12,000 m³   15,415 m³

Source: Mekonnen, M.M. and Hoekstra, A.Y. (2012)   OurWorldInData.org/water-access-resources-sanitation/ • CC BY-SA

Figure 35 – Amount of water required for the production of a tonne of various foods (multiply by 35.3 to calculate cubic feet)[157]

And the amounts in Figure 34 significantly understate the amount of water required. In addition to water needed to make the raw materials for your turkey sandwich or hamburger, you have to add the water for

- running the farm that produced the materials, including the humans living on the farm;
- infrastructure, such as roads, to enable the food to get to market;
- trucks and transportation needed to get the food to market;
- buildings and employees for the wholesale and retail infrastructure to sell you the food;
- credit card and banking infrastructure and employees for you to buy the food;
- regulatory infrastructure and employees required to ensure the safety of the food, buildings, roads and employees;
- and on and on.

Consumption of bottled water has skyrocketed in recent decades. Projected global consumption for 2017 was 391 billion liters (103 billion gallons)[158]. While most of that just recycles through the hydrological system, it takes twice as much water to make a plastic water bottle as is contained in the bottle. Ever-increasing amounts of water are being "trapped" inside of plastic water bottle material and ultimately thrown away.[159]

However, our primary use of water is not for washing or for lawns, but for agriculture – to grow food.

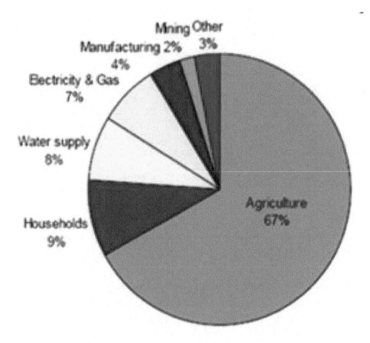

Water use in the world 2005

Figure 36 – Water use in the world 2005[160]

Water has always been considered as almost a free, inexhaustible resource, so we have not paid attention to how much we have used. That is now changing as we are increasingly using more water than nature can supply.

Rivers That Run Dry

Some formerly-mighty rivers no longer reach the ocean, including:

- The Colorado River, primarily in the U.S., flows 2,333 km (1,450 mi), from the Rocky Mountains, to the Gulf of California, supplying Los Angeles, San Diego, Las Vegas, Phoenix and parts of northern Mexico. "In its natural state, the Colorado River poured about 16.3 million acre feet (20.1 km³) into the Gulf of California each year." Now, no water makes it that far. It began stopping from time to time in the early 60s and some water has made it all the way to the Gulf

139

of California only once since the late 90s.

- The Rio Grande River flows 3,033 km (1,885 mi) in the United States, from Colorado to the Gulf of Mexico. Less than a fifth of its historical flow now reaches the Gulf, and in some years, none reaches it. There are parts of the Rio Grande upstream that are also usually dry; further downstream, tributaries contribute to the flow. Complications arise in the downstream part because raw sewage and medical waste from the Mexican city of Nuevo Laredo flows into the river.

- The Yellow River runs 5,464 km (3,395 mi) through China to the Pacific Ocean. Beginning in 1972, it has frequently run dry before it reaches the sea, primarily due to the demands of irrigation.

- The Indus River, primarily in India, flows 3,180 km (1,980 mi) from Tibet, through India to the Arabian Sea in Pakistan. Because of reduced flow from damming, little water is flowing through its delta, allowing salty water to intrude, affecting fishing and agriculture.

- The Teesta River flows 315 km (196 mi) in India from the Himalayas into the Brahmaputra River in Bangladesh, and now no longer makes it all the way there.

- The Murray River in Australia is 2,375 km (1,476 mi) long, from the Australian Alps to the Indian Ocean near Adelaide. Agriculture of irrigated crops is the primary usage of the Murray's water. Only dredging of silt at the mouth of the river is keeping it flowing.

- The Amu Darya River flows 2,400 km (1,500 mi) from Afghanistan, through Turkmenistan and Uzbekistan, and once flowed into the Aral Sea. Today, due to intensive irrigation upstream, flow now ends some 110 km (70 miles) upstream.

- The Syr Darya River also used to flow into the Aral Sea. It starts in Kyrgyzstan and Uzbekistan and flows 2,212 km (1,274 mi) toward the Aral Sea, into which it trickles.

- Only 10% of the Nile's river water now reaches the ocean, and this could worsen as the Grand Ethiopian Renaissance Dam is completed in the early 2020s, creating significant tensions between Egypt and Ethiopia.[161] Ethiopia is not a party to the treaties allocating water in the Nile, 80% of which is supplied in the Ethiopian highlands. Other upstream countries, Kenya, Tanzania, Burundi and Uganda are also not parties to earlier treaties between Egypt (or Great Britain) and Sudan.

It's not just the major rivers that are struggling. Countless smaller rivers run dry altogether, in sections or during certain times of the year. In the U.S., these rivers include the Hillsboro River in Florida; Walla Walla River in Washington; Santa Fe River in New Mexico; the Hila, Salt and Santa Cruz Rivers in Arizona; Big Wood River in Idaho; Ipswich River in Massachusetts; San Juaquin and Kern Rivers in California; multiple rivers in Nebraska, Colorado and Montana; Beaver and North Canadian Rivers in Oklahoma.[162]

These flow reductions have several causes, but the biggest cause by far is crop irrigation.

Disappearing Aquifers

An aquifer is an underground layer of rock that includes water. That water can be pumped to the surface for use, both by cities and by agriculture. Aquifers fill up over centuries and millennia with water that percolates down from the surface from rain and from snow melt, including melting glaciers from the last Ice Age.

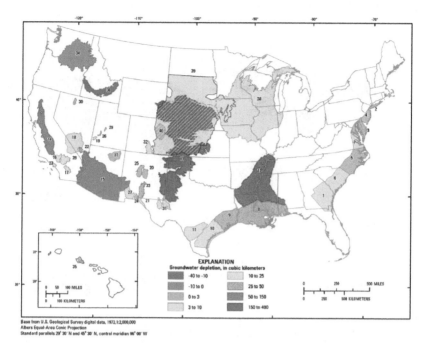

Figure 2. Map of the United States (excluding Alaska) showing cumulative groundwater depletion, 1900 through 2008, in 40 assessed aquifer systems or subareas. Index numbers are defined in table 1. Colors are hatched in the Dakota aquifer (area 39) where the aquifer overlaps with other aquifers having different values of depletion.

Figure 37 – Groundwater depletion in the U.S.[163]

The Ogallala Aquifer stretches down the middle of the United States, through wheat-growing country, and supplies some 30% of the groundwater used for irrigation in the U.S. It also provides drinking water for the vast majority of the inhabitants living over it. Since 1940, the Ogallala Aquifer has shrunk in height by more than 90 meters (300 feet). In parts of western Kansas, the aquifer has declined by more than 60 percent during that period; in some parts, including parts under Texas, it is already exhausted. In other parts, 358 miles of surface rivers and streams supplied by aquifers have dried up, and streams continue to dry up at the rate of 6 miles per year.[164] A 2013 study by Kansas State University forecasted that the aquifer would be 69% depleted by 2060.[165]

In California's Central Valley, a major agricultural production area and one-sixth of the U.S. agriculture area, groundwater is being rapidly depleted.

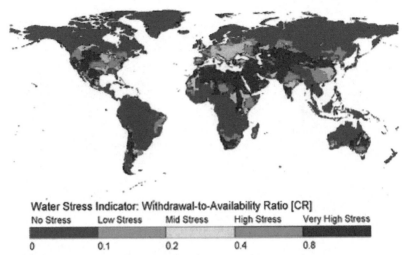

Water Stress Indicator: Withdrawal-to-Availability Ratio [CR]

| No Stress | Low Stress | Mid Stress | High Stress | Very High Stress |

| 0 | 0.1 | 0.2 | 0.4 | 0.8 |

Figure 38 –Water availability stress indicator[166]

NASA satellites, monitoring changes in Earth's gravitational pull, found that 21 of the world's 37 largest aquifers have passed their sustainable tipping points – humans are withdrawing more water than rain and snow melt are replacing ("recharge" is another word for replacing the water in an aquifer).[167]

According to the *Desert Sun*, "The Indus Basin of northern India and Pakistan is among the hotspots where groundwater is being depleted most rapidly. Others include the aquifers of the Arabian Peninsula, the Murzuk-Djado Basin and the Nubian Aquifer System of northern Africa, the Canning Basin mining region of northwestern Australia, and the North China Plain, among others. In the United States, groundwater levels are dropping especially quickly in California's Central Valley and the southern High Plains, and also declining along portions of the Atlantic and Gulf coasts."[168]

"Perhaps Saudi Arabia provides the most spectacular example of overdrawing a resource." The Saudis drilled 2,000 feet deep into the huge Arabian Aquifer. "The dunes turned green with grain, transforming the desert nation into a leading exporter in the 1980s and 1990s. Now the aquifer has been all but emptied. In 2016, wheat wasn't even planted; the Saudis are growing alfalfa in Arizona and California."[169]

That pattern is repeating itself in various places around the world, including in southern Peru, where a desert has been used for intense farming by pumping groundwater. Groundwater levels have been falling and will continue to fall until farming is no longer sustainable.

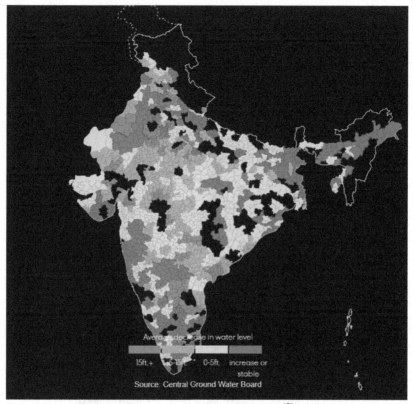

Figure 39 – Average decrease in water levels in India, 2005 – 2010[170]

In 60% of European cities with more than 100,000 people, groundwater is being used at a faster rate than it can be replenished.[171] Cities around the world that have experienced aquifer reductions between 10 to 50 meters (33 to 164 feet) include Mexico City, parts of which are sinking a foot and a half each year, Bangkok, Manila, Beijing, Madras and Shanghai.[172] Indonesia is moving its capital city away from Jakarta, parts of which have sunk 2.5 meters (8 feet) in ten years. This sinking is primarily due to the extraction of groundwater for drinking and bathing.[173]

The reservoirs in Chennai, India, population 5 million, have run dry due to a combination of over-pumping, lack of rain and poor water infrastructure.[174]

Clearly, these trends are not sustainable with existing population levels, much less the 50% increase in population projected by 2100.

One of the effects of pumping ground water from aquifers is the sinking of the ground above the aquifer. Parts of major cities, including Beijing, Shanghai, Mexico City, are sinking. This sinking can, among other things, disrupt infrastructure as the soil shifts underneath roads, bridges, buildings and pipelines. Also, the sinking land may fill in the spaces used by water, reducing the total capacity of the aquifer.

Figure 40 – Subsidence in the San Joaquin Valley of California. The sign at the top of the telephone pole, noted by the arrow, indicates where the land surface was in 1925; the sign in the middle of the pole indicates where the land surface was in 1955.[175]

And the problem feeds on itself. As surface waters become less available, more wells are drilled, lowering aquifers and decreasing the water from them that flow into surface waters. In addition, retreating water tables along coastal areas allow sea water to begin to mix with fresh water, leading to undrinkable water.

Some of the water that is extracted from aquifers returns to the aquifers, as it seeps back into the soil. Some of the water that is extracted from aquifers evaporates and contributes to the rain-evaporation hydrological cycle. However, much of the water that is extracted from aquifers drains into the sea and is effectively redistributed, geographically.

The Great Lakes

The Great Lakes, which run along the U.S. - Canadian border, make up the largest group of freshwater lakes in total area in the world and contain 21% of the Earth's surface fresh water. They provide a tempting source as water stresses increase throughout the United States. However, the Great Lakes should be considered as being more of an aquifer than a renewable resource, since only 1% of their volume is replenished each year. If water in excess of 1% of the volume is diverted, the Great Lakes will begin drying up.

Seas That are Drying Up

Because the Amu Darya River, no longer reaches the Aral Sea and the Syr Darya River now trickles instead of rushes into the Aral Sea, the Aral Sea, once the fourth largest lake in the world, has shrunk into a group of small lakes with about one-tenth the water that it used to contain.

The Dead Sea, located between Jordan and Israel, is drying up due to reduced flows from the Jordan River, which is being tapped by Syria, Jordan and Israel.

The Salton Sea in California is drying up, primarily due to reductions in flows from the Colorado River.

Polluted Water

The water that flows in rivers and is held in lakes is increasingly filthy. The United Nations Environment Programme estimates that 70% of industrial waste is dumped, untreated, into waters by developing countries and 80% of the world's wastewater goes untreated[176]; the World Health Organization estimates that 2.3 billion people lacked access to sanitation facilities in 2017[177]. The *Wall Street Journal* describes the extent of the pollution in one river in India:

Today, the Yamuna is a foul sludge for much of its 855-mile [1,376 kilometer] run. In Delhi, it is black and nearly motionless, covered in many areas with a foam of industrial chemicals, floating plastic and human waste.

Every 100 milliliters [3 ounces] of the Yamuna in Delhi contains 23 million fecal coliform bacteria, up from 12,250 in 1988, scientists say. Anything over 500 is unsafe for bathing, India's government says. The comparable standard in Vermont is 235.

Illnesses ranging from diarrhea to brain worms are reported along the river's edges. By the time the Yamuna exits Delhi, it is so defiled that scientists have declared the next 300 miles [483 kilometers] "eutrophic," or incapable of sustaining animal life.[178]

According to an article in *Nature Geoscience*, 60% of the groundwater in the Indo-Gangetic Basin, supporting more than 750 million people in Pakistan, India, Nepal and Bangladesh is not drinkable or usable for irrigation due to contamination.[179]

China has long been the poster child for water pollution. According to a governmental study, more than 80 percent of the water from underground wells used by farms, factories and households is unfit for drinking or bathing because of contamination from industry and farming. Cities face a similar challenge. In Shanghai, for example, 85% of the water in the city's major rivers was undrinkable in 2015, according to official standards, and 56.4% was unfit for any purpose. [180]

The World Water Council says that water pollution is arguably the leading worldwide cause of death and disease, accounting for the deaths of more than 14,000 people daily.[181]

In the United States, wells are increasingly being poisoned by fertilizer runoff and by manure runoff from spreading manure as fertilizer.

Water is a precious resource that we insist on fouling.

Water is Being Taken Out of Circulation

The fracking phenomenon has dramatically increased the supplies of oil and natural gas, and decreased their associated cost to the consumer.

As one of those tradeoffs discussed in Part I of this book, fracking uses gargantuan amounts of water, from several hundred thousand gallons to over nine million gallons per well. Most of that water is made toxic in the process and is not immediately recoverable, although some of it can be reused in the fracking process, and some of the water can be treated in special-purpose plants. Most of the water is injected deep underground, where it contributes both to earthquakes and to the elevation of the earth above the injection wells.

For our purposes, that water is being removed from availability for other uses and is no longer available for human consumption. In effect, we are reducing the amount of accessible fresh water.

Seasonality

Water does not flow and rain does not fall at the same rate during the year. While, on average, some regions may have enough water, there may be times of the year when water is scarce or nonexistent. Researchers, writing in the journal, *Science Advances*, found that "two-thirds of the global population (4.0 billion people) live under conditions of severe water scarcity at least 1 month of the year. Nearly half of those people live in India and China. Half a billion people in the world face severe water scarcity all year round."[182]

Complications From Fighting Climate Change

An article in *New Scientist* magazine[183] describes how planting crops to absorb CO_2 can have unintended consequences. In summary, extensive planting of crops to absorb CO_2 requires water that cannot be used for other purposes, creating increased water stress.

Peak Water

Both water supply and water consumption are primarily local

The U.N. in its World Water Development Report, said that the world could suffer a 40% shortfall in water by 2030, as global demand increases by

55%.[184] (One implication of this projection is that current global demand is approximately equal to current global supply. Therefore, under current conditions, human carrying capacity from a water perspective equals approximately 7.5 billion people, the human population of the Earth in 2017.)

Ownership of Water

Throughout the world, including in the U.S., ownership of water in lakes, rivers and aquifers, and also when it falls from the sky, is based on a long history of who claimed rights first, who won rights in fights and wars, claimed legal rights of down-stream users and legislation. In some instances, water is a private right, and in some instances, it is publicly owned. Vast and complex systems of law have been developed dealing with questions of who has the right to use water and how it may or must be used. Throughout the world and throughout history, water resource use has been one of the most highly regulated of economic activities. And this does not just apply to consumption and irrigation. There are questions, for example, of whether rafters can use rivers that flow through private property. The result is a patchwork mess that often stands in the way of rational use of water.

One common approach to ownership of water is that the person who owns the land on the bank of a lake or river or on top of an aquifer has the right to use the water. That right may be subject to the rights of other owners. The fundamental rule of water use in rivers is that each landowner must leave the natural flow of the river unchanged. That rule has evolved into one which requires that use of the water does not cause an unreasonable injury to another user.

As more users claim more water, governmental entities have stepped in to regulate who can use how much water.

Historically, the person who controls the water upstream has priority use over those downstream. Downstream, anyone who uses a certain amount of water for a specific purpose retains the right to that amount of water for that purpose. However, this right can disappear if usage of the water is discontinued.

As water has become scarcer and as nations have dammed rivers to provide reservoirs and hydroelectric power, disputes have arisen between nations. Today, one of the motivations for water-starved China to annex Tibet is that many large rivers originate in its mountains. Water ownership is key to China's ability to grow economically, but its control of upstream sources of water is creating conflict, particularly with India. Essentially all of India's important rivers begin in Tibet. Recently, China announced that it is blocking a tributary of the Brahmaputra River, which is important to India, to construct a hydroelectric dam.

China is also said to be planning a 1,000 km (621 mile) tunnel to divert water from the Brahmaputra into its Xinjiang region, which it has denied. The intention is to change the Taklamakan desert into an area that can grow crops on a large scale.[185] This project, if pursued, will likely lead to increased tensions with both India and Bangladesh.

Countries have created treaties on the use of rivers that they share, including pacts governing the Nile River through Sudan and Egypt and the Mekong River through Laos, Thailand, Vietnam and Cambodia. However, in a time of drought, or when population or agricultural pressures increase, treaties may not be honored and the country upstream usually has the upper hand.

Complications that arise in an age of water scarcity, even when agreement can be reached, are illustrated by the case of the disappearing Colorado River.[186] In the U.S., water usage is governed by each individual state. Seven states entered into an agreement dividing the Colorado River Basin into two areas: the Upper Division (the states of Colorado, New Mexico, Utah and Wyoming) and the Lower Division (Nevada, Arizona and California). The division was based on rainfall patterns in the years leading up to 1922, when the agreement was reached. The treaty attempted to divide the water in the river equally between the two Divisions. Subsequent agreements further allotted the water among the states in the two Divisions. Water was also allocated to Mexico in a treaty signed in 1944. In addition, the Lower Basin can use a defined amount of any surplus (which California has been using).

As it turns out, the rainfall assumptions made when the treaty was signed and which were the basis for the allocations, appear to have been higher than the long-term average. Therefore, total flows in the river are lower in the long term than assumed in the treaty.

Additional complications arose when Native Americans, who live on reservations in the Basins, asserted rights, reducing originally-agreed-upon allocations.

The water being received by Mexico is often below its allocation and is increasingly brackish. There are no water quality levels provided for in the agreements, and these issues are not being dealt with.

As cities served by the Basins, including Los Angeles, Phoenix, Salt Lake City and Las Vegas, continue to grow, and as farming increases, requiring additional irrigation, pressure on both the river and the various treaties continues to increase.

In a recent environment of drought and shortage, "interim guidelines" for allocation in the event of shortages were issued by the Department of the Interior.

The United States Supreme Court ruled in 2018 that the U.S. Government is authorized to join with Texas against New Mexico with regard to New Mexico's alleged diversion of water from the Rio Grande in excess of agreed amounts.

Worldwide, the arcane, complex and inefficient patchwork of rights to water will inhibit rational allocation and will provide the bases for disputes and conflict.

Investor Rick Rule summarized the water situation in the U.S. in an interview, when he said,

> Water is the most mispriced commodity in the world. Because water is allocated politically, it is believed to be a right, as opposed to a commodity. The consequence of that – as an example, here in the U.S. Southwest, we have taken sources of water, like the Colorado River, and we have allocated approximately 130% of the flow of the river to various claimants. This is sort of hard on the river. You have a circumstance where water flows uphill to votes rather than downhill for money. And you can't allocate something that doesn't exist.
>
> And also because of the structure of the American water business. Because of the fact that most of it is delivered politically rather than via markets. The rents that go to water, while they are insufficient to maintain supply, go to

municipalities. And they go to fund current political goals as opposed to maintaining the infrastructure for the production and distribution of water.

It is believed, on a country-wide basis, that we have deferred as much as 3 trillion dollars in sustaining capital investments in the water business. I can't tell you when this theme comes home to roost. But when it does come home to roost, this might be one of the great resource themes of all time.[187]

How Bad Is It?

A study by McKinsey concluded that there would be an aggregate shortfall of water demand in 2030 of approximately 66% of existing supply.

Aggregated global gap between existing accessible, reliable supply[1] and 2030 water withdrawals, assuming no efficiency gains

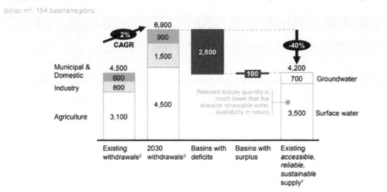

1 Existing supply which can be provided at 90% reliability, based on historical hydrology and infrastructure investments scheduled through 2010; net of environmental requirements
2 Based on 2010 agricultural production analyses from IFPRI
3 Based on GDP, population projections and agricultural production projections from IFPRI; considers no water productivity gains between 2005-2030

SOURCE: Water 2030 Global Water Supply and Demand model; agricultural production based on IFPRI IMPACT-WATER base case

Figure 41 – Aggregated global gap between existing accessible, reliable supply and 2010 water withdrawals, assuming no efficiency gains.

The Good News

If these trends continue, we are in serious trouble. However, trends that cannot continue will stop. In addition, creative people will begin to address problems, once they understand them.

People in the future will likely look back on our time and wonder, what the hell were they thinking, about several things. Near the top of their list will be using highly-treated drinking water to irrigate lawns and golf courses (and they will probably shake their heads that irrigated lawns and golf courses existed at all). They will wonder why we treated water only to urinate and defecate into it and then send it back for treatment. They will wonder why we fed storm drainage into our sewers, vastly complicating sewage treatment. It has been estimated that only 10% of treated water is used for consumption and cooking. Of course, having only one source for water makes sense from an infrastructure standpoint, since it requires only one set of expensive pipes and pumps. However, viewed from the perspective that water is vital to life and we are running out, the solution is some combination of not irrigating at all, and implementing infrastructure for partially treated water, clean enough for irrigation and flushing purposes, but not up to human consumption standards (grey water).

The good news is that, since we have been extraordinarily wasteful of water, there are a number of significant changes we can implement, and technology will continue to change the game.

The bad news is that implementing many of these changes will be expensive, if for no other reason than the problem is so huge and so extensive. And, it will be difficult because of ingrained attitudes toward water, such as, it should be free. And, current allocations of water have been agreed through contentious negotiations and struggles over decades and centuries, and will not be easily undone. Finally, conservation efforts will have unintended consequences in the distribution of water.

It seems odd that being wasteful is good news, but our historical waste provides the opportunity to implement a number of effective, straightforward approaches to tackling the water problem.

Available water can be increased using several strategies:

Conservation

The best way to conserve water is to not use it in the first place. In order to promote conservation, we must think of water differently and the cost of water has to increase to reflect its actual value. Perceptions must change such that water is seen as precious instead of being taken for granted, which is a non-trivial attitudinal / cultural challenge. Billions of humans would need to take such actions as taking shorter showers (no baths), turning off the tap when doing such things as washing hands or brushing teeth, running a full load in the washing machine using a front load model, fixing leaks, creating as little waste water as possible, using less water to flush, and running only a fully-loaded dishwasher.

Leaky infrastructure must be repaired. It is estimated that water main breaks and leaking pipes waste 1.7 trillion gallons (6.4 trillion liters) of water in the U.S. each year.[188] A similar problem exists, often to a much worse extent, in other countries.

More fundamentally, water must be conserved through a combination of pricing and regulation. Precious water is too valuable and too critical to be almost free. It should be priced at a level that incorporates not only its direct cost, but also its indirect cost and its increasing scarcity.

The increased price of water would result in the replacement of all lawns with either low-water varieties of grass (mandatorily irrigated, if at all, by drip irrigation) or xeriscaping. Golf courses should not exist at all, or at least not have extensive, irrigated fairways and greens.

Since agriculture is the largest user of water, agriculture must be fundamentally changed. Crops should be raised in areas which provide the level of water that they need. Raising water-hungry rice in an area that requires irrigation from aquifers is a very inefficient and wasteful use of water. Drip irrigation, precise seed planting and precise application of fertilizer should be widely adopted.

The *Economist* magazine gives the example of an almond grower in California who employed analysis of soil composition, water sensors, exact application of drip irrigation, matching seed density to soil capabilities, and aerial and satellite analysis and became 20% more efficient in his use of water.[189] Of course, all of this technology comes at a price in terms of equipment, labor and taxes.

Obvious misuses of a scarce resource include bottled water, water parks, man-made snow, fountains and decorative lakes.

Since water is the basis for creating goods and energy as well as food, the cost of living from appropriately pricing water will increase. This increase in price will result in increased social pressures, particularly for the poor.

Conservation means not only using less water; it means thinking about water differently.

- All reclaimable water should be reclaimed.
- Purified water should be used only for drinking and cooking;
- All other requirements, including industrial uses, should use grey water.
- Water should be caught when draining from roofs and rerouted or stored to be used on the spot instead of going into streams to be processed for use later. Of course, catching rainwater at its source would have unintended consequences downstream.

Recycling

Necessity is the mother of invention. People living in desert areas are leading the way in preserving the precious water they have.

And Israel leads the way by reusing approximately 90% of its wastewater (in second place, at approximately 20%, is Spain). The primary use for recycled / gray water in Israel is agricultural irrigation.[190]

Desalination

While fresh water is becoming a scarce resource, salt water is plentiful.

Desalination (desal), removing salt and other minerals from sea water, is extremely expensive, but technology is advancing quickly. Because there is so much water in the oceans, compared with the very little available fresh water, salt water has the potential to provide a virtually inexhaustible source of water.

Dsal is attractive when there are no other alternatives, even at a cost of 8-10 times average water costs in the U.S. Countries such as Saudi Arabia and

Israel rely on desalination; Israel now gets 55 percent of its domestic water from desalination. The biggest plant in North America was recently opened near San Diego.

Desalination is very energy intensive and therefore has a relatively large carbon footprint, raising climate change concerns, and is vulnerable to the cost of energy. It is facing regulation, including of its intake, so that fish and fish eggs are not harmed. Using current processes, about half of the saltwater that is piped in is made drinkable. Along with drinkable water, the desal process produces large quantities of brine, very salty water, that includes minerals. The brine is typically diluted with other water before being returned to the ocean. If not reintroduced to the ocean correctly, brine can be corrosive to the ocean's ecosystems, particularly the seabed, since brine is denser than sea water.

It is likely, for now, that desal cannot produce water in sufficient quantities to support agriculture.

Experts, particularly those that are environmentally inclined, generally recommend that all other alternatives, including water conservation, recycling and water re-use be pursued before turning to desal.

Desal's younger sibling is brackish water, generally from deep reservoirs. Brackish water still needs to be cleaned up, but it is a potential source of (nonrenewable) water in a time of desperation.

Pricing

Most – almost all – charges for water in the U.S. do not include a cost for the water, itself. Charges are generally for the costs of treatment and distribution, but not for the water.

Culturally, since we have demanded that water be essentially free, we have used it in uneconomic ways, such as growing rice in the desert and creating lush landscapes through irrigation. Charging a reasonable price for water will be strongly resisted and will create significant dislocation for those who are effectively misusing water. However, it will be critical to water conservation that water is properly priced.

Regulation

Several areas around the world have passed laws restricting the use of water, usually in response to a drought.

In 2018 California passed a law which restricts personal indoor water usage, regardless of drought, as the greater of 55 gallons a day or a standard to be recommended by a governing board to account primarily for differences in various geographic areas of the state. The maximum declines over time; beginning January 1, 2030, the standard is the greater of 50 gallons a day and the board standard. For comparison, an 8-minute shower uses about 17 gallons of water, a load of laundry uses about 40 gallons of water, a bathtub holds upward of 80 gallons of water and a dishwasher uses 6 gallons of water. The law also establishes a process to set standards for outdoor residential use, again by geographic area.[191]

California's bigger water challenges are in the agricultural area, but those are more difficult to address.

Summary

On average, we are on the edge of water unsustainability. Some parts of the world, including India and the central and western parts of the U.S., are already in serious trouble when it comes to water sustainability, and all the trends are heading in the wrong direction. Draining aquifers is the equivalent of eating seed corn. It is a one-time event, and once the aquifer water is depleted, all of the agriculture, industry and consumption the aquifer supported will also be gone. Efficiently providing water for primary needs will take massive changes in attitude, culture, regulation and technology.

Water will, in all likelihood, become a primary limiting factor in determining the Earth's ultimate carrying capacity, regardless of the amount of technology applied.

As a thought experiment, let's accept the UN's prediction that by 2030 the Earth will only supply 60% of the water necessary to support the Earth's system, that the Earth's population in 2030 will be 8.5 billion, and that water usage efficiency can be improved by an average of the 20% achieved by the almond farmer in California, discussed above. These very- approximate assumptions would lead to a carrying capacity in 2030 of under 7 billion people. (This reconciles with the 7.5 billion estimate from most of the same data, above, since there is an implied assumption that demand for water per capita will grow more rapidly (55%) than the population (13%).)

This analysis begs a lot of questions and rests on a number of averages, but it provides another approximate data point in our quest to determine the human carrying capacity of Earth. (That there would be 8.5 billion people on an Earth that has a carrying capacity of less than 7 billion indicates a population in Overshoot. Any population above 7 billion would be consuming more resources than is sustainable. It would be denuding the field and probably heading for population collapse, absent a reduction in consumption.)

Topsoil

We think of water as the critical resource for growing food. But water is irrelevant if the soil does not contain the nutrients needed to grow food. Plants can grow where the soil is fertile, either because it is naturally fertile or because artificial fertilizer has been applied. Naturally- fertile soil is generally called topsoil, "the upper, outermost layer of soil, usually the top 2 inches (5.1 cm) to 8 inches (20 cm). It has the highest concentration of organic matter and microorganisms and is where most of the Earth's biological soil activity occurs."[192]

Topsoil is required for the production of food on the scale necessary to supply current and future human populations.

Hundreds of years are required to naturally form an inch of topsoil, although farmers and environmentalists employing regenerative farming methods are actively creating topsoil much more rapidly. Once formed, topsoil is subject to erosion from wind and rain, and to depletion from growing crops that extract the nutrients out of the topsoil. A study by Cornell University reports that the U.S. is losing soil 10 times faster – and China and India are losing soil 30 to 40 times faster – than the natural replenishment rate.[193] According to *Time* magazine, "Some 40% of soil used for agriculture around the world is classed as either degraded or seriously degraded – the latter means that 70% of the topsoil, the layer allowing plants to grow, is gone."[194] According to David Pimentel, professor of ecology at Cornell, "Soil erosion is second only to population growth as the biggest environmental problem the world faces."[195]

The pre-industrial approach to replacing nutrients was to leave stubble in the field after harvest or to grow a cover crop which, when it died, would replenish the field with nutrients. In order to meet today's demand for food, too many fields are being used over and over again without sufficient replenishment. Artificial fertilizer, consisting of nitrogen, potassium and phosphate, is used to compensate for nutrient-depleted fields. Therefore, crop yields are becoming ever-more dependent on ever-increasing amounts of fertilizer.

Further, moderately degraded soil holds less than half the water than healthy soil in the same location. This means that much of the irrigation of degraded soil is wasted as it simply runs off. In effect, we are pumping precious aquifer water into the ocean.

The true cost of soil, like the true cost of water, is not priced into the cost of food, so that farmers do not receive compensation which they could invest in maintaining their fields.

Desertification

Desertification refers, not just to the growth of deserts, although there is some of that, but more generally to the degradation of land. During desertification, soil loses its productivity and cover vegetation is removed.

A committee of the European Commission published a comprehensive review of soil loss and land degradation in 2018. Among its conclusions were

- Globally, a total area half of the size of the European Union (4.18 million km^2 [1.6 million miles^2]) is degraded annually, with Africa and Asia being the most affected.
- Land degradation and global warming are estimated to lead to a reduction of global crop yields by about 10% by 2050. Most of this will occur in India, China and sub-Saharan Africa, where land degradation could halve crop production.[196]

Degraded land is able to produce less food, in effect decreasing the Earth's carrying capacity.

Competition for arable land

As demand for food increases and arable land becomes completely utilized, questions will arise as to how we can best use existing arable land. Uses for arable land in addition to raising food crops include housing, roads, parks, commercial buildings and warehouses, wind and solar farms, pastures for animals, raising non-food crops like cotton and flax and raising corn and sugar cane for biofuels.

D'Amour, et. al., in a publication for the National Academy of Sciences, estimated that an additional 1.8-2.4% of global croplands will be lost to urban expansion by 2030.[197]

Peak Phosphorus

Phosphorus is derived by mining phosphate rock and is included as a Planetary Boundary. Historically, phosphorus was derived from bat guano, however, many guano resources have been exhausted. We have reached peak guano and are using guano faster than bats can create it.

Peak phosphorus has been estimated to occur as early as 2030 and as late as hundreds of years from now.

Estimates of total resource exhaustion (mindful of the lessons learned from peak oil) are

Estimates of Remaining Phosphate Reserves

Author	Estimated lifetime of reserves	Assumptions/notes
Steen (1998)	60–130 years	2-3% increase demand rates, 'most likely' 2% increase until 2020 and 0% growth thereafter if efficiency and reuse measures are implemented
Smil (2000)	80 years	At 'current rate of extraction'
Smit et al. (2009))	69–100 years	Assuming 0.7-2% increase until 2050, and 0% increase after 2050
Vaccari (2009)	90 years	At 'current rates'
Fixen (2009)	93 years	At 2007-2008 production rates

⊠SEI

Figure 42 – Estimates of Remaining Phosphate Reserves[198]

Arno Rosemarin, PhD, Senior Research Fellow at the Stockholm Environment Institute concludes that economic phosphorus reserves in the U.S. will be depleted by 2035 – 2040; and economic global reserves will be depleted within 75-100 years (new finds and revised estimates could extend this by 50-100 years).[199]

Rosemarin also discusses the possibility of recovering significant amounts of phosphorus from human solid waste.

Fertilizer is critical for raising crops and will become even more so as population and consumption pressures mount to grow more and more food from increasingly marginal soil. However, the Planetary Boundary for the production of nitrates has been exceeded by 300%. The production of fertilizer will increasingly degrade, and in a sense, poison, the ecosystem as nitrates and phosphates drain into rivers and streams.

Runoff of nitrogen and phosphorus fertilizers from fields into rivers can accumulate in oceans to create dead zones. The nitrogen and phosphorus provide food for algae, which then bloom and decompose. This process depletes the water of oxygen, creating these dead zones.

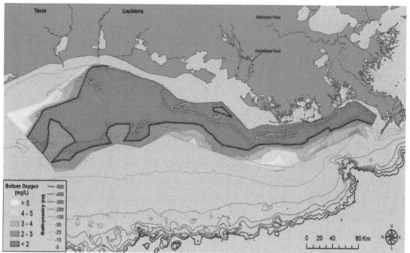

Figure 43 – The dead zone in the Gulf of Mexico in 2017 – the size of the State of New Jersey.[200]

The dead zone in the Gulf of Mexico is just one of many, worldwide.

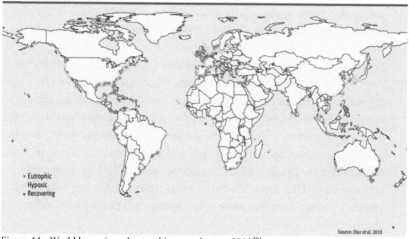

Figure 44 - World hypoxic and eutrophic coastal areas, 2010[201]

Runoff is also impacting local water supplies. Des Moines, Iowa, is located close to two rivers in an intensely-farmed area of the United States. Increasingly, during growing season, the fertilizer runoff has been contaminating river water to the point that the City of Des Moines cannot supply un-tainted drinking water to its citizens when algae blooms occur.

Nanoparticles, increasingly used in cosmetics and other products, and therefore increasingly being washed into rivers, streams and the ocean, have unknown effects on fish, animals and humans. Such particles are difficult-to-impossible to clean from drinking water, as are drugs, hormones and medicines that humans are increasingly excreting into their sewers.

Fish

Huge, refrigerated fish processing factories electronically track fish and cast nets, including drift nets, that are limited to 2.5 km (1.6 miles) long in international waters by the United Nations General Assembly (the U.S. restricts nets to 2.8 km (1.7 miles) in American waters). These nets bring in huge amounts of fish and other creatures. Another approach is long-lining, in which as many as 75 miles (121 kilometers) of line with hundreds of thousands of baited hooks are dragged behind the boat or left in the water overnight.

According to the United Nations Food and Agriculture Organization, in 2013, 32% of the world's fish stocks were being exploited beyond their sustainable limit, up from 10% in the 1970s, even though the total catch has remained approximately constant for three decades.[202]

Some whale species have been hunted almost to extinction. A 1986 ban on commercial whaling by the International Whaling Commission (IWC) has allowed some whale populations to begin to recover. However, some countries, primarily Japan, abuse an exemption that allows hunting whales for research purposes and in 2019 withdrew from the agreement altogether. Norway has withdrawn from the IWC and there is concern that it is endangering the minke whale. Two whale species, the blue (Antarctic population) and the gray (Northwest Pacific population), are considered critically endangered; five more whale species are currently considered as endangered.

Because of the kind of efficiency enabled by huge nets and very long lines, we are overfishing the oceans, which means we are reducing the breeding populations of some types of fish and other seafood below the point at which they can recover. For example, Pacific bluefin tuna stocks are down by 97% from early 1960s levels; the bluefin tuna is considered to be the sixth most threatened species in the world by the World Wildlife Fund.[203]

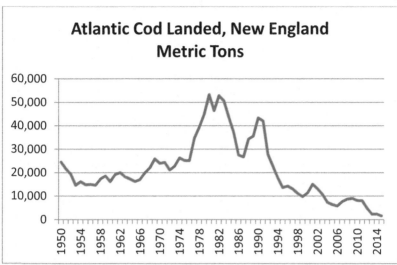

Figure 45 – Atlantic cod landed by ships fishing off the coast of New England, 1950-2015, in metric tons.[204]

Figure 45 illustrates the dramatic increase in cod caught due to mass fishing techniques, to a peak of over 50,000 metric tons in the early 1980s. Since then, cod caught has collapsed to only a few thousand metric tons in recent years as breeding capability has diminished due to overfishing.

The International Union for the Conservation of Nature classifies various species as to their level of endangerment in its Red List.[205] In 2014, 1,414 species of fish were included as being at risk for extinction. Fish like the bluefin tuna are endangered because they are purposefully fished. Other species that are most threatened by overfishing, according to Greenpeace, include Atlantic halibut, monkfish and all sharks.

The Maltese Ray, the second most endangered fish, is not of interest to fishermen, but is caught in their massive nets with other fish. This "bycatch" includes sea turtles, seals, dolphins, the New Zealand sea lion and sea birds.

Small fishers, because of their large numbers in aggregate, also produce a significant amount of bycatch. A 2018 study by the University of Exeter reported the findings of monitoring just 43 harbors in Ecuador, Peru and Chile. 46,000 turtles were caught and more than 16,000 were killed annually by small fishers.[206]

An article by Deborah Zabarenko for Reuters includes an extreme use of extrapolation from past trends, while at the same time describing the magnitude of species collapse:

> The world's fish and seafood populations will collapse by 2048 if current trends in habitat destruction and overfishing continue, resulting in less food for humans. Marine biodiversity - the variety of ocean fish, shellfish, birds, plants and micro-organisms - had declined dramatically since the 1960s. Some 29% of species were already in collapse. Extrapolating these trends, scientists calculate that by 2048 all species, from mussels and clams to tuna and swordfish, would be in collapse, which the researchers defined as having catches decline 90% from the maximum catch.[207]

The ocean ecosystem is diverse, consisting of many species of fish and other animals, which depend on each other in vast food chains and environmental support. Removing a species can have several effects. For example, if the removed species provides food for other species, those species which have lost their food will suffer. Their loss will destabilize other populations as they prey on new species in order to survive. If the removed species is a predator, its prey may begin to overpopulate, in turn threatening further food supplies.

Increasingly, humans are using fish farms to supplement wild catch and to reduce pressure on wild populations. In 2014, fish farming accounted for approximately half the fish people ate.

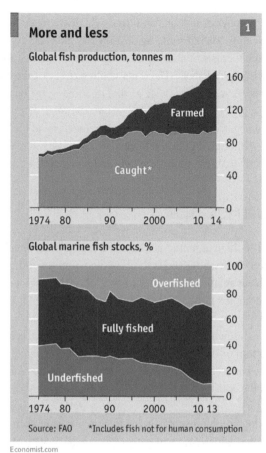

Figure 46 – Global fish production Global marine fish
stocks[208]

Raising fish for food in underwater enclosures is an efficient way to increase
the yield of fish available for food. Downsides include creating a significant
amount of waste in a small area, which can enable algae blooms, which
starve the water of oxygen. Parasites often decrease yield. And there is
concern that changes in the food the farmed fish consume may decrease the
nutritional value to humans of the farmed fish.

Open-ocean fish farming is in its infancy. Open-ocean fish farming consists
of creating huge, submersible fish cages in the open ocean, and raising fish
in those cages. Open-ocean fish farming significantly reduces the waste
concentration and parasite problems associated with current, shallow-water
farming.

There are a number of indoor fish farms, which are made up of huge tanks and tubes to allow fish to swim against the current. This type of fish farming has several challenges, including the need to replace the water, in some cases, once every two days. The other challenge is that the energy requirements are more than twice as that of some water-based fish farms.

Humans are negatively impacting both fish species and the ocean's ecosystem. Although it does not appear that the system as a whole is near collapse, there are clear signs of stress, and many species are near or past collapse.

The bottom of the food chain

One way of looking at nature is that it is one, massive, interlocking chain of consumption. Everything needs food. In the animal world, predators eat prey, which eat smaller prey or may eat plants. The interconnectedness of life in this complex system is remarkable.

Although we humans do not give them much thought, there are creatures near the bottom of the food chain on which the entire cycle depends. At least two of these basic creatures are at risk, endangering the vitality and the viability of the entire chain.

Phytoplankton are microscopic algae that are at the bottom of the ocean's food chain, and which also generate approximately 50% of the Earth's oxygen.

According to a report issued by Dalhousie University in Canada, phytoplankton declined 40% between 1950-2010, and the decrease is continuing at the rate of about 1% per year. While the causes are not clear, the decline is primarily attributed to climate change. Whatever the cause, this dramatic decline at the base of the food chain is making the entire food chain ever more fragile.[209]

A study, published in the journal *Plos One*, measured a decline in flying insect species in public lands in Germany by 75% over the last 25 years.[210]

Lynn Dicks at the University of East Anglia was quoted in *The Guardian* as saying, "If total flying insect biomass is genuinely declining at this rate – about 6% per year – it is extremely concerning," she said. "Flying insects have really important ecological functions, for which their numbers matter a lot. They pollinate flowers: flies, moths and butterflies are as important as bees for many flowering plants, including some crops. They provide food for many animals – birds, bats, some mammals, fish, reptiles and amphibians. Flies, beetles and wasps are also predators and decomposers, controlling pests and cleaning up the place generally."[211]

The reasons for the decline are not known, but are thought to be pesticides, the destruction of wild areas and, potentially, climate change.

Ironically, a German study indicated that wind farms were contributing to insect die-off, estimating a loss of approximately 1.2 trillion flying insects a year.[212]

A study concluded that the number of birds in the U.S. and Canada had declined by approximately 3 billion or 29% over the past 50 years.[213] A study in France concluded in 2018 that there had been a one-third reduction in the bird population in some rural areas over the last 15 years. The scientists who conducted the study concluded that a reduction in insects was due to pesticides, similar to the reduction in Germany. This reduction has led to less food for birds and therefore a declining bird population.[214] These dramatic reductions have led to generalized concerns about the impact on the global food chain from a loss of species.

Honeybees are not near the bottom of the food chain, but are critical to the food chain since they pollinate plants. The decline in the population of honeybees has been dramatic, including a collapse of 42% of bee colonies in the U.S. in 2015. The causes of the decline have not completely determined, but potentially include pesticides, loss of habitat, climate change and diseases carried by mites.[215] In 2018, the European Union banned the outdoor use of "neonicotinoid" pesticides, associated with the decline in bee population.

At a time when humans desire and require continually-increasing amounts of food, the underlying food chains are in danger.

Technology and Food

It is clear that if there is to be sufficient food of a broad variety to feed an increasing number of humans on a planet on which almost all arable land is being farmed and arable land is decreasing in area, technology must be a significant part of the solution.

Capitalism-enabled technology has the potential to help generate more food from a finite planet, but perhaps not enough.

GMOs

Farmers have been genetically modifying food for centuries, intentionally and unintentionally employing Mendel's laws of inheritance to breed crops and animals for desirable characteristics. This process has resulted in sturdier, more productive crops and animals.

Since the late 20th century, scientists have taken genetic modification several steps further, specifically altering DNA and genes to create plants and animals having particular characteristics, such as resistance to a certain pest or disease. These modified plants, animals, viruses and bacteria are called genetically modified organisms or GMOs.

The term, GMO, is most often used to refer to genetically modified plants, however, a GMO salmon was approved in the United States. That salmon, which grows faster on fish farms, is the first GMO animal to be approved for consumption.

Although GMOs are controversial and some of them are banned in some parts of the world, including Europe, the U.S. and many other countries have used them extensively, with no adverse issues, so far. (The Union of Concerned Scientists, Greenpeace and others are concerned that the risks of GMOs have not been adequately identified and managed.) For example, approximately 88% of the corn crop and 90% of the cotton crop in the U.S. was modified in 2011. David Zilberman, a University of California at Berkeley agricultural and environmental economist, says, "(GMO) has lowered the price of food ... It has increased farmer safety by allowing them to use less pesticide. It has raised the output of corn, cotton and soy by 20 to 30 percent, allowing some people to survive who would not have survived without it. If it were more widely adopted around the world, the price [of food] would go lower, and fewer people would die of hunger."[216]

On the other hand, 300 scientists issued a joint statement in *Environmental Sciences Europe*, which included, "...the totality of scientific research outcomes in the field of GM crop safety is nuanced; complex; often contradictory or inconclusive; confounded by researchers' choices, assumptions, and funding sources; and, in general, has raised more questions than it has currently answered."[217] In other words, for some scientists, the jury is still out regarding safety, not only to humans, but also to the environment. Some experiments with GM food on animals have yielded indications that some GM foods are not safe.

GMO crops will be required to provide the yields necessary for an increasing population that will be demanding increasing amounts of food.

However, "an extensive examination by *The New York Times* indicates that the debate [over GMOs] has missed a more basic problem [than safety of GMOs] – genetic modification in the United States and Canada has not accelerated increases in crop yields or led to an overall reduction in the use of pesticides." *The New York Times* used United Nations' data to compare crops in the U.S., where GMO is widely used, and in Europe, which uses few GMO crops. "An analysis by The Times ... showed that the United States and Canada have gained no discernible advantage in yields – food per acre – when measured against Western Europe..."[218] A recent National Academy of Sciences report reached a similar conclusion.[219]

These findings are controversial, and they are deeply troubling. It is highly unlikely that, with current capabilities, we will be able to feed increasing populations in the future. If GMO is not effective in increasing yields, the challenge of finding sufficient food in the future will be increased, significantly.

Scientists are addressing GMO in different ways, hoping, for example, to use modifications to directly increase the rate of photosynthesis within plants, allowing more efficient growth. By some estimates, this process could increase rice and wheat yields by roughly 50% or use less water and fertilizer for same amount of food.

But there appear to be unintended consequences to gene editing. A study in 2018 published by *Nature Medicine* found that some edited cells, which are intended to treat disease, actually trigger cancer.[220]

Additionally, there is concern that current food is not as nutritious as that grown prior to the implementation of modern methods.

The commercially grown vegetables, fruits, and grains that we are eating today have significantly lower nutritional content than these foods had 100 years ago, or even just 30 years ago. We now have solid, scientific evidence of this troubling trend. For example:

- In wheat and barley, protein concentrations declined by 30 to 50 percent between the years 1938 and 1990.
- Likewise, a study of 45 corn varieties developed from 1920 to 2001, grown side by side, found that the concentrations of protein, oil, and three amino acids have all declined in the newer varieties.
- Six minerals have declined by 22 to 39 percent in 14 widely grown wheat varieties developed over the past 100 years.
- Official U.S. Department of Agriculture (U.S.DA) nutrient data shows that the calcium content of broccoli averaged 12.9 milligrams per gram of dry weight in 1950, but only 4.4 mg/g dry weight in 2003.[221]

The primary implication of this study is that the Earth has to produce as much as double, in the case of wheat and barley, the amount of wheat today (assuming no additional deterioration in nutritional content since 1990) to supply the same amount protein, as compared with the same amount of plants, that was supplied by wheat in 1938. This means that increasing the amount of wheat (corn, barley and broccoli) that is grown does not necessarily increase the amount of actual nutrition supplied, significantly increasing the challenge of supplying nutrition to a growing population.

Herbicides and pesticides

Herbicides and pesticides have been critical in improving yields from plantings. Improvements in both will continue to contribute to increasing yields.

However, there is a point at which increasing reliance on chemicals, including fertilizers, results in unintended consequences. For example, glyphosate, the predominate weed killer and the primary active ingredient in the widely-used herbicide, Roundup, is, as reported by *The Guardian*, "so pervasive that its residues were recently found in 45% of Europe's topsoil – and in the urine of three quarters of Germans tested, at five times the legal limit for drinking water. … Its residues have been found in biscuits, crackers, crisps, breakfast cereals and in 60% of breads sold in the UK. … environmentalists claim that glyphosate is so non-selective that it can even kill large trees and is destructive to wild and semi-natural habitats, and to biodiversity."[222]

In 2015, the International Agency for Research on Cancer of the World Health Organization classified glyphosate as "probably carcinogenic to humans (as were insecticides malathion and diazinon).[223] The European Parliament considered revoking permission for glyphosate use in Europe but ultimately renewed its license for five years. Given the degree of human reliance on glyphosate, the fact that banning is being seriously considered at such high levels clearly indicates the level of concern.

In 2018 a plaintiff in the U.S. was awarded damages of $289 million, following his allegations that Roundup caused his terminal cancer. (Roundup's manufacturer appealed and damages were reduced to $20.5 million, which is also being appealed.) To the extent that these regulatory and judicial reviews continue against glyphosate and Roundup, agriculture will lose one of its primary productivity tools.

Also in 2018, a federal appeals court in the U.S. ordered the Environmental Protection Agency to ban the pesticide chlorpyrifos, citing scientific evidence of harm to children and farmworkers. It was formally banned in 2021, following delays during the Trump administration.

Another unintended consequence of the extensive use of herbicides is that weeds are increasingly evolving resistance to them. This means that it will take the application of an increasing number of chemicals to do the job, and will create the possibility that herbicides will be less useful in the future. This would lead, in turn, to lower crop yields.

An article in *The New York Times* summarizes the challenge:

> Superweeds — that is, weeds that have evolved characteristics that make them more difficult to control as a result of repeatedly using the same management tactic — are rapidly overtaking American commodity farms, and Palmer amaranth is their king. Scientists have identified a population of Palmer amaranth that can tolerate being

sprayed with six different herbicides (though not all at once), and they continue to discover new resistances. By now, it's clear that weeds are evolving faster than companies are developing new weed killers: Just six years ago, in response to the onset of resistance to its marquee product, Roundup (active ingredient: glyphosate), Monsanto began selling a new generation of genetically modified seeds bred to resist both glyphosate and dicamba. By 2020, scientists had confirmed the existence of dicamba-resistant Palmer amaranth. The agribusiness giant took a decade to develop that product line. The weeds caught up in five years.[224]

In 2018, the European Union enacted a ban on almost all "neonicotinoid" pesticides for outdoor use. These pesticides have been, sometimes controversially, associated with the decline in bee colonies.

The good news is that technology is providing some answers in the form of intelligent machines that patrol a farm, looking for weeds and when finding them, zaps them with a laser.

Since these machines are bulky and expensive, they can provide only limited mitigation to the use of herbicides.

Precise use of resources

Earlier, when discussing water conservation, we used the following example, which also describes the precise use of resources. "The *Economist* magazine gives the example of an almond grower in California that employed analysis of soil composition, water sensors, exact application of drip irrigation, matching seed density to soil capabilities, and aerial and satellite analysis and became 20% more efficient in his use of water. Of course, all of this technology comes at a price in terms of equipment, labor and taxes." In addition to conserving water, these approaches optimize the use of seed and fertilizer.

Meat grown in the lab and processed from plants

Academics and start-up companies are working to create meat in the laboratory that tastes as good as, has the same consistency as and may be more nutritious than meat currently sold in stores. Lab-grown meat exists today and scientists and companies are working to improve its taste and consistency to make it acceptable to consumer and address issues of scaling and cost.

There are two types of lab-grown meat. The first is meat grown from a culture of animal cells. The second is meat reconstructed from plant proteins and products. This variation is potentially attractive to vegetarians and vegans.

Both types of lab-grown meat are now widely available in an increasing number of stores, albeit at prices significantly higher than those for meat from animals.

Benefits of lab-grown meat include reducing the land and water required to raise animals by an estimated 99 percent and a reduction in greenhouse gasses emitted in the process. Hormones and antibiotics used in raising animals are not needed in the lab. However, the total environmental impact has not been determined, nor has the analysis expanded to include electricity and heat required to produce lab-grown meat.

Plant-based meat has been widely distributed in the U.S. and is being included in the menus of many fast-food hamburger restaurants. Jim Thomas, co-executive director and researcher with the ETC Group, an organization that tracks how new technologies impact food systems, said, "This has nothing to do with trying to solve the problems of our food system. This is just about trying to create new niches and new hype to sell to consumers." He went on to note that plant-based meat is "ultra-processed," and that highly-processed foods should generally be avoided. [225]

It is not clear whether the meat grown from cow cells will be vegetarian. It is also not clear whether lab-grown pork products will be kosher or halal. However, Rabbi Yuval Cherlow, a prominent Orthodox rabbi in Israel, said that meat from a genetically-cloned pig would be kosher for consumption by Jews, including when eaten with dairy products. [226]

It is too early to understand all of the implications of lab-grown meat, including whether it will be accepted by the consumer and whether it will cost too much. However, those experiments are under way, and early indications are that there is at least a niche market for alternative meat.

<u>Vertical farms</u>

Japan may be leading the way in cultivating plants vertically. In essence, floors in a building are filled with hydroponics (in a variation, aeroponics, the roots of hanging plants are sprayed with water containing nutrients), perhaps in multiple layers on one floor, and use LED lighting. This significantly multiplies the area on which food can be grown, provides control over resources needed to cultivate the plants, and also allows food to be grown essentially anywhere.

The primary downside, which currently makes food from vertical farms more expensive and uncompetitive, is that, instead of consuming free sunlight, a vertical farm must provide energy to light layers and floors of growing plants.

Additional Steps to Increase the Food Supply

<u>Reduce waste</u>

As with water, we waste an enormous amount of food. We can effectively increase the food supply by wasting less.

There are many reports in the press about the amount of food that is wasted, but these reports typically do not distinguish between avoidable and unavoidable waste. Unavoidable waste is inherent in every action that we take.

An interesting study, focusing primarily on the United Kingdom, and published by the Royal Society, quoted a previous study that 25% by weight of purchased food was wasted (which is different from the waste when compared to the amount harvested).

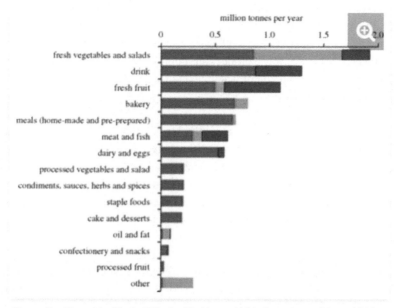

million tonnes per year

fresh vegetables and salads
drink
fresh fruit
bakery
meals (home-made and pre-prepared)
meat and fish
dairy and eggs
processed vegetables and salad
condiments, sauces, herbs and spices
staple foods
cake and desserts
oil and fat
confectionery and snacks
processed fruit
other

Figure 47 – Wasted food in the UK, classified by avoidable (brown), possibly avoidable (green) and avoidable (blue) from WRAP. 2009 *a* Household food and drink waste in the UK. Banbury, UK. ISBN: 1-84405-430-6.

The study found that approximately 64% of waste was avoidable (42% of the avoidable waste came from preparing or serving too much food and drink, and approximately 54% was due to not using the food or drink in time before spoilage). Therefore, approximately 16% of food production could be reclaimed, instantly increasing available supplies by 21%.

Reducing food waste would require significant changes in infrastructure, transportation, storage, and, most importantly, human attitudes. However, the potential increase in available food would be meaningful.

The study concluded, "In developing and emerging economies, this [conservation] would require market-led large-scale investment in agricultural infrastructure, technological skills and knowledge, storage, transport and distribution. … Where international markets and local policies and investment are lacking, large-scale capital investment in infrastructure in developing countries has often failed. For long-term sustainability, development across the FSC [food supply chain] in the developing world requires locally supported government policies and investment alongside any market-led private investment with reach through into developed world markets. … the greatest potential for the reduction of food waste in the developed world lies with retailers, food services and consumers. Cultural shifts in the ways consumers value food, stimulated via education, increased awareness of the FSC and food waste's impact on the environment have the potential to reduce waste production. Improved food labelling and better consumer understanding of labelling and food storage also have food waste reduction potential."[227]

A prevalent cause of food waste is the use of sell-by, or best-if-used-by dates for food. There is little or no correlation between these dates and the dates at which food is no longer fit for consumption. In many cases, the actual sell-by date, the date by which food should be sold in the stores, assuming an average time in the home before consumption, is significantly beyond the sell-by date given on the food's packaging. In the extreme, low-acid foods like canned green beans are probably risk-free for up to five years.

Without going into a long discussion of sell-by or best-if-used-by dates, a consistent, analysis-based approach to determining these dates would reduce food waste.

One response to food waste is a small, but growing, group of entrepreneurs who are selling misshapen fruit and vegetables at a discount.

Reduce obesity

Another approach to conservation is for people to consume only what they need and no more. We should concentrate on calories and nutrition. According to the World Health Organization, in 2014, more than 1.9 billion adults (39%) were overweight, 600 million (13%) of which were obese.[228]

It will be increasingly important in a food-constrained world to be efficient in consuming the nutrition necessary to sustain life, and not eat the excess that others will need.

Don't plant organically

There is disagreement about the difference in crop yields from "conventional" farming, compared with organic farming. Essentially all studies indicate that organic farming is less productive, up to 33% less productive. However, some studies indicate that the difference in yield can be reduced to 8-9%.[229]

Climate change

Climate change can't be all bad. Ironically, increasing CO_2 in the atmosphere, which contributes to climate change, also tends to increase plant yields.

Stop planting crops for biofuels

Biofuels from corn are a politically-inspired waste of good land and energy. Approximately 40% of the U.S. corn crop is used to manufacture ethanol. Biofuels from sugar cane have some value, but that value should be compared to the value that the land currently devoted to sugar cane could provide if planted in food.

Employ some of the principles of regenerative agriculture

Some environmentalists are taking the concept of organic farming further by, for example, eliminating all pesticides (contrary to some popular belief, organic farming incorporates the use of some pesticides). The primary focus of regenerative agriculture is to restore the health of the soil. Earlier, we examined loss of topsoil and increased water runoff due to degraded soil conditions.

Regenerative agricultural practices include:

- no tillage,
- diverse cover crops,
- in-farm fertility (no external nutrients),
- no pesticides or synthetic fertilizers, and
- multiple crop rotations.

Regenerative agriculture, like organic farming, emphasizes the natural as opposed to the synthetic and artificial. There are few widespread studies on the productivity of regenerative agriculture, but initial indications are that regenerative agriculture's yields are on par with those of conventional agriculture. Initial indications are that regenerative agriculture also creates a significantly smaller climate change footprint. The restoration of topsoil will become increasingly important, and the techniques of regenerative agriculture can be used to help restore that topsoil.[230]

Re-think the definition of food

As traditional foods become limited and in greater demand, there will be pressure to reconsider what is classified as acceptable food. Humans around the world currently eat essentially all parts of animals, including their internal organs. They eat a wide variety of animals, including dogs, cats, horses and kangaroo; and eat a wide assortment of insects.

More than 1,900 species of insects are part of the diet of at least two billion people, including beetles, caterpillars, bees, wasps, ants, grasshoppers, locusts and crickets.[231] In 2020, the European Union's Food Safety Authority approved the sale of bugs as "novel food," opening the way for sale of locusts, crickets, grasshoppers and mealworms across Europe.

Insect burgers and insect balls went on sale in Switzerland in 2017.

Grasshopper pizzas were trending in Las Vegas in 2019.

Since domestic animals will begin competing with humans for food, there will be increasing pressure to restrict or eliminate domestic animals, including cats and dogs.

However, a Swedish scientist took the definition of food to its limits, by noting that people would have to consume human corpses in order to combat climate change and food sustainability.[232]

Then, the Bad News

We may be entering a period of diminishing returns with regard to the rate of improvements in food productivity. Past improvements have been very rapid and have been the result of "low-hanging fruit." Future gains may come more slowly and at greater cost and effort.

This decrease in productivity has been reflected in recent statistics. Patricio Grassini and his co-authors noted in an article in Nature Communications that, "investment in R&D in agriculture in China has increased threefold from 1981 to 2000. However, rates of increase in crop yields in China have remained constant in wheat, decreased by 64% in maize [corn] as a relative rate and are negligible in rice. Likewise, despite a 58% increase in investment in agricultural R&D in the United States from 1981 to 2000 (sum of public and private sectors), the rate of maize yield gain has remained strongly linear, implying that the marginal yield increase per unit of research investment has decreased substantially over time. This highlights the need to increase the level of investments in agricultural R&D in order to sustain current and future increases in crop yields."[233]

A Conundrum

I will leave the food section on a philosophical note.

Let's do another simplistic thought experiment.

Assume a world population, some of whom are obese, some of whom are well fed and most of whom are "food insecure" or starving. Say, the world during Malthus' time.

What is the result of increasing the amount of food, say through a green revolution?

Part of the answer is that the world can support more people, since returns from the green revolution will go primarily to the wealthier and more powerful. The other part of the answer is that the degree of food insecurity, malnourishment and starvation will decrease.

The world's population will have increased from one billion when Malthus lived to an estimated 10 billion in 2060 due to two primary factors: there was food (and other resources) to support them and life expectancy increased, partially because of improved nutrition, but also due to antibiotics and other improvements in medicine. This increase was partially offset by a decline in the number of children born to each woman.

Population growth is forecasted to decrease due to the winding down of the one-time effects of longer lives and fewer children. Around 2100, the human population will primarily depend on the availability of food (and other resources).

Simplistically, and back to Malthus, increasing the amount of food enables an increase in population (and a decrease in overall food insecurity), which, in turn, stresses the planet, its other species and its natural resources.

The conundrum: was the green revolution, in the long term, a good thing or a bad thing?

The answer, I believe, is that for a few hundred years, it was a good thing as the overall quality of life increased for an increasing proportion of the population. A significant transition occurred when human population and consumption resulted in the degradation of the environment and to unsustainability of human activities at their current level.

Energy

Our energy future can be summarized as: continuing dominance by carbon-based fuels, increasing use of renewable energy for electricity and a continuing decrease in Energy Return on Energy Invested (EROI). It is unlikely that peak oil, peak coal or peak natural gas will occur within the next twenty years.

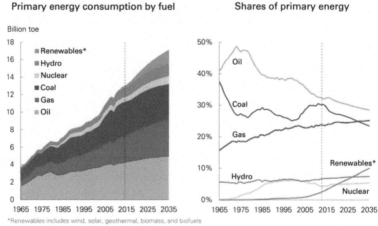

Figure 48 - Projected world energy consumption through 2035 (Although the projection is by BP, it does not differ materially from that of the International Energy Agency, and BP does a better job of presentation.)[234]

Revisiting EROI

Earlier, we discussed Energy Returned on Energy Invested (EROI) and the estimate that an EROI of 14 or more is probably required to sustain a complex society.

The problem is that EROI is decreasing for the high-density, carbon-based fuels we have relied on in the past. We have used up the easiest-to-get-to, highest quality oil and natural gas and are increasingly going "colder and deeper" to find additional reserves.

181

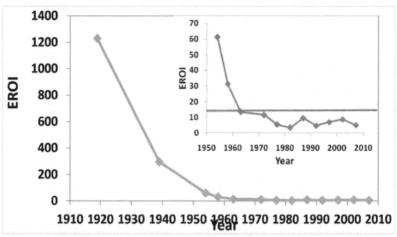

Figure 49 – EROI for oil and gas discoveries over time (I placed the red line on the insert to mark the 14:1 level.)[235]

Calculating the separate EROIs for oil and for natural gas is difficult, because they are often found together. Figure 48 illustrates how the EROI for oil and natural gas has dramatically decreased over time. According to Figure 48, in 2010 the EROI for newly-discovered oil and natural gas was 8 – well below the complex-society minimum of 14.

EROI for U.S., Selected Fuels, 2010

Biodiesel	1.3
Ethanol from corn	1.3
Solar collector	1.6
Solar flat plate	1.9
Bitumen tar sands	3.0
Ethanol from sugar cane	5.0
Shale oil	5.0
Photovoltaic, without accounting for intermittence	6.8
Oil – current discoveries	8.0
Geothermal (no water heating)	9.5
Natural gas 2005	10.0
Nuclear (diffusion enrichment–obsolete)	10.0
Potential minimum EROI to support complex societies	14.0
Wind, without accounting for intermittence	18.0
Oil – current production	20.0
Geothermal (hot water heating)	32.4
Coal	80.0

| Hydro | 100.0 |
| Nuclear (centrifugal enrichment) | 105.0 |

Figure 50 – EROI for selected fuels, potential minimum EROI line added[236]

The good news is that wind's EROI is a healthy 18. The bad news is that the EROI for solar is below 7 and that the EROI for shale oil is 5. The even worse news is that the EROIs for solar and wind are significantly overstated, since compensating for storage and intermittence (the fact that the sun does not shine all the time and the wind does not blow all the time) are not included in the calculations.

Weißbach, et al., calculated the effective, or "buffered," EROI for various energy sources. Their calculations encompassed energy storage over an entire life of the energy source. Their conclusions are summarized in the following chart.

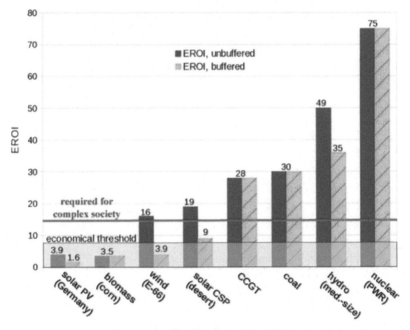

Figure 51 – EROI for various fuel types[237] PV is photovoltaic, CSP is concentrating solar power, CCGT is combined cycle gas turbine. "Wind: Location is Northern Schleswig Holstein (2000 fullload hours). Coal: Transportation not included. Nuclear: Enrichment 83% centrifuge, 17% diffusion. PV: Roof installation. Solar CSP: Grid connection to Europe not included." I added the "required for complex society" red line.

The authors include the following in their conclusions:

… All EROIs are above the physical limit of 1 which means they all "produce" more energy than they "consume". Not all of them are above the economical limit of 7, though … Solar PV in Germany even with the more effective roof installation and even when not taking the needed buffering (storage and over-capacities) into account has an EROI far below the economic limit. Wind energy seems to be above the economic limit but falls below when combined even with the most effective pump storage and even when installed at the German coast. Biogas-fired plants, even though they need no buffering, have the problem of enormous fuel provisioning effort which brings them clearly below the economic limit with no potential of improvements in reach.

Solar CSP is the most hopeful option among the new solar/wind technologies, in particular because of the smaller influence of the buffering. However, pump storage is often not available in regions with high solar irradiation. Choosing less effective storage techniques like molten salt thermal storage and the connection to the European grid probably brings the EROI again far below the economic limit. It is also important to keep in mind that small units are much more ineffective, as is an installation in sun-poor regions owed to the non-linearity …

Ted Trainer, in a journal article in which he analyzed "the EROI of whole systems for 100% renewable electricity supply capable of dealing with intermittency," concluded, "The general finding is that 100% renewable supply systems probably have values that are too low to sustain energy intensive societies."[238]

These, more sophisticated, calculations continue to ignore the EROI of infrastructure required for each energy type, e.g., pipelines, connections to the grid.

In the end, we are increasingly using energy that is not returning sufficient EROI to support a complex society. As a result, society will necessarily have to go forward with fewer things and become simpler.

Energy has historically been plentiful and cheap to the point that we take it for granted. When we turn on a light switch, we get light at a low cost. When we fill up our gas tank, we get gasoline at a low cost. We have been the beneficiaries of what will likely turn out to be a unique period in time – the time of the discovery and use of high-EROI fuels – a time of unsustainable, unique, and very enjoyable energy abundance.

We have likely reached peak EROI, which argues that we are at or near peak complexity in our society as we deplete the remaining high-EROI sources of energy.

If this is true, high-energy EROI fuel will not be available to support the future. Society and technology will be required to simplify. Humans will have to adjust their attitudes about and expectations of increasing benefits from high-EROI sources of energy.

If renewable energy has an all-in EROI of, as a guess, 8, then we can support a society and technology compatible with that EROI, as compared with our current society and technology, which require an EROI of something on the order of 14.

The Cost of Conversion to Renewable Energy

It is far from clear, actually it is unlikely, that non-carbon-based energy will be able to supply humanity's energy needs in the future, absent a significant implementation of nuclear fission or a breakthrough in developing nuclear fusion.

And the cost will be massive.

Upgrading the electric grid, investing in mines and refining of metals and other commodities needed to create windmills, electric panels and storage capability will cost tens of trillions of dollars.

As with any undertaking, there will also be secondary effects and unintended consequences.

The Irony of Inexpensive, Renewable Energy

Much of the increase in human population, from 7.8 billion in 2020 to 10 billion around 2060, will be in Africa. Many Africans have lagged behind in development and in consumerism. Therefore, inexpensive, renewable energy would give them the basis for their rapid attainment of higher standards of living.

It is fair that Africans be able to strive for standards of living achieved in the rest of the world. However, this process of catching up would mean that their consumption would also increase rapidly, increasing their contribution to the strain on natural resources. The world will face the conflict between Africans' (and others in developing countries) reasonably wanting to improve themselves and the reality of Overshoot.

Materials

"Companies in all sectors need to
prepare themselves for a world where
raw materials may be in short supply." -
KPMG[239]

In general, as with oil, we are accessing and using the materials that are the easiest and the least expensive to mine. As those materials are depleted, we access materials that are increasing difficult to get to and increasingly expensive to mine.

We will look at the massive amounts of materials required to form the basis of our civilization, beginning with the foundations of renewable energy.

It is ironic that supplying renewable energy requires the use of a significant amount of materials, impacting the environment and creating greenhouse gasses.

More importantly, the mineral-production infrastructure and the identification of mineral reserves are not sufficient to support a rapid increase in the demand for renewable energy.

"Building one wind turbine requires 900 tons of steel, 2,500 tons of concrete and 45 tons of plastic."[240] In addition, miles of copper wire and the equivalent of thousands of batteries must be supplied in order to make that wind turbine functional. Wind turbines have an expected life of 20-25 years, after which they will be torn down and replaced.

Solar panels are generally sold with a 20-year warranty.

"If, as the IEA [International Energy Agency] predicts, there are 125 million electric vehicles (EVs) on the road by 2030, it will require roughly 10 million tonnes of copper – a 50% increase over current annual global copper consumption (20 million tonnes). ... Given how much aluminum, metallurgical coal, copper, aluminum, zinc and rare earths are required for each wind turbine and each EV – and how much lithium and cobalt are needed for EV batteries – it begs the question: Will the transition to a low-carbon economy lead to 'peak metals' (the point of maximum metal production? ... Even if there are sufficient theoretical amounts of base metals in the earth's crust, there's a big difference between what is theoretically retrievable and what is economically recoverable or politically viable. ... And even when a deposit proves to be economically recoverable and can get all the permits it needs, it typically takes 10 to 20 years for a mine to go from discovery to production. ... [A Dutch study concludes] The current global supply of several critical metals is insufficient to transition to a renewable energy system. ... Exponential growth in renewable energy production capacity is not possible with present-day technologies and annual metal production.'"[241]

The IEA summarized these thoughts in graphic form:

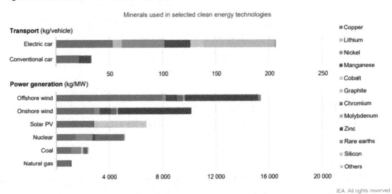

Figure 52 – The rapid deployment of clean energy technologies ... International Energy Agency[242]

Many of the minerals required for renewable energy appear to be in sufficient supply. However, some critical minerals, such as cobalt, more than half of which is supplied by the Democratic Republic of the Congo, are difficult to acquire.

Rare earth minerals, although not actually rare, may not exist in sufficient quantities to support renewable energy.

In addition, any meaningful transition to renewable energy will be difficult to support with current technology and infrastructure.

The number of materials used in everyday life is impressive. As an example, Christine V. McLelland has produced a list of materials used in the creation of a Subaru.

Name of material	Amount in lbs.	Use
Aluminum	240	Light metal used in body of car.
Antimony	Trace	Used to make car upholstery fire resistant.
Asbestos	1.2	Used in brake pads.
Barium	Trace	Used to coat electrical conductors in the ignition system.
Cadmium	Trace	Electrolytically deposited as a coating on metals (steel) to form a chemically resistant coating.
Carbon	46	Used to make iron ore into steel. Steel contains 1% carbon. Also used to add strength to rubber.
Clays	Trace	Used to make ceramics in engine (ex. spark plugs)
Coal	NA	Used to make electricity to produce autos.
Cobalt	Trace	Makes thermally resistant alloys** ('superalloys') in engine.
Copper	42	Used for wiring throughout automobile.
Fluorspar	Trace	Directly or indirectly used to manufacture aluminum, gasoline and steel.
Gallium	Trace	Used in mirrors, transistors and LEDs.
Gold	Trace	Used in the electronics systems.
Iron Ore (see MAGNETITE)	4960	Used to make steel for the frame and engine of the auto.
Lead (see GALENA)	24	From the mineral galena, used in the battery. (960 lbs. of lead ore needed)
Magnesium	4.4	An alloy used to strengthen aluminum and zinc.
Manganese	17.6	Makes an alloy with steel that is tough and resistant to wear for parts such as the axles, pistons, crank shafts and gears. Used in batteries.
Molybdenum	1.0	Used to strengthen steel and lubricants.
Mica	Trace	Fills the shocks.

Nickel	9.0	Used as plating for stainless steel.
Nitrogen	Trace	Used for ceramic materials (spark plugs) and in battery.
Oxygen	Varies	Used for the combustion in engine.
Palladium	Trace	Used as an alloy in electrical contacts.
Petroleum (see gusher, oil rigs, and pipeline pictures)	980	From petroleum we produce plastics (used for the body and interior), rubber tires, paint, synthetic fabrics, gasoline and lubricating oils. Also to make electricity used in the production of the auto.
Quartz sand	170	Used for silica to make glass (85 lbs.)
Silicon	41	Ceramic components.
Strontium	Trace	Used for phosphorescent paint on dials.
Sulfur	2	Used in battery.
Tin	Trace	Alloys with copper, makes solder and lead.
Titanium	Trace	Used to make metallic alloys and as a substitute for aluminum. Also used in paint, lacquers, plastics and rubber.
Tungsten	Trace	Used in filament of light bulbs and for spark plug manufacturing.
Vanadium	1	Used to form alloys that are tough and resist fatigue. Used in axles, crank shafts, gears and other critical components.
Zinc Ore	18 (720 of zinc ore)	Galvanizes screws to be resistant to rust and corrosion. As a filler in rubber tires. Auto industry is the largest consumer.
Zirconium	Trace	Alloy of steel and glass, and used in light bulb filaments.

Figure 53 – From "What Earth Materials Are in My Subaru," Christine V. McLelland[243]

Every American Born Will Need...

27,365 lbs. Salt

11,655 lbs. Clays

15,107 lbs. Phosphate

6.97 million cu. ft. Natural Gas

72,381 gallons Petroleum

51,720 lbs. Cement

968 lbs. Copper

23,011 lbs. Iron Ore

419 lbs. Zinc

3,656 lbs. Bauxite (Aluminum)

1.88 Troy oz. Gold

1.42 million lbs. Stone, Sand, & Gravel

828 lbs. Lead

355,951 lbs. Coal

plus 48,856 lbs. Other Minerals & Metals

3.188 million pounds of minerals, metals, and fuels in their lifetime

©2017 Minerals Education Coalition

Learn more at www.MineralsEducationCoalition.org

Figure 54 - Minerals, metals and fuels need in lifetime of American[244]

If the future is electric vehicles, following is the amount of materials Tesla would require to produce 20 million cars a year as a percentage of 2019 production of those metals, keeping in mind that we need 100% of the 2019 production of these metals for other purposes.

METALS TESLA NEEDS TO BUILD 20M CARS A YEAR

Tesla Production @ 20m	Material Required (t)	Production 2019 (t)	% of Production
Graphite	1,028,775	1,100,000	94%
Nickel	750,410	2,460,000	31%
Lithium	127,302	77,000	165%
Copper (vehicle)	1,820,000	21,000,000	9%
Manganese	20,811	19,000,000	+0%
Cobalt	68,315	122,000	56%
Aluminum (battery)	16,544	64,000,000	+0%
Aluminum (vehicle)	3,380,000	64,000,000	5%
MagREO (NdPr, Dy, Tb)	18,000	46,000	39%

Battery graphite, nickel, cobalt, lithium, manganese, MagREO (NdPr, Dy, Tb): Adamas Intelligence
Production: USGS, BMO, Morgan Stanley, BP, Fitch, Excl. synthetic graphite
Copper, aluminum (vehicle): UBS estimates of Chevy Volt

MINING.COM
EVMETAL
INDEX

Figure 55 – Metals Tesla Needs to Build 20M Cars a Year[245]

Industry and technology require materials that are not well known in order to keep high-tech processes running. These materials are used to alloy metals, create efficient batteries, produce high-performance magnets, create solar cells and for many other applications.

In response to an Executive Order by President Trump in 2018, the following were designated as "critical materials" – "a non-fuel mineral or mineral material essential to the economic and national security of the United States, the supply chain of which is vulnerable to disruption …": aluminum, antimony, barite, beryllium, bismuth, cesium, chromium, cobalt, fluorspar, gallium, germanium, graphite, hafnium, helium, indium, lithium, manganese, magnesium, niobium, platinum group metals, potash, rare earths, rhenium, rubidium, scandium, strontium, tantalum, tellurium, tin, titanium, tungsten, vanadium, uranium, zirconium.[246]

The depletion of minerals, metals and fuels can be illustrated through the parable of an imaginary mineral, maxite.

The Parable of Maxite

It is pretty straightforward to understand that if a resource is finite in supply, to the extent it is being used at all, there is no question that it will be used up. The only question is, how much time will it take before it is used up? As with peak oil, "used up" does not necessarily mean "all gone." It most likely will mean that all of a resource that can practically and economically be accessed has been used. While it may not be all gone, for all practical purposes it is inaccessible and, therefore, unusable.

Let's imagine a natural resource that we will call maxite. Let's assume there are a million tons of maxite in the Earth. Humans discover a use for maxite and begin to mine it. Since a lot of maxite is near the surface of the Earth, it is relatively inexpensive to mine, so that maxite can be mined and sold for $1,000 a ton. Initial mining production is 10,000 tons a year. If no other uses are found for maxite and the number of people using it remains the same, there is a 100-year supply of maxite.

However, China finds additional uses for maxite, and humans around the world start buying products with maxite in them. Production increases to 50,000 tons a year. There is still a 19-year supply.

However, miners now have to dig deeper to get to the maxite. Also, the quality of the ore is declining, so that a lot more rock has to be mined in order to produce the same amount of maxite. New technology and tools must be employed in the mining. The price of maxite goes up to $5,000 a ton.

The increasing price causes the rate of adoption of maxite to decrease, so that at the end of year 5, production is 100,000 tons per year and the price has increased to $50,000 a ton. There is still about a 7-year supply remaining, but by the end of an additional five years, mining has ceased. Even though there are still some 200,000 tons left, it is simply too expensive in time and energy to mine maxite, given that no one will pay the $1,000,000 per ton price.

Within a period of about 10 years, a resource with a 100-year supply at $1,000 per ton was, for all intents and purposes, totally depleted, even though there was a significant amount still left in the ground, and its last sale was at $1,000,000 per ton.

In addition, since there was no practical substitute for maxite, all of the tools and instruments that were made from maxite could no longer be made, nor could the processes and goods that relied on the tools and instruments that included maxite.

All non-renewable resources are, essentially, maxite: aluminum, gold, uranium, iron, phosphorus, molybdenum, oil. We have been fortunate enough to live during the period when there was a reasonable amount of "maxite" available at reasonable prices. Although depletion curves will differ for different natural resources, there are now so many people asking for those resources, that many are being critically depleted.

Consider copper as a real-world example of how the maxite process is currently unfolding.

There is a point at which recovery of remaining resources is not profitable, so that peak copper is reached.

From 1991 to 2015, world production of copper doubled. In 2015, we mined approximately 18.7 million tons out of estimated available resources of some 2.1 billion tons, indicating that there are more than 100 years of copper yet available. However, the quality of the ore is declining and the cost of mining ever-deeper and more difficult to reach copper is increasing. Applying Hubbert's model from crude oil to copper shows peak copper arriving in somewhere between 8 and 40 years from now, at a much higher cost of extraction.

The quality of ore that is now available to be mined is declining. By some estimates, in 2003, the average amount of copper in the mined ore was a little less than 1%; today it is approximately 0.62%. During that period, cost to mine ore has approximately doubled. [247]

A picture is worth a thousand words.

This is the Bingham Canyon copper mine, located south of Salt Lake City in Utah.

Figure 56 - Bingham Canyon copper mine[248]

The mine, dug out of what once was a mountain, is now approximately 2.5 miles (4.0 kilometers) wide and 0.75 miles (1.2 kilometers) deep.[249]

In order to mine ore that is approximately 0.2% copper, immense equipment must be used.

Figure 57 – Haul truck[250]

Haul trucks at the Bingham Canyon mine include trucks that carry 255 tons (231 Imperial tons) of ore. If all of the copper in the ore carried by one truck, 510,000 pounds, could be recovered, each truckload would result in 1,020 pounds of copper.

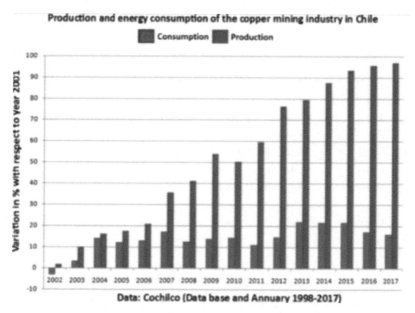

Figure 58 – Production and energy consumption of the copper mining industry in Chile.[251]

These pictures vividly illustrate the extent to which we now have to go in terms of energy and technology to extract some minerals, as their supplies become increasingly depleted.

And copper is becoming increasingly difficult to mine just as demand for its use in electric vehicles and in the enhanced electric grid is increasing dramatically.

Projections of Depletion

In 2007, *New Scientist* magazine, published an article predicting the time to exhaustion of various materials, assuming we continue consuming them at the rate we were consuming them in 2007. This kind of analysis is flawed, however, it does emphasize the materials we are at risk of exhausting and for which additional sources or substitutes must be found.

Future rates of consumption will probably be higher than assumed in the study, due both to increasing population and increasing consumption by that population. The good news, is there are likely additional undiscovered resources of each material. Although the *New Scientist* presented the data in graphic form, following is a table containing some of the data:

Material	Used For	Projected Year of Exhaustion
Indium	Displays	2020
Silver	Jewelry, Catalytic Converters	2036
Antimony	Drugs	2037
Tin	Cans, Solder	2047
Zinc	Galvanizing	2047
Lead	Pipes, Batteries	2049
Gold	Jewelry, Dentistry	2052
Uranium	Weapons, Power	2066
Copper	Wire, Coins Plumbing	2068
Nickel	Batteries, Turbine Blades	2097

Figure 59 – Predicted year of exhaustion for selected materials[252]

According to Armin Reller (University of Augsburg) and Tom Graedel (Yale University), if we continue with the average global usage rate of metals and other materials (aluminum, copper, nickel, phosphorus, etc.) that are manufactured into products that we use daily (electronics, vehicles, fertilizers, etc.), there are resources available for only another 58 years. If the rest of the planet consumed at half the rate of the United States today, we would have resources for only 20 years.[253]

Each of these estimates / predictions will likely prove to be in error by substantial margins. However, each of these predictions indicates that there is trouble ahead at some point in the relatively near future.

One significant change that has the potential to increase the available amount of several minerals is mining the ocean floor. In essence, large machines will vacuum mineral nodules, including nickel, cobalt, gold, copper, zinc, iron and manganese, from the ocean floor and pump them to the surface for processing. There are environmental hurdles to be overcome for this technology to be effective, including the disturbance of huge amounts of silt.

Prototypes are now testing out the concept, and commercialization is anticipated to begin in the early 2020s.

We can take steps to defer the ultimate peak date for each material, however, those dates cannot be extended forever in an environment of population growth and ever-increasing demands for the material trappings of the good life.

Solutions

The steps that can be taken are well known and have been known for decades. However, they have been taken tentatively, if at all:

- Produce goods for the long term – the disposable culture is extremely wasteful of materials. The bias should be for long-lasting goods.
- Repair goods instead of disposing of them and buying new ones. This is a variation of the disposable culture. We have become accustomed to throwing out items, even if they are repairable. We cannot have new iPhones every year.
- Recycle – recycling can be problematic in that it often requires a significant amount of energy and additional raw materials, and at times yields low quality output. However, as the world runs out of materials, it will be increasingly important to reclaim whatever can reasonably and efficiently be reclaimed.

Waste

All of this consumption results in the production of massive amount of waste, perhaps approaching the limit of the environment to cleanse itself.

Capitalism enables the creation of a cornucopia of goods and services. Since there is demand for the ever-greater amounts of things capitalism can provide, there is an associated, essentially unavoidable creation of incredible amounts of waste.

Since waste is mostly flushed or tidily carried away by the trash service, it is easy to ignore the harm inflicted on the environment by mountains of waste. Out of sight, out of mind.

Each stage of the creation, delivery and consumption of goods and services involves the creation of waste material and energy. As a simple example, consider the creation and sale of a piece of furniture from Ikea.

- A tree is felled. Much of it is discarded as waste as not being the right size or quality.
- The remainder is shaped and drilled, creating waste.
- The metal pieces have also generated waste as they were created and shaped.
- The truck that delivered the wood and metal generated waste energy, both because of the laws of thermodynamics and also because of engine idling at stoplights, etc. On average, diesel engines, such as those in the truck, are about 45% efficient, meaning that, before losses from idling, about 55% of the diesel energy is wasted.
- The machines that create the wood pieces and metal parts use electricity. Between 8-15% of electricity is lost in transmission. Leaving machines on while not operating them wastes additional electricity.
- Wrapping the pieces into a set involves losses in paper, cardboard, labels, ink, etc.
- Delivering the set to the store involves additional diesel waste.
- The store wastes energy through electricity transmission losses and leaving electrical appliances on while not using them.
- The consumer incurs gasoline engine inefficiencies, which, at around 70%, are higher than diesel inefficiencies.
- The wrapping is mostly waste when discarded.
- The energy generation by diesel, gasoline and electricity generated carbon dioxide and pollutants into the atmosphere.
- The web extends ever-outward, and includes advertisers, lawyers, accountants, laying concrete for roads, electricity for traffic lights and food for all the humans involved.

Some of this waste, such as the inefficiency of internal combustion engines, which convert about 20 – 35% of the energy in gasoline into power for the engine (the remainder is released as heat)[254], results from laws of physics. This waste can be reduced to some extent, but most of the waste will remain. Other waste results from the mismatch between the form of raw materials and the finished form we desire. Again, we can be more efficient, but it is unlikely that we will find a tree in the shape of a bed. 3D printers have the potential for minimizing waste in the manufacturing process.

However, waste is inherent in and a key component of the consumption process.

Convenience and the increasing cost of labor have led us to throw away things – from Styrofoam coffee cups to plastic bags to iPhones – in staggering numbers. "The U.S. accounts for about 120 billion paper, plastic and foam coffee cups each year, or about one-fifth of the global total. Almost every last one of them—99.75 percent—ends up as trash, where even paper cups can take more than 20 years to decompose."[255]

From gargantuan garbage dumps at the edges of our cities to the filthy air over Beijing and Delhi to the dead zones in our oceans to plastic "islands" four times the size of Texas in our oceans to human and industrial waste in our rivers to spent uranium fuel rods from nuclear reactors, we are overwhelming our environment's ability to function.

The most common form of plastic pollution is cigarette butts. Of the 6 trillion cigarettes smoked worldwide, annually, some 4.6 trillion are littered in the environment. Additionally, these butts contain toxic materials that are released into the environment.

Figure 60 – Pollution in the Caribbean[256]

"Every minute, one garbage truck worth of plastic is dumped into the ocean. Yearly, a colossal 1.4 billion tons of trash ends up in our beautiful oceans. Of this waste, much of it is plastic."[257]

Some of the plastic is funneled into circulating currents, or gyres, such as the North Pacific Ocean Gyre, which is four times the size of Texas. Some of it will be ingested by fish and by the people who eat fish.

Even though a huge amount of plastic goes into the oceans, most of our plastic trash winds up in landfills.

Figure 61 - Landfill[258]

To add to the pollution problem, technology has enabled an all-but-invisible form of plastic, called microplastic.

Microplastics are small pieces of plastic, less than 5 mm (0.2 inches) in length, such as microfibers from clothing, microbeads and plastic pellets. They are also the products of the wearing down of larger plastics. Although individually small in size, in aggregate in 2014, they were estimated to amount to 15 – 51 trillion individual pieces, weighing between 83,000 – 236,000 metric tons (91,492 – 260,145 U.S. tons). They are used in facial cleansers, cosmetics, air blasting and medicines.[259] It has been estimated that each American ingests, through eating, drinking or breathing, between 74,000 and 121,000 microplastic particles per year.[260] There is evidence that microplastics in the oceans are permeating all parts of the food chain.

There is no clear evidence that microplastics are harmful, however, they are a growing presence and are increasingly unavoidable at any location on

Earth.

In 2006, the latest year for which data are available, the U.S. generated 251 million tons of trash, or 4.6 pounds per person per day. 55% of this goes to landfills, 33% is recycled and 12% is incinerated. When trash is buried in landfills, it does not decay. Landfills release methane, a potent greenhouse gas. Some landfills capture this methane to burn to generate electricity.[261] In the past, "recycling" has primarily meant "shipped to China where much of it is disposed in landfills."

When they are allowed to decay, it is estimated that a Styrofoam cup requires about 50 years to biodegrade, an aluminum can 200 years, diapers 450 years, a plastic bottle 450 years and fishing line 600 years.[262]

Another critical waste discussion involves the air we breathe.

Figure 62 – Air pollution in Delhi[263]

The primary measure of air pollution is the amount of PM 2.5 in the air. PM 2.5 are tiny particles suspended in the air. The World Health Organization considers 10 micrograms per cubic meter of PM 2.5 as "safe" (as an annual mean; 25 micrograms per cubic meter as a 24-hour mean), and anything above 300 mpcm as "hazardous." (There are standards for other types of air pollution, such as ozone.) While Delhi registers concentrations in excess of 600, it is not in the top ten of a list of the world's 19 most polluted cities. The top 19 include 9 in India, 4 in China (Beijing does not make the list), 3 in Saudi Arabia, 1 in Iran, 1 in Cameroon and 1 in Pakistan.[264]

Our waters are also becoming extraordinarily filthy.

Figure 63 – Water pollution in India[265]

The website, Whatagreenlife, has compiled a list of some of the most polluted rivers in the world. River pollution generally comes from untreated industrial waste, untreated human waste and sewage, pesticides and fertilizer.

- Citarum – Indonesia. Every day approximately 300 tons of waste is dumped by 1,500 factories.
- Volga – Russia
- Seine – France
- Rhone – France
- Yangtze – China
- Ganges – India
- Danube – Europe
- Nah Ghadir – Lebanon
- Mekong – Asia[266]

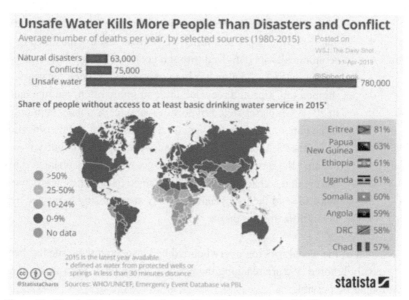

Figure 64 – Unsafe Water Kills More People Than Disasters and Conflict[267]

Unsafe water kills approximately six times more people than disasters and conflicts, and is responsible for approximately 780,000 deaths a year.

Not only are we, as a species, consuming too much, we are excreting too much.

Decreasing the amount of solid waste will be based on the "reduce, reuse and recycle" principle.

A thorough discussion of this principle is beyond the scope of this book, but in summary:

- Reduce – consume only the minimum that you need. For example, insist on reasonable portions of food. Do not buy a new iPhone every year. When you go out in your car, bundle tasks into one trip.
- Reuse what you can. Do not use disposable items, mostly paper and plastic, when a reusable approach is available. Repair instead of replacing. Do not needlessly purchase a replacement of an item, such as an iPhone, which is not broken.
- Recycle –This applies to activities such as composting household food waste. Unfortunately, recycling manufactured materials, plastics, paper, etc. is most often impractical due to the energy and

additional materials, including chemicals, required. To the extent that recycling is desired, it may have to be legally mandated or economically incentivized through taxation. Much of the waste people in the U.S. believe is being recycled has been for years shipped to China and recycled there or, more often, put in a landfill. In 2018, China restricted import of many recyclables, including some paper and most plastics. As the West looks to other locations in Southeast Asia to take its garbage, country after country is banning the receipt of foreign garbage, particularly plastics. This has created a challenge in the U.S., since many cities now have no place to send their recyclables. Many are choosing to put the items in landfills or burn them.

Much of the world is being overwhelmed by waste, and the issue has been mostly ignored. We are reaching the point at which ignoring waste will no longer be possible.

Another substance that may be overwhelming our atmosphere is carbon dioxide.

Climate Change and the Population / Consumption Challenge

The projected population collapse in *The Limits to Growth* occurs at approximately the same time as dates used as deadlines for various (generally ineffective) governmental actions relating to climate change. In other words, if *The Limits to Growth* scenario is correct, the climate change problem more or less takes care of itself in a be-careful-what-you-ask-for kind of way in a sustainability collapse. Human population begins to collapse before the dates incorporated in the various climate change goals by various governments.

For example, former U.S. President Barack Obama, as part of the Paris Accord on climate change, pledged that the U.S. will reduce CO_2 emissions by 26-28% below 2005 levels by 2025.[268]

Even supporters agree that the Paris Accord will have very little effect. The 2025 date for doing not much in the way of climate change is very close to the projected (approximate) 2030 date of the beginning of the collapse of human populations according to *The Limits to Growth*. In terms of time, Overshoot is far more urgent than climate change.

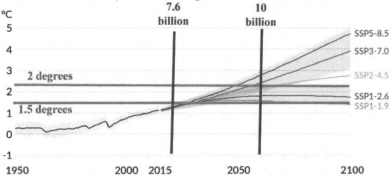

a) Global surface temperature change relative to 1850-1900

Figure 65 – IPCC's forecast of future temperature under five scenarios (SSPs). I have added the 1.5 and 2° red lines and the two purple population lines. The purple lines indicate reasonable ranges for Earth's carrying capacity for humans.

More fundamentally, climate change is a symptom of Overshoot. It is an indication that capitalism has gone too far in its use of energy resources.

If you "solve" Overshoot, you probably solve climate change; the converse is not necessarily true. If you solve climate change, you probably do not solve Overshoot.

However, there is some overlap. One, widely-accepted "solution" to climate change is to reduce greenhouse gas emissions by 80-90% below, say, 2005 levels. If this is achieved through a reduction in economic activity, the consumption challenge in sustainability would probably be solved. If emissions are reduced by entirely replacing carbon-based energy with renewable energy, which is not likely in this century, there would be no effect on population and humans would continue to consume. The Overshoot problem would not go away and could possibly be exacerbated as constraints on carbon dioxide production are relaxed.

Even though I am arguing the primacy of the Overshoot problem, climate change and Overshoot interact at many levels.

The warming of the atmosphere that has already taken place, due to natural and human causes, and the increase in atmospheric CO_2 due primarily to human activities, are significantly changing the world's oceans, in turn impacting ecosystems and habitat.

- Oceans are getting warmer.
- The oceans are absorbing more atmospheric CO_2 making their waters more acidic (actually, less alkaline), and thereby stressing various forms of life.
- Warming air is changing the dynamics of the hydrologic cycle.
- Spring is coming earlier in some locations.
- There will be increasing conflict between the use of farmland for raising crops and for hosting solar panels or wind farms.
- When water heats up, it expands, in turn increasing sea levels (indeed the majority of recent increases in sea level have been due to this thermal expansion).
- Higher ocean temperatures may enable stronger hurricanes and typhoons.
- Krill, a small organism at the bottom of the food chain, reproduce in significantly smaller numbers when ocean temperatures rise, creating devastating effects throughout the food chain

The Price Conundrum

Julian Simon won his wager with Paul Ehrlich that the world was not running out of things based on prices of commodities decreasing over the term of the bet. Decreasing prices are indicative of increased supply. Increased supply contradicts forecasts of shortages and associated emergencies.

Figure 66 – GCSI commodity index

205

In reality, it turns out that Simon picked his dates and the particular commodities included in the wager well. Picking other commodities or other dates could have yielded a different result.

As measured by the GCSI commodity index, commodity prices have generally increased over the past 45 years, until the Great Financial Crisis (GFC). Since the GFC, prices have been decreasing.

The reasons for the changes are complex, including the incredible consumption of commodities by China during its economic and geopolitical rise, and the subsequent peaking of China's consumption of some of those commodities.

However, due to many factors, including the ending of the pandemic, the disruption of supply chains due to the pandemic and for geopolitical reasons and a shortage of labor due to the pandemic, commodity prices have begun what appears to be a significant uptrend.

It is likely that 2020 marked a low in commodity prices for at least several decades to come.

So, Where Are We?

We have built the case that:

- humans have reached or are close to reaching Earth's carrying capacity for them;
- if carrying capacity has not been reached, it will likely be reached within the next forty years or so;
- forty years is not enough time to be able to take meaningful actions to reduce population;
- focus must be made on reducing levels of consumption, while, at the same time, taking whatever educational and regulatory actions can be taken to address population growth in the longer term.

Along the way, we have discussed various predictions, which indicate that all is not well with our planet. In fact, many systems are beginning to fail.

Following is a recap of Earth's carrying capacity for humans under various assumptions, as discussed in this book. The Earth's population in 2019 was approximately 7.7 billion and the Earth's projected population in the late 2050s is 10 billion.

Projected Carrying Capacity (billion)	Primary Assumptions Behind the Projection	Notes
1-2	Relative Prosperity	
2.0-3.0	Long-term steady state following Overshoot	Following collapse from 9-10 billion
3.4	Current food production practices within Planetary Boundaries	
< 4.0	Long-term steady state following Overshoot	Following collapse from > 8 billion
5.0	Eco-footprint in 2013	Projected carrying capacity by this measure gets smaller every year
< 7.0	In 2030 from thought experiment regarding projected water usage	
7.0	Paper by O'Neill, et. al. in *Nature Sustainability*	Extensive analysis of carrying capacity at planetary boundaries and therefore a low standard of living.
7.5	Deduction from U.N water projection	
9.0	Median of estimates in literature in one study	

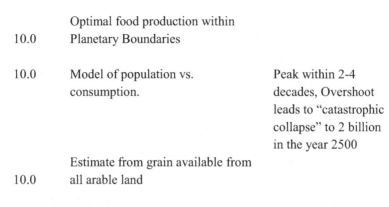

10.0	Optimal food production within Planetary Boundaries	
10.0	Model of population vs. consumption.	Peak within 2-4 decades, Overshoot leads to "catastrophic collapse" to 2 billion in the year 2500
10.0	Estimate from grain available from all arable land	

Figure 67 – Summary of predictions for Earth's carrying capacity of humans

- The U.N. in its World Water Development Report said that the world could suffer a 40% shortfall in water by 2030, as global demand increases by 55%.

- The Food and Agriculture Organization of the United Nations projects that by 2050, we will need 70% more food to feed an ever-increasing population, which will demand greater quantities and a greater variety of food, including meat.

- "Today the pace of arable land degradation is estimated at 30 to 35 times the historical rate. Desertification is degrading more than 12m hectares [29.6 m acres] of arable land every year – the equivalent of losing the total arable area of France every 18 months." AheadOfTheHerd Newsletter

- Some foods today are yielding significantly lower nutrition than in the past.

- Roundup, a key herbicide, has lost a key court case. If regulatory and judicial rulings continue against glyphosate and Roundup, agriculture will lose one of its primary productivity tools.

- According to *Scientific American*, December 2014, "On current trends, the world has about 60 years of topsoil left."

- According to a study by the European Commission, "Land degradation and global warming are estimated to lead to a reduction of global crop yields by about 10% by 2050."

- GMOs may not materially improve yields and may be losing their effectiveness in reducing the amount of herbicides required to grow crops.

- The EROI of our energy sources is steadily decreasing to the point that there will not be sufficient EROI to support a society of today's complexity.

- According to the United Nations Food and Agriculture Organization, in 2013, 32% of the world's fish stocks were being exploited beyond their sustainable limit, up from 10% in the 1970s, even though the total catch has remained approximately constant for three decades.

- Four of the eight proposed and quantified Planetary Boundaries have already been exceeded - atmospheric concentration of CO_2, radiative forcing, extraction of nitrogen from the atmosphere and biodiversity loss - indicating stress in the resiliency of the Earth system.

- There has been a 75% decline in flying insect species in parts of Germany over the last 25 years.

- According to a report issued by Dalhousie University in Canada, there has been a 40% decline in the amount of phytoplankton from 1950-2010, and the decrease is continuing at the rate of about 1% per year.

- A study in France concluded in 2018 that there had been a one-third reduction in the bird population in some rural areas over the last 15 years.

- If population is to increase by 33% in 40 years, as forecast by the U.N., then some combination of available resources and improvements in efficiency must increase by 33% in 40 years just to maintain the current status quo. If humanity wants to improve its standard of living by, say, 1% per year over those 40 years while population is increasing (and assuming that increase is even possible), then some combination of available resources and improvements in efficiency must approximately double over that timeframe.

Critical resources will become increasingly scarce as human population relentlessly increases to 10 billion, and then higher. Humans are placing the Earth's resources under severe stress to the point that we have achieved, or will have achieved peak-many-things within the next 40 years or so.

Including peak humans.

The sooner we begin to provide room for ourselves by reducing consumption and reducing population, the smaller the price we will have to pay as we run up against limit after limit after limit.

However, the evidence indicates that there will be a significant price to be paid.

Achieving Sustainability

"It is difficult to get a man to understand something, when his salary depends on his not understanding it."
Upton Sinclair[269]

"The human mind isn't a terribly logical or consistent place. Most people, given the choice to face a hideous or terrifying truth or to conveniently avoid it, choose the convenience and peace of normality. That doesn't make them strong or weak people, or good or bad people. It just makes them people."
— Jim Butcher, *Turn Coat*[270]

Achieving sustainability is pretty straightforward in concept and perhaps impossibly difficult in practice. There must be fewer of us. We all must consume less, much less, and we must eliminate the capitalistic cycle.

Population control is an urgent necessity. The number of sustainable humans is dependent on their level of consumption, and vice versa. Unless there is a population collapse, human population will inevitably increase past Earth's carrying capacity, if it has not done so already. The primary focus in the near term must be on a significant reduction in consumption – and on a continuing hope that the technological cavalry will arrive.

Sustainability will only occur "on its own" following a catastrophic collapse in population after we denude our field. To prevent this dystopian future, humanity must make a conscious effort to achieve sustainability to avoid collapse.

So, how can we achieve sustainability through these conscious efforts? What do the likely futures look like?

Personal Responsibility

"We have met the enemy and he is us." Walt Kelly's Pogo[271]

It is just this simple, and just this difficult: human behavior must change. You must quit consuming; I must quit consuming.

Now.

Capitalism-enabled behavior must stop.

Even though it must stop, it is not likely to stop.

Consumerism can be compared to a heroin addiction. The high is great, but the side effects are destructive. Habituation means that there are diminishing returns. And, it is very painful and difficult to kick a powerful addiction.

Many, including many environmentalists, blame corporations or government for environmental damage. They are actually asking corporations and governments to enforce policies that the majority of consumers and voters do not support. Environmentalists are asking corporations and governments to force us to eat our vegetables – because they are good for us, you understand.

Putting aside the question of whether environmentalists are, in some sense, right, citizens vote for governments, and consumers vote their preferences with their wallets. This makes it difficult for governments and corporations to stray far from the demands of their constituencies.

Consumers bear some amount of regulation and taxation, but at any given point in cultural evolution, there is a limit.

In particular, as consumers' tastes change and as technology changes, businesses flourish and collapse. From an ecological perspective, this can be a good thing, as the increase in demand for hybrid and electric vehicles indicates.

Voters' demands also change, as various clean air and clean water laws indicate. We have taken the lead out of our paint and out of our gasoline; we have addressed acid rain and the hole in the ozone layer.

The global success in addressing the hole in the ozone layer also provides a cautionary tale. It is only a partial success, and such success as there has been required decades to achieve.

In the end, voters and consumers must "walk the walk" as well as "talk the talk," by changing their own, personal behaviors, by demanding changes in consumer goods and by demanding legislation.

Corporations and governments may implement changes at the margin, however, they are unlikely to be able to impose on people the massive changes required to achieve sustainability. That change must come from us.

Two Alternative Scenarios

It is not clear whether we are currently in Overshoot, although I think it is likely that we are. There is a reasonable argument that we are past carrying capacity, but we may not be there, yet. We are facing a future having two principal, alternative scenarios:

1. Current human population / consumption is below carrying capacity, providing time for purposeful, intentional adjustment to sustainability.
2. Current human population / consumption is at or beyond carrying capacity, meaning that the field is being denuded. The longer the period of denuding, the lower the resulting carrying capacity leading to an inevitable collapse. This scenario demands immediate and drastic action.

Both alternatives entail the end of capitalism.

Intentional Sustainability

This book addresses sustainability principally in terms of natural resources. There are social forms of sustainability, such as inequality and social justice that will not be considered here. The things that are being sustained are energy and natural resources; the "for whom" such resources are being sustained is principally humanity, generally ignoring Earth's other species of plants and animals. There are a number of sustainability considerations which are important, but outside the scope of this book.

Let's consider what efforts and changes will be required to achieve this definition of sustainability.

A.A. Bartlett made many insightful observations about sustainability in "21 Laws of Sustainability:" Here are some important ones:

- All countries cannot simultaneously be net importers of carrying capacity.
- When large efforts are made to improve the efficiency with which resources are used, the resulting savings are easily and completely wiped out by the added resources that are consumed as a consequence of modest increases in population.
- Humans have an enormous compulsion to find an immediate use for all available resources.
- (Eric Sevareid's Law) The chief cause of problems is solutions. [This goes back to our discussion of tradeoffs and unintended consequences. For example, implementing wind farms to solve the problem of renewable energy kills large numbers of birds, scars the landscape and requires additional spending additional resources to address the intermittency of wind energy.]
- Starving people don't care about sustainability.[272]

Amy Larkin, a rare environmentalist who bridges the gap between environmental concerns and business, has created a "Nature Means Business" framework, which is summarized as:

1. Pollution can no longer be free.
2. All accounting and business decisions must incorporate long-term effects.
3. Government has a vital role to play.[273]

A study published in *Nature Sustainability*[274] concluded:

> We find that no country meets basic needs for its citizens at a globally sustainable level of resource use. Physical needs such as nutrition, sanitation, access to electricity and the elimination of extreme poverty could likely be met for all people without transgressing planetary boundaries. However, the universal achievement of more qualitative goals (for example, high life satisfaction) would require a level of resource use that is 2–6 times the sustainable level, based on current relationships.

We do not know whether we have passed Earth's carrying capacity for humans, but if we have not, it is highly likely that we are close. That means that growth must cease (or if we are past carrying capacity, growth must become negative, or we must achieve "ungrowth.")

Growth

The current cultural imperative of growth is relatively recent, measured by human history. Prior to the Industrial Revolution, humans had limited ways to improve growth on a per capita basis. The slow evolution of technology, from fire and the wheel, through agriculture and the use of metals, enabled some limited growth. The Industrial Revolution leveraged energy and capitalism to enable an increase in human productivity that resulted in an explosion of growth.

That growth fed on itself as increased profits were deployed to transform more resources and support more people. Ultimately, growth and consumption became ends in their own right.

That growth explosion began in the "gilded age" of the 1920s, but was upended by the Great Depression. The significant change in Western, particularly U.S., values regarding consumption came after World War II, with the resumption of the consumer society. Since that time, consumption has comprised some 70% of the U.S. economy, and growth has become central to Western cultures.

Growth has become our secular religion.

There is the expectation that, since growth occurred during the 50s and 60s, it should continue in perpetuity. We take it for granted that there will always be more.

Worse, given the amount of debt we have incurred, future economic prosperity depends on future growth in an amount sufficient to both repay a portion of the debt and also to provide increased prosperity.

The consumer-capitalism society seemed to arise from the intersection of human nature, the availability of consumer loans and financing, the waning of the cultural taboo of debt from the economic scars of the Great Depression, increased leisure time, a rapidly-growing economy and the rise of advertising.

Over time, growth has become no less than the primary driving force behind the global economy, its culture and its way of life. Even "communist" China is in the midst of changing its economy to one that is consumer-based.

A basic assumption, which has underpinned our lives for generations, is that our standard of living will improve because of growth. Our economy is based on consumption; a growing economy requires increased consumption. Debt is a way to bring future consumption forward. Our over-indebtedness and fiscal deficits require economic growth in order to provide any hope of paying of pensions and entitlements and the repayment of the debt that has been incurred.

Because we are near, or have passed, the Earth's carrying capacity for humans, we cannot sustainably grow anymore; certainly not much more. No growth in population; no growth in consumption. This inability to grow will have profound effects on our expectations and our definitions of who we are.

All species are hard-wired to want offspring, so population increases are all but certain, up to the limits of carrying capacity. Humans are unique among species by not having any natural predators to keep population in check, except themselves and viruses. Humans aspire to not only increasing standards of living, but also to climb out of paralyzing poverty. At the same time, we have debts incurred during an orgy of consumption which must be repaid.

And that is the fundamental conundrum facing our species.

Growth can only be achieved through the availability of unused resources or by using currently-existing resources more efficiently than they have been used in the past. If there are no available, unused resources, there can be no growth. If population is to increase by 50% in 40 years, as forecast by the U.N., then some combination of available resources and improvements in efficiency must increase by 50% in 40 years just to maintain the current status quo. If humanity wants to improve its standard of living, say by just 1% per year, over those 40 years while population is increasing (and assuming that increase is even possible), then some combination of available resources and improvements in efficiency must increase by approximately 110% over that timeframe.

That conclusion is worthy of repetition.

Given existing population forecasts for the next 40 years, and assuming increasing standards of living by 1% per year over that timeframe, resources required in 40 years will be more than twice currently-used resources. More than twice the energy or twice the energy utilization, or some combination of the two. More than twice the land, or twice the land utilization, or some combination of the two. More than twice the water, or twice the water utilization, or some combination of the two. More than twice the niobium, iron, phosphate, etc.

If sustainability, as defined by eco-footprint measurements, was 1.7 global hectares (4.2 acres) per capita in 2014, the equivalent sustainability levels in 40 years under the growth assumptions, above, would be 0.77 global hectares (1.9 acres) per capita. That is approximately the current resources provided by Cuba or Iran.

In addition, growth in social, economic and technical complexity generally depends on the availability of excess energy.

How Growth Overwhelms

Even a small amount of economic growth can, over time, overwhelm any amount of finite resources.

Today, the United States considers growth of 2% a year as too slow, aiming for 3-4%. China is unhappy with anything below 6% a year.

If the U.S. economy grows at the "too-slow" rate of 2% per year, it will double in 36 years. In 2056, it would be twice as big as in 2020. Our economy would consume twice as much of everything.

If the U.S. economy were to achieve its dream of growing at a rate of 4% per year, it would double in 18 years, or by 2038. In 18 years, it would consume twice as much of everything.

If China's economy grows at its minimally-desired rate of 6% per year, it will double in 12 years. In 12 years, it would consume twice as much of everything.

Given that the Earth is at or past Overshoot for human consumption, these rates of growth would literally be devastating.

We face a profound crossroads. If we do not address sustainability by dramatically reducing population and consumption, our economy can collapse under the conditions of Overshoot. If we begin to significantly address both issues and cease growing economically, we will encounter significant social, economic and cultural stress.

Continuing growth almost certainly cannot occur for longer than a few decades. Any trend that cannot continue will stop. We will achieve sustainability, one way or the other, but any growth, in population or consumption, will ultimately lead to dystopia and collapse.

Humans lived for millennia before the Industrial Revolution without experiencing significant economic growth. Can we do it, again?

Possibly.

But only by controlling population and consumption.

And only by replacing capitalism with another basis for the economy.

What To Do About Population?

Earlier, for argument's sake, I basically gave up on the whole population problem, noting that population was inevitably going to increase to carrying capacity, if it is not already past carrying capacity. This will occur in such a short period of time that there was nothing we can practically do to prevent that from happening in the required timeframe.

I would like to expand my thoughts on population to encompass the longer term. We should not restrict our attention and analyses only to the period between now and around 2060, when Earth's human population is projected to reach 10 billion. Ten billion seems to be an upper limit for human carrying capacity. Since population is projected to increase, although at a slower rate, after 2060, it is critical to take steps now that will reduce population growth and then reduce population as soon as possible. There are steps we can take to address population, while reducing levels of consumption and waiting for the technological cavalry.

The most effective ways to reduce birth rates in the longer term are to educate girls so that they have opportunities outside of the home, and to provide education on family planning to enable couples to have only the children they want and for families to be financially secure.

According to Robert Engleman of the Worldwatch Institute, there are nine ways to control population:

1. Assure universal access to a range of safe and effective contraceptive options and family planning services for both sexes.
2. Guarantee education through secondary school for all, with a particular focus on girls.
3. Eradicate gender bias from law, economic opportunity, health, and culture.
4. Offer age-appropriate sexuality education for all students.
5. End all policies that reward parents financially based on the number of their children.
6. Integrate teaching about population, environment, and development relationships into school curricula at multiple levels.
7. Put prices on environmental costs and impacts.
8. Adjust to population aging rather than trying to delay it through governmental incentives or programs aimed at boosting childbearing.
9. Convince leaders to commit to ending population growth through the exercise of human rights and human development.[275]

Population can also be controlled through the power of the state. Perhaps the best example of this is the "one-child" policy of China. That policy was introduced in 1979 and went through various revisions and changes before being phased out in 2015, was generally replaced by a two-child policy and then, in 2021, a three-child policy. Simplistically and with exceptions, the government of China outlawed couples having more than one child. One unintended consequence of the policy was increased infanticide of females, since many Chinese preferred male offspring. The effect of the policy is disputed, since it is difficult to distinguish between the reduction in births due to the policy and the reduction due to a natural reduction in fertility rates. While China asserts that some 400 million births did not take place which otherwise would have taken place, some demographers calculate a number of half that many.

One metric that can be measured is the change in the male:female ratio at birth. That ratio increased to a maximum of 117:100 from a baseline of 111:100, leading to estimates of approximately 30 million "extra" males in China.[276]

Dr. Paul Ehrlich, author of *The Population Bomb*, his wife, Anne, together with John Holdren, have voiced extreme concern about the unsustainability and dangers of population growth, to the point that they have suggested what would otherwise be considered radical intervention. It is important to understand when reading these recommendations that the Ehrlichs and Mr. Holdren passionately consider population growth to be an existential crisis; one that unavoidably and certainly demands drastic, immediate action. Their recommendations include compulsory abortion; mandatory, involuntary sterilization after a couple's second or third child; and implantation of a sterilization capsule at puberty that may not be removed, except by official permission.[277]

Population growth can be significantly and quickly (over a period of decades) reduced through force of law, however, with unintended consequences.

It is possible that population control could be influenced by economic incentives. Potential incentives could be awarded for taking sex education, for taking contraceptives, for sterilization or, directly, for not having children. There have been few studies on the potential success of such programs. While direct rewards for not having children seem to result in marginal success, other changes in behavior have not been promising.

I simplistically assumed that population does not matter in the short term because it practically cannot be controlled in that timeframe. However, population must be controlled in the longer term, or nature will control it for us.

James Carli, writing on HuffingtonPost.com, put it dramatically, yet accurately (he was referring to climate change, but his words apply as well to sustainability):

> So, I think considering all of this, the most ethical course is that if you love children – which I wholeheartedly do – then the answer is to consciously not have them, and to spare them the pain of watching the whole beloved system fall into absolute pieces. It's basic mercy. It's compassion. Hell, it's even harm reduction. So, get your tubes tied, ladies, snip-snip, gentlemen, and enjoy the rest of the world while we've still got it, without having to wake up every day worried and guilty about the anguish your offspring would otherwise have to endure.[278]

But, population is only one part of the problem.

What To Do About Consumption?

We cannot reduce population in the short term; we must reduce population in the longer term.

But consumption is a critical and immediate problem. We must dramatically reduce consumption, both in the short and in the longer terms.

How much less do we need to consume?

Historically, consumption beyond that required for survival was generally restricted to the wealthy and powerful few.

The consumer society, bringing consumption to the middle class, was effectively created after World War II, following a false start in the 1920s, which was interrupted by the Great Depression and by World War II. (World War II was a time of significant consumption of natural resources, but by nations at war and not by individuals.) Prior to that time, culture and economics were not focused on consumption. After that time, consumption became central to our senses of wellbeing and of purpose.

And, it became the foundation of our economic system. Because we were able to live without a focus on consumption in the past, we can theoretically return to that kind of culture. Because we have built our culture, expectations and economy around consumption, the transition likely will be wrenching.

By far, the largest consumers are the rich countries of the West (including Japan). However, consumption is also a significant part of developing and third-world economies.

Consumption as Percentage of GDP
for Selected Countries, 2016

Afghanistan	112.1
Bangladesh	69.1
Mexico	66.3
Canada	58.3
Australia	57.8
Germany	53.6
Russia	53.4
China	50.8
Sweden	44.4
Singapore	37.5

Figure 68 – Consumption as percentage of GDP, select countries, 2016 (China is for 2015)[279] The comparable number for the U.S. was 68%.

Of course the answer to the question of what to do about consumption is different for each resource and for each part of the world. A comprehensive answer is beyond the scope of this book. However, we can think about the magnitude of the problem and contemplate solutions on a high-level, global basis.

One benefit of the eco-footprint approach is that it provides a direct, quantitative approach for estimating how much is too much for each country.

The high-level answer is straightforward: since the human population, absent a catastrophe, will not decline in the near future, all humans must immediately reduce their consumption by 33%, on average. The U.S. must immediately reduce its consumption by 75%. Of course, those reductions assume there will be no additional humans, when the human population is predicted to grow by 33% in the next forty years or so. Therefore, the actual answer for all humans is an immediate reduction of closer to 50% than 33%, in order to conserve resources for new humans to consume.

It may seem obvious that in order to consume resources, there must be resources to consume. In order to grow, there must be unclaimed resources to be devoted to that growth. But, so long as resources are neither renewable nor recyclable, and as long as they are being consumed, they will ultimately be exhausted.

Reducing consumption to reserve resources for future consumption is conceptually the same as delaying the time until resource exhaustion.

Barriers to reducing consumption include that consumption is a primary foundation of our economy and culture, and that the issue of over-consumption is not at the forefront of any conversations or debates. This significant, existential problem is not on anyone's radar, except for the United Nations and a few environmentalists.

Again, let's do some simplistic calculations, begging a lot of questions. If consumption currently comprises 70% of the U.S. economy, and we reduce that by 75% to address the challenges of Overshoot, denuding and collapse, consumption will comprise only 17.5% of the U.S. economy. The remaining 52.5% will not be replaced by anything; it will simply go away – it must go away. We have to get by with significantly fewer, or no, clothes, vacations, iPhones and strawberries in December.

That magnitude of reduction in consumption is unlikely to happen voluntarily. The best we can expect is to take steps to begin to incrementally reduce consumption. While this more-realistic approach is more likely, although still not very likely, the result of not immediately, drastically reducing consumption is that Overshoot, denuding and collapse become increasingly probable. At some point, nature will require a reduction in consumption, and the longer we wait, the more drastic that unavoidable reduction will be.

There are actions that can be taken and technology trends that can help.

- **Conserve** - which we have discussed extensively in the sections on water and food. There is a complication associated with conservation, which has various names – let's call it the Paradox of Thrift. If you save on one thing, you will likely spend that savings on something else. This has been demonstrated in countless studies, including a study of those who saved energy by, for example, increasing insulation. They then spent those savings by turning down the thermostat in summer or by taking a vacation or buying new clothes, all of which may cost more energy than was saved by installing the insulation. We have not found a way to permanently capture those savings so that they are not spent elsewhere.

- **Emphasize repair and reuse** – completely revise attitudes toward disposable items. As a starting point, all things must be repaired, and nothing may be thrown away.

- **Recycle** - which has its own challenges. We will need to use every scrap of what we have, but often recycling requires energy or other resources which makes it, on the whole, not worthwhile.

- **Engage the climate change community** - While some climate change activists may think that sustainability complicates and dilutes their message, one of the primary solutions to both climate change and to sustainability is a radical reduction in consumption. It is crucial that the climate change community realize that the sustainability crisis will occur more quickly than the climate change crisis, the implications of the sustainability crisis are direr and solving the sustainability crisis solves the climate change crisis.

- **Do what we can about population**

- **Adjust the prices of resources to reflect their full economic value / cost.**

Pricing

Although I am a recovering free-market capitalist, I still believe that free markets generally allocate resources significantly better than other approaches. It will become increasingly important that ever-scarcer resources be properly allocated. However, markets fail in some critical instances for three principal reasons:

- Political bodies grant subsidies, impose taxes and enact regulations. This means that the real cost of a resource is not directly paid by society (the free market is not entirely free). Essentially every item consumed in the U.S. is, or contains some component that is, either subsidized or regulated.
- The "tragedy of the commons" – the abuse of and lack of accountability for common resources that no one owns.
- Some effects, for example the loss of species or the effect of chemicals on unborn children, are inherently not quantifiable.

The first two of these fallacies arise because of a fundamental failure in economic theory. Economists, whether Marxist, socialist or capitalist, have been primarily focused on the deployment of labor and capital, and the relative importance of each. The complex equations that central banks use to analyze economic systems do not even include terms for energy or natural resources. And until relatively recently, economists of all stripes in academia were also ignoring these factors.

However, as economist Steve Keen has written, "An equation in which energy plays an essential role, and which is compatible with the Laws of Thermodynamics, can easily be derived by observing that the very idea of either labor or capital without energy is an impossibility. Labor without energy is a corpse; Capital without energy is a sculpture. Instead, labor and capital are means by which available energy is harnessed to generate output, which in its essence is useful work."[280]

Sometimes, actually, often, politicians subsidize items to buy votes; sometimes to support an industry in their district; sometimes to support what they consider a social good; sometimes to help the poor. The costs of these subsidies are paid indirectly through taxes and are hidden from the market and from the consumer.

The U.S. government subsidizes ethanol, solar power, wind power and electric cars because they want to support those industries (and particularly, in the case of ethanol, make corn farmers happy). Farmers' prices are supported to help them through the cycles of farming, and to buy their votes. Oil has been subsidized because it is a critical component of our economy, and to gain the support of a powerful industry. Homeowners are supported via the deduction of mortgage interest on their income tax returns because home ownership is highly valued, and to buy homeowners' votes. The Affordable Care Act is subsidized because health insurance premiums incurred by the insured would increase even faster if they were not. The price of water, itself, is maintained around zero because the electorate expects it – in general, water rates pay for the associated infrastructure, but not the cost of the water, itself. The list of subsidies is lengthy and can be found at http://funding-programs.idilogic.aidpage.com/

"In the United States, the federal government has paid $74 billion for energy subsidies to support R&D for nuclear power ($50 billion) and fossil fuels ($24 billion) from 1973 to 2003. During this same timeframe, renewable energy technologies and energy efficiency received a total of $26 billion."[281]

Each subsidy of a natural resource distorts the market-pricing mechanism, leading to misuse of that resource. To allow the efficient allocation of natural resources, all subsidies must cease.

In a time of scarcity and efficient pricing of resources, it is likely that prices for resources will rise, perhaps significantly. Rising prices will disproportionally impact the poor. Although the entire economy will have to learn to do without a large number of consumer goods, carefully-considered subsidies for essential items for those who cannot afford them may be required.

(Actually, price levels will be affected by two primary forces: scarcity of supply and the collapse of the consumer-based economy. This collapse will result in a significant reduction in demand for both goods and services. The ultimate effect on prices, as with the example of oil prices examined at the beginning of Part II of this book, will be complex.)

The Tragedy of the Commons applies when some public resource is used but the price of that resource is not reflected in the cost of the item in which it is used. The classic example is cows grazing on public land. The cost of the land, its maintenance and of the grass on the land are not included in the cost of the cow's meat. Even worse, the care of the land is no one's responsibility and therefore the land can be denuded through over-grazing because there is no one to protect it.

The best contemporary examples of the Tragedy of the Commons are air and water pollution, over-fishing and aquifer depletion. Since no one owns the air and the cost of pollution is not included in costs of products, air pollution increases until regulated by the government. No one is in charge of the health and viability of fish, so overfishing is rampant. No one owns an entire water system, so the water can be misused, e.g. for growing rice in an arid area. Climate change is another example of a potential cost to everyone that is being incurred because there is no penalty for emitting carbon dioxide and the price of emitting carbon dioxide is not included in the manufactured product.

I am including "negative externalities" in the tragedy of the commons. Negative externalities are consequences to someone for which someone else is responsible. One example is the effect of upstream water pollution on downstream users of water. The upstream pollution damages the environment and imposes costs on the downstream users, but the upstream polluter, who benefits from the pollution, does not have to pay the cost to either the environment or the downstream user.

Prices for natural resources must increase if we are going to conserve them. (That increase may be relative to other prices, rather than an absolute increase, as the prices for other items may decline due to a drastic decline in consumption.)

Since markets are failing with regard to the Tragedy of the Commons, governments must set the price and charge for common resources. It is far from clear how the cost of water from a depleting aquifer or the cost of eroding topsoil should be computed and allocated. A pricing mechanism called cap and trade is theoretically workable but has not been particularly politically successful.

Cap and trade has primarily been used in allocating the ability to emit carbon dioxide and the chemicals that have created a hole in Earth's protective ozone layer. A maximum amount of emissions is determined and every emitter is given rights to emit their ratable proportion of the maximum emissions. If one emitter is able to change their processes such that they do not need all of their rights, they can sell those extra rights to others. Over time, the maximum amount of allowable emissions is decreased to the desired level. This period of time allows emitters to adjust their processes and employ technology.

One approach would be to establish a cap and trade system for each common resource. In practice this would create a massive bureaucracy and the temptation for political interference and corruption. However, it is not clear there is an effective alternative.

A version of cap and trade has been implemented by the State of California in reaction to a severe drought in 2012-2016. The state implemented Groundwater Sustainability Agencies (GSAs) to monitor water users in areas across the state. The goal of the GSAs is to achieve sustainability by the early 2040s. As a result of restrictions on water use, farmers must choose which crops to grow, based on profitability of the crop, but taking into account the water usage of the crop. A farmer may choose to let some of his land go fallow and sell his water rights to other farmers. By selling water rights, depending on the price of water, the farmer may make more money than by growing crops. Over time, this system should lead to the efficient use of water.

The success of the program is critically dependent on the proper allocation of water rights. Another major issue is the competitiveness of crops grown in California, subject to the "true," sustainable price of water, with crops grown around the world, subject to subsidized prices.

California's establishment of GSAs is a critical experiment in determining what can and cannot be accomplished by cap and trade of the use of resources.

Another, equally-complicated approach to solving the Tragedy of the Commons is to create a trust that would be responsible for managing each common asset. For example, a trust could be set up to manage an aquifer or a species of fish. Trusts that do not cross countries' boundaries would be difficult to create, but would be significantly easier to create than trusts that involve multiple countries.

There is no effective approach to pricing for unquantifiable outcomes, such as the effect of chemicals on unborn children. The causes of these outcomes must be regulated by governments.

The economy as a whole will suffer from increased prices, whether absolute or relative, but, again, the poor will suffer the most. In many cases the poor will have to do without (everyone will have to do without, but the effect on the poor will be much greater). However, particularly with regard to essential resources, governments may have to subsidize prices for the poor in an exception to the rule that there must be no subsidies.

Most likely, the world will move to an entirely different kind of economics – a no-growth economy, which will be discussed below.

In that economy, we will need to measure and value things differently as well as price them differently.

Gross Ecosystem Product

China has been pioneering an effort to measure and place a value on the ecosystem so that its impacts and changes can be better understood. This effort, called the Gross Ecosystem Product (GEP), will also provide the ability to measure and understand linkages between the ecosystem and other systems, such as the economy and the broader society / human development. GEP will also provide a basis for measuring / quantifying sustainability.

This is an extraordinarily ambitious project, which is in its early days.

Two, partially overlapping presentations on GEP are

- Research Enter for Eco-Environmental Sciences of the Chinese Academy of Science.
  https://events.development.asia/system/files/materials/2017/12/201
  712-gross-ecosystem-product-gep-and-ecological-asset-accounting-
  eco-compensation-methodology-and.pdf

- International Union for Conservation of Nature, China.
  https://seea.un.org/sites/seea.un.org/files/presentation_3_gep_introd
  uction_29190213_pdf.pdf

Finally, in our quest for resources, we can think outside the box and come up with a Hail Mary, named after the desperate, last-second, throw-the-football-into-the-end zone-and-pray play in American football.

Hail Mary

Groups of thoughtful people and individuals, including the late, eminent astrophysicist, Stephen Hawking, are increasingly coming to the conclusion that there are not sufficient resources on Earth to support an expanding human population. As they think through alternatives, many are focusing on expanding away from Earth to other planets and to moons of other planets. Basically, the Hail Mary play is to live elsewhere and use resources that exist in those places (at least until they are exhausted), effectively expanding humans' "field."

The obstacles to the extra-planetary Hail Mary are daunting. Earth has a probably-unique, or at least rare, combination of moderate temperature, atmospheric oxygen and water. Life on this planet has evolved to precisely fit into the ecosystem that Earth provides. It is highly unlikely that we will find another habitat that even comes close in suitability for humans. The Hail Mary solution means we will have to find ways to grow plants and animals and generate oxygen that nature may not provide on other planets. Colonizers of other planets will have to improvise based on the materials and conditions available on that planet.

In addition, distances in space are unimaginably huge. We have just begun discovering planets outside our solar system, but the closest planet that has been discovered, so far, outside of our solar system, is some 4.25 light years (40 trillion kilometers (25 trillion miles)) from Earth. At 62,100 kilometers per hour (38,600 miles per hour), the current speed of Voyager 1, our first, interplanetary explorer, it would take approximately 74,000 years to travel from Earth to that planet, which is probably uninhabitable in any event.

Over the next decades, it is likely that humans will attempt to develop small colonies on Mars and perhaps on a moon of Jupiter or Saturn. These will be very limited, difficult undertakings.

We will not solve problems associated with colonizing other planets before we reach carrying capacity for humans on Earth.

Outside of colonizing space, what would a possible future look like?

The Future

*"It is as if humankind were packed into a bus racing
through an impenetrable fog. Somewhere ahead is a
cliff: a calamitous reversal of humanity's fortunes.
Nobody can see exactly where it is, but everyone knows
that at some point the bus will have to turn." – Charles
C. Mann, The Atlantic[282]*

*"The central challenge of our age must be to decouple
human progress from resource use and environmental
deterioration."[283]*

*"This is the way the world ends
Not with a bang but a whimper."
W.B. Yeats, The Hollow Men*

I have made the case that capitalism has been too successful, sending humans to or past their carrying capacity, and that the steps required to be taken to avoid denuding and collapse are highly unlikely to be taken. Where does this leave us?

The Good News

While it appears that humans will experience increasing distress, it is important to revisit the reason that Malthus and Ehrlich were either wrong or early – technology they could not imagine has profoundly changed the rules of the game of human existence.

The world today is brimming with incredible changes in technology that have the potential to meaningfully effect sustainability. Financial commentator, John Mauldin, when discussing the possibility of significantly extended, healthy life spans, summed up the optimists' view as follows: "I know I'll get letters saying that life extension will add to overpopulation and the consumption of the planet's resources. I disagree. I think the talent and ideas these additional lives give us will unleash ways to use our resources more efficiently."[284]

I agree. Humans are extremely creative, and additional time to be creative through extended life spans could lead to impressive innovation. The optimists' view is entirely realistic and plausible.

At their most fundamental, my views are based on the facts that time is either short or already up. Any changes, technological and/or social, must be agreed by most of the humans on the entire planet. Agreement among the world's humans is a daunting undertaking, requiring time, money and resources.

In the last half century, we have experienced social changes, such as civil rights and the role of women in the West. However, in spite of being in progress for decades, these changes are still substantially incomplete.

While waiting on the technological cavalry, let's explore the alternative.

The Dream

In some kind of perfect, fair, equitable world, we would determine a level of sustainability for each human, and rich countries would reduce their consumption to those limits, while poor countries would increase their consumption to those limits.

For example, we noted in our discussion of eco-footprints that Canada is well-endowed with resources at 14.92 global hectares (multiply hectares by 2.5 to calculate acres) per capita and is consuming less than half of its endowment, at 7.01. (These statistics are for 2014, and have changed and will continue to change - as population increases, eco-footprints decrease.) However, Canada's consumption is more than four times the world average sustainable level of 1.67, even though it is below its own level of available natural resources. The United States has capacity of 3.76, while consuming more than twice that at 8.22, which, in turn, is five times the world-average sustainable level. Bangladesh is consuming at 0.72 with capacity of 0.38. Bangladesh is not sustainable by itself, in spite of low levels of consumption. In our hypothetical, fair, equitable world, Canada should give up some of its spare capacity to Bangladesh in order for it to increase its consumption to the sustainable average of 1.67. In fact, Canada should contribute its surplus to the rest of the world, and reduce its standard of living by some three-quarters, in effect decreasing its standard of living to that of Honduras or Morocco, which are at the world's sustainable average. The U.S. should also decrease its consumption by more than 75% to 1.67 to provide room for other countries to increase theirs.

We do not live in that fair world.

Even if humanity were to fully comprehend the crisis, it is highly unlikely that hundreds of millions of people would spontaneously and materially give up their standards of living.

Change is Very Hard

I was a lecturer for a course called Business Process Management at the McCombs School of Business at the University of Texas at Austin. Basically, it was a course in how to effect successful corporate change.

Implementing change is complicated and involves several processes and tools, but, at bottom, the critical issue regarding change is humans' resistance to change. Humans resist change for many reasons. In a corporate setting, they may be comfortable with the way things are, or afraid they will not adequately adapt to the new environment, or they may be afraid they will lose status or rank or they may disagree with the change. The process of change requires buy-in from the group so that they will support the change.

From my experience in implementing change in the corporate world, I came up with a very rough rule of thumb that, given any significant change, one-third of employees would actively embrace it; one-third would not care much, either way; and one-third would resist it.

As a general rule, the larger and more complex the organization, the more difficult it is to implement change. Actually, the difficulty of change increases exponentially with the size of the organization, to the point that meaningful change in large organizations becomes virtually impossible. Changes such as those at IBM when it moved away from mainframe computers to services are all the more impressive because of their extreme difficulty and rarity.

I believe that these rules can be extended to organizations other than corporations and to cultures and societies. A significant number of people will actively resist change; the difficulty of change increases exponentially with the size of the entity undergoing change.

The exception to the rule is that significant change can occur following some disruption or emergency, such as war, famine, epidemic, natural disaster, revolution or economic collapse, in which external forces mandate that the organization change or die.

Given that context, imagine attempting truly significant change in a world of more than 7.8 billion people of differing races, religions, incomes and cultures in an environment in which people are far from convinced that there is an emergency. Of those who are convinced, many are not highly motivated. Substantial change, absent disruption or emergency, is all but impossible.

This is not just academic theory. We have a real-world example unfolding today.

The Climate Change Example

There are significant, ongoing efforts by governments, scientists and others to convince all of humanity to change their habits and sacrifice in order to address climate change. Decades of discussions and pleas by politicians and celebrities, including an Oscar-awarded film and a Nobel Prize, have led to very little effective action. Even the much-acclaimed Paris Accord will, by its supporters' own admission, have little direct effect on climate change.

Sustainability is decades behind climate change in human consciousness. It does not feature the star power of Al Gore or Leonardo DiCaprio or Arnold Swarzenegger or Prince Charles. It does not have the scientific backing of the equivalent of the U.N.'s Intergovernmental Panel on Climate Change.

Climate change has heat waves, droughts and hurricanes to bring the public's focus back to the subject at hand, appropriately or inappropriately. Sustainability plays out in more of a boiling-frogs scenario. Humans adapt to increasing crowding and increasing waste and pollution, slowly "boiling" into dystopia.

Sustainability must be addressed now.

If the inability to effectively address climate change is a good precedent, then the odds of effectively addressing sustainability in any meaningful timeframe appear to be small.

Quality of Life

If we are not going to consume and grow, what are we going to do with ourselves?

Essentially every environmentalist group gets to the point in their thought processes that we have just gotten to – we are in serious trouble and have to reduce our population and change our economic model. Then they begin talking about investing in the environment and in the quality of life, as opposed to continuing to invest in the material possessions that capitalism makes so plentiful and which are so tantalizing.

Social and cultural philosophers emphasize the need to move beyond capitalistic economics in the narrowest sense, towards moral and social progress, increased happiness, well-being, and human fulfilment. In *How Much Is Enough?*, Robert and Edward Skidelsky argue that progress should be measured not by the traditional, yardsticks of growth or per capita incomes but by the seven elements of the good life: health; security; respect; personality; harmony with nature; friendship; and leisure.[285]

Various writers emphasize the need for a "new consciousness" and a "transformation of the human heart."

Psychologist Eric Fromm distinguishes between being and having:

> By being or having I do not refer to certain separate qualities of a subject as illustrated in such statements as "I have a car" or "I am white" or "I am happy." I refer to two fundamental modes of existence, to two different kinds of orientation toward self and the world, to two different kinds of character structure the respective predominance of which determines the totality of a person's thinking, feeling, and acting.

> In the having mode of existence my relationship to the world is one of possessing and owning, one in which I want to make everybody and everything, including myself, my property. In the being mode of existence, we must identify two forms of being. One is in contrast to *having*, as exemplified in the Du Marais statement, and means aliveness and authentic relatedness to the world. The other form of being is in contrast to appearing and refers to the true nature, the true reality, of a person or a thing in contrast to deceptive appearances as exemplified in the etymology of being.[286]

Arthur Lyon Dald offers another good example of going beyond the consumer society,

> The alternative is to build a stronger sense of human purpose through education and community action, facilitating a process of maturation from egotism to altruism. Elements of that purpose should include: a vision of future society that is worth effort and struggle to build; a recognition of the importance of family, community and social relationships; an appreciation of the importance of work done in a spirit of service; an introduction to the rational tools of science and the value of knowledge and crafts; a connection with nature, beauty and the arts; and an understanding of the ethical, moral and spiritual dimensions of life that lead to the refinement of character. With these elements, cultivating a culture of change becomes possible while encouraging a diversity of local expressions of social advancement.[287]

Discussion from people such as Fromm and Dald usually includes some hand waving and a comment that the details have to be worked out, but they all know it can be done.

They discuss the need for increased public goods without considering the cost of those goods or the source of the money to pay those costs as the consumer economy implodes.

They discuss the proper characteristics of a new way without considering that those characteristics, while desirable, may not be achievable.

One component of the new way is often a "decent livelihood." The word, decent, begs quite a few questions, but even more fundamentally, in a constrained world, there may not be the basis for whatever a decent livelihood is.

In the world of Overshoot, we humans get the livelihood bound by the environmental constraints, not the livelihood we would prefer.

That's an important point. Throughout human history, there have been few practical limits on the consumption of Earth's resources. If early settlers chopped down all the timber in one place, then they could move to another place. If a farmer depleted a field of its nutrients, they could move to a different field; if the fish in one section of the ocean are depleted, fishermen could fish in another part of the ocean. If drillers run out of oil, they can dig deeper or go to the Arctic.

The underlying assumption, particularly in the resource-rich U.S., has been that there is always more; always somewhere else to go. Usually more difficult to reach, but still available.

Of course, from time to time, populations have not been able to move and have died out.

We are now talking about the entire Earth, not a field or an area.

There is nowhere to go.

There is not more.

We have entered a time when more is not assured. The life we can live will not be based on finding more resources. The life we can live will be dictated by the resources that are available, since essentially all vital resources will become scarce.

It is worth repeating that we will get the livelihoods that results from the environmental constraints, not the livelihoods we would prefer.

My reaction to the usual environmentalist's conclusion of what must be done in the face of unsustainability is simple: investing in the environment and investing in the quality of life are good things, but miss three key points:

1. Such an economy is contrary to human nature and the way human nature has played out over its history (see Jonah Goldberg's *Suicide of the West*[288] for a great discussion of human nature the way it is, as opposed to the way we wish it was). A worldwide "kumbaya" moment may be remotely possible, but it is not the way to bet. Actually, given the need to compete for scarce resources, conflict is much more probable than love and understanding.
2. The attitudes and infrastructure of the dominant world system are

built around consumption and growth, and those people who do not have that consumption and growth would like some. The vested interests in the status quo will be very difficult to overcome.

3. Investment requires resources. If humanity is at the boundary at which there are no further incremental resources to be used, then no investments can be made.

We are so accustomed to being all that we can be and just doing it that it may even be inconceivable that we not only cannot do anything we want, we cannot do many things we would like, or even need to do.

Worse, if we are at or past the limit, our population is subject to significant stress if anything changes – which it will. Drought, flood, famine, disease. We are close to continually living on the edge of disruption.

Everything is scarce, so that everything must be allocated – by price or by regulation.

Let's think about the end game, and then consider how we might get there from here.

The End Game

In the end game, all accessible non-renewable resources will have been consumed or depleted over time, as billions of humans relentlessly search for the remaining, economically-recoverable reserves of everything.

Part of this process will result in the loss of ability to find, access and use some resources. Advanced mining and manufacturing will essentially cease for lack of resources, so that although some goods, say molybdenum, may still be present in reasonably-sized reserves, we would not be able to mine those reserves nor use the molybdenum even if we were able to produce some. So, while some resources continue to exist, they will be non-existent for all practical purposes.

Our ability to produce refined energy will also diminish dramatically as the availability of natural resources declines.

Two of the four critical foundations of modern prosperity, the availability of natural resources and of abundant, high quality energy, will be eroding.

Step-by-step, civilization will unwind. In the end, humans will have access to only renewable resources. The number of humans supportable in this scenario, which varies in estimates from 1-4 billion, will depend on humans' ability to maintain renewability. Humans will be hunter-gatherers and organic farmers, and the layer of retained civilization will be very thin. Essentially the entire, 10,000-year process of civilization will be reversed.

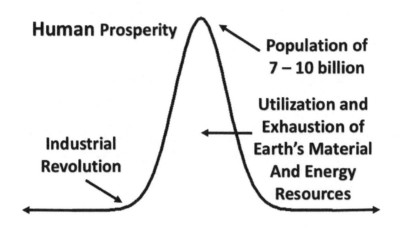

Figure 69– A visualization of the implications of Overshoot[289]

One implication of all of these ideas is that normal human existence, as experienced over millennia, has been interrupted by a relatively brief period following the Enlightenment and the Industrial Revolution. During this period, (some) humans have been able to achieve extraordinary prosperity through capitalism's enablement of the consumption and exhaustion of Earth's resources. When this unusual period is over, humans will generally continue an existence roughly as experienced before the Industrial Revolution.

This is a pretty grim outcome, and all but inevitable. The only question is when.

The exception to the "only renewable resources" requirement is the use of recycling to reclaim previously-used materials. While recycling is important, it requires the use of materials and energy, which must be set aside for recycling. The output of the recycling process, including the quality of the end product, must justify the use of the energy and materials dedicated to the recycling process.

At the beginning of the Enlightenment, and even in the 1950s, the horizon for resource depletion appeared to be infinitely far away.

At the beginning of the Enlightenment, say 1700, the population of the Earth was something above 600 million, the vast majority of whom consumed very little. In 1950, the Earth's population was approximately 2.5 billion. At the beginning of the consumer society, consumption was still constrained. Population and consumption were within the bounds of sustainable.

Today, the U.S. is consuming a little less than ten times its consumption, as expressed in real GDP, as it did in 1950.

Today, the horizon is close at hand, or we may have already crossed it. Given 7.7 billion consumers, soon to be 10 billion consumers, demand will rapidly overcome any finite supply. Recall the example of oil discovery earlier in this section.

> To provide an idea of scale, in 2015, the world consumed a little less than 35 billion barrels of oil. In 2016, what may be the largest oil discovery in history, of approximately 20 billion barrels of oil, was found in West Texas. Simplistically, that gargantuan oil field will supply the world for a little less than seven months at the rate of oil consumption in 2015, assuming that the estimated volume of oil is correct and that all of the oil is economically accessible.

Perhaps the largest oil field ever discovered in the U.S. will optimistically supply seven months of current demand for oil.

Although maxite and molybdenum have been used as examples of depletion, future prosperity does not depend on their continued availability. There are, however, critical resources, such as oil, water, topsoil, fertilizer and fish on which continued existence, much less prosperity, depend.

As resources become scarcer, competition for resources will increase.

Winners and Losers

As resources are depleted and the consumer society disappears, it is likely that the thin layer of civilized behavior that humans have acquired over the last few thousand years will begin to erode. Human nature and human instinct that prevailed over the past millennia will begin to re-emerge.

A friend of mine described a "game" she helped organize for a United Nations young people's project. Two teams were created, which would inhabit an island. Half of the island was verdant and well-supplied with water, and occupied by one team; the other half was desert and occupied by the other team.

At the beginning of the game, all of the participants agreed that the water was to be shared. As the game progressed and it became clear that there wasn't enough water to go around, a wall went up between the two halves and guns came out. The "our" in "our water" evolved from "everyone" during good times, to "only the verdant people on whose land the water flowed" during stress.

The outcome of this game seems to be a good description of the way humans generally behave. We have more-or-less arbitrarily created countries that now "own" resources.

Assume for a moment that "we" are past carrying capacity, so that resources should be shared, equally.

What, exactly, are the odds of that happening?

Close to zero, if the U.N. exercise described above and a review of human history are any indications.

In addition, those with guns will attempt to take critical resources from those with no guns or smaller guns. That's what people have done for millennia and there is no reason to think we will change now.

Much of the literature on sustainability assumes that we will find a way to get along and share. Since I do not even begin to agree with that assumption, we will explore likely outcomes undertaken by real humans.

Perhaps the biggest challenge to be faced is that of growth.

The Cultural Conundrum of Growth

The primary barrier to achieving sustainability is that we have been too successful over the past three hundred years in increasing life spans and standards of living. Those past, extraordinary successes have created expectations that historical, positive trends will always continue for the wealthy West, that they are within the grasp of developing nations, and they provide hope for those who are still in poverty. We demand more.

No one wants to give up their dreams, particularly for their children (even though, ironically, by depleting resources and incurring debt, we are significantly diminishing our children's futures – we seem to be either extraordinarily hypocritical or clueless).

Nor does anyone see any reason to give up their dream of an increasingly wealthy future. Except for a few environmentalists and academics here and there, no one is discussing limits. Even though there is increasing scarcity of, and stress on, natural resources. Even though we are incurring previously-unimaginable levels of debt to artificially maintain our standards of living. Even though international migration and the anger and pain around the world of people whose jobs were replaced by technology and globalization are indicating that stress is increasing on those who are not at the top of the economic ladder. We continue to hold onto the dream of increased prosperity for us and for our children.

All of our past successes and the strength of our expectations and hopes for a better future will likely ensure that no meaningful steps will be taken toward sustainability until well after carrying capacity is reached and the accumulated stress on resources becomes apparent, even to those who are economically sheltered from those stresses.

As anthropologist Joseph Tainter has noted, "It takes protracted hardship to convince people that the world to which they have been accustomed has changed irrevocably."[290]

The Organization for Economic Cooperation and Development in Article 1a, adopted in 1960, committed "to achieve the highest sustainable economic growth and employment and a rising standard of living in Member countries."[291] The religion of growth has since been adopted by communist and formerly-communist countries, by developing countries and by third world countries. Even green parties support growth to provide resources for public goods. Economic growth enables improvements in health, welfare, education, life-span, poverty and the arts.

Stephen Quilley, an associate professor of social and ecological innovation, has noted that, "even the most sophisticated critiques from the left, such as Piketty's (2014) Capital in the Twenty First Century, focus on the need to reignite economic growth."[292]

William E. Rees, a professor and author on sustainable development, puts it this way, "Virtually the entire global community subscribes to the compound myth of endless technological progress and continuous economic growth. Economists and political leaders everywhere still act with unbridled confidence in human ingenuity to overcome natural limits."[293]

Many people in various environmental movements have attempted to address the growth challenge by proposing different futures in which the effects of growth are mitigated and less harmful to the planet. These proposals broadly fall under the categories of "green growth" and "decoupling." Green growth means continuing to grow, but in a more eco-friendly way. Decoupling means continuing to grow, but using fewer natural resources per unit of growth in the future than we do now.

Both of these proposals are good and worthwhile. However, they both miss the point that there are so many people living today, that the number of people will increase significantly in the future, and that all of these people will want to increase their living standards.

As outlined in an article in Foreign Policy[294], this tsunami of consumption will likely overwhelm any attempts to improve the greenness of growth. In addition, green growth and decoupling do not address, and most likely will enable, population growth. The primary benefit of green growth is that it extends the time horizon until the exhaustion of a particular resource, assuming it does not enable population growth.

Another group proposes "agrowth." Agrowth is basically the creation of a society that has values and objectives that do not explicitly include growth.

Yet another group of environmentalists believes that the Earth is beyond its carrying capacity for humans and must go through a period of degrowth. Degrowth is a reduction in some combination of population and consumption that will lead to a sustainable level of each - a controlled version of collapse. The degrowth group believes we should understand what is going on and purposefully downsize to avoid uncontrolled collapse.

Since growth of any kind is probably not a practical option, green growth, decoupling and agrowth are probably not practical strategies. Several decades ago, there were several paths for humans to follow that could have led to sustainability, including one outlined in *The Limits to Growth*. However, it is now likely too late, absent significant technological innovation, and it is time to consider how to achieve sustainability without growth.

Sustainable growth is an oxymoron.

If growth will no longer be the measure of success, the future must encompass other ways to think about ourselves and other ways of defining success and prosperity.

How Much of What is Enough?

When thinking about how much is enough, there is an underlying question of, how much of what is enough?

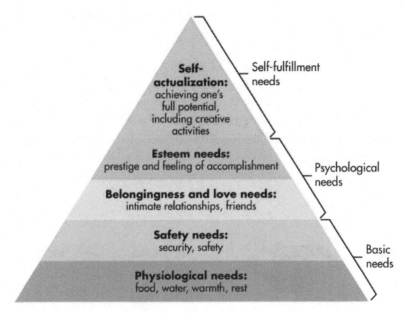

Figure 70 – Maslow's hierarchy of needs[295]

Abraham Maslow (d. 1970), evolved the concept of humanity's "hierarchy of needs." Each level is not exclusive, and humans pursue several needs at the same time. But, in general, as each lower level of needs is fulfilled, humans look to achieve higher needs. Humans look to survive before looking for esteem and expressing themselves in the arts.

Social Instead of Economic Goals

When environmentalists and academics consider many of the issues discussed in this book, they often conclude, "Of course, if you cannot achieve economic goals, they must be replaced by social goals. We need to talk about the quality of our lives, about relationships, about community and about meaning." They redefine prosperity as something that transcends the material and addresses health, happiness and work satisfaction.

While I believe that focusing on social goals and the quality of our lives are good ideas and that their adoption will be a necessity, it is far from clear humans want to focus on relationships and meaning to the exclusion of material growth, particularly when doing so involves significant sacrifice. Convincing people to give up half or more of their income and wealth to be able to better focus on community and interpersonal relationships would be a significant challenge.

When considering prosperity and the requirement for the West to sacrifice prosperity, it is important to realize that today more than 3 billion people live on less than $5 a day, and 80% of the Earth's population lives on less than $10 a day. These people desperately want to be able to successfully negotiate Maslow's first level of physiological needs. As the developed world declines in prosperity, it will be important to assist those who are impoverished in increasing their prosperity.

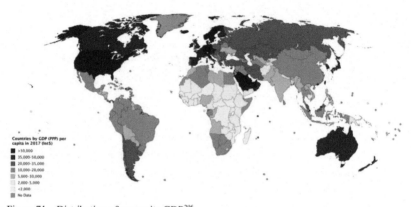

Figure 71 – Distribution of per capita GDP[296]

In the *Handbook on Growth and Stability*, ethnobiologist James Meadowcroft asserts that "meeting the basic needs of the poor should come before satisfying additional material demands of the rich."[297]

It is more fundamental than that. In an era of no growth, there should be no additional material demands of the rich. If the needs of the poor are to be addressed, given that there can be no growth, it will only be through redistribution.

I will continue with a Western frame of reference, understanding that there is a mass of humanity that is suffering.

There have been many thoughts about the proper way to live, perhaps beginning with Socrates, Confucius and the Buddha; extending through Jesus and Muhammed; and then taken up by philosophers following the

Enlightenment. Essentially none thought that the accumulation of material goods was a worthy goal, and some condemned it. However, modern Western civilization has not listened to any of these notables and has placed material goods at the centers of their cultures.

As material goods become increasingly expensive and unavailable, it will not only be important, but also mandatory, that other values become central to society. But, how much consciousness-raising can be accomplished during a time of crisis and stress?

Development must be redefined to address not just physical growth, but also development on the interpersonal and social dimensions. Development must be interpreted as "qualitative improvement in human well-being" and "unfolding of human potential."

The emphasis must be (and this tears at my formerly-capitalist soul) on redistribution and equity. There must be value in simply being and in doing non-economic tasks, such as walking, gardening, enjoying music and reading (begging the question of where the music and reading will come from and how it will be distributed).

There must be voluntary simplicity, and humans must be willing to make a virtue of this necessity.

At the end of the day, prosperity really does go beyond material pleasures. It transcends material concerns. It resides in the quality of our lives and in the health and happiness of our families. It is present in the strength of our relationships and our trust in the community. It is evidenced by our satisfaction at work and our sense of shared meaning and purpose. It hangs on our potential to participate fully in the life of society.

While this new era of mutual respect and help is to be wished for, it is unlikely. Humans have not yet demonstrated these traits on a continuing basis among any group over its history.

Utopia Versus Dystopia

We are left with two, starkly different paths:

1. Utopia. We all learn how to get along and share, valuing the intangible over the material. We immediately and rapidly reduce

our standard of living to that compatible with sustainability. We place the goal of no growth at the center of our cultures.

2. Dystopia. We continue to increase population and consumption. As available resources decrease, inequality continues to increase as fewer and fewer people prosper. As population increases and consumption grows further and further from sustainability, the overall quality of life for most humans begins an inexorable decline (there is an argument to be made based on GPI that that decline began in the 1970s for the U.S. - a decline of some 33% from its peak to 2005). There is increasing crowding, pollution and competition for resources. Dystopia most likely leads to population collapse from an increasing shortage of resources – from the denuding of the field.

Our complex, technology-based society cannot continue to prosper without increasing inputs of energy and material.

Earlier, I expressed significant skepticism that humanity would voluntarily reduce consumption, in some cases like the U.S., by more than 75%, to achieve sustainability. Since humans will likely resist this reduction, the alternative is the likely scenario that the quality of human life will deteriorate over time as portions of humanity, and then humanity as a whole, reach limit after limit. As population relentlessly increases and increasingly stresses the environment, humans will probably incur what a group of scientists has termed "widespread misery." Although the process will be complex, and will move at different speeds in different countries, humans will likely generally denude the field until it cannot support them well and then denude it further until the field cannot support many of them at all. Population will likely begin to decline through a combination of starvation and disease and the unwillingness of potential parents to bring children into that kind of world. War is always a possibility.

Our future appears to be one of more people, fewer things and increasing inconvenience: A slow, relentless deterioration of quality of life in the West, and an inability to improve quality of life in developing and undeveloped countries. At some point, we will begin the collapse that results from Overshoot.

Humans will not be simply resigned to their fates. As conditions worsen and dystopia deepens, humans will increasingly come to grips with the changes going on around them. Responses will be varied and complex, because from Overshoot essentially all paths lead to worsened conditions in the short term.

In addition to increased competition, people will react by actively and creatively attempting to solve the problems. Recent history, particularly in the U.S., is replete with profound social changes, such as dealing with segregation, equal rights for women, homosexuality and the physical ills associated with smoking. Each change has required many years and many decades for the creation of the consensus necessary for change, and that change is incomplete in all cases.

In the face of immediate physical crises, responses may be quicker and more coordinated. Because of the presence of crisis, it is likely that many decisions will be counterproductive and that there will be unintended consequences to even otherwise good decisions. However, humans will begin to proactively react to and cope with the consequences of Overshoot. These crises and responses will likely have different magnitudes, occur at different times and have different attributes in different locations. The end result, however, must be sustainable relationships with the environment.

Signs of Dystopia

Although the trend to dystopia is in its early stages, it has progressed to the point that there are ever-more-visible signs that it is under way.

The ends of capitalism and sustainability are impacting people deeply. They are leading to increasing feelings of despair, degradation and diminution.

That people are experiencing more and more hopelessness in a time of unparalleled general economic prosperity is astounding.

The view of the rest of the world about the deterioration of the U.S. may be summed up by "an old man in Stockholm" who was quoted on Twitter as saying, "What has happened to your country? You pulled out of the Paris climate accord, you let anyone have machine gun, your president spouts hate. The America of my youth won World War II and was a model to the rest of the world. What happened?"

What is happening to bring us so low?

In the midst of this overall economic prosperity:

- The economic system has broken due to unsustainable debt and entitlement levels. Attempts by the Fed to fix the problem have only made it worse. "Financial repression," the policy of forcing interest rates downward toward zero, is severely distorting economic incentives leading to inflation in asset prices and wealth inequality. It is stifling the investment and creativity necessary to generate economic growth. It is crippling the return on savings and negating ability of pensions to generate sufficient returns to be able to provide promised levels of payments on retirement. This broken system is creating a negative environment, weighing on the actions of individuals and corporations.

- Inequality is increasing, resulting in rising indignation and concern that the system is not working any more for the average person.

- Society and politics are growing increasingly fragmented and polarized. Everyday life is burdened by the volume and shrillness in the news and on social media.

- Ironically, the mantra of diversity is leading to the silos of identity politics. Races, genders and ethnicities are bonding ever more tightly and asserting their views more strongly.

- Outrage is rampant and sometimes appears as if it is the dominate emotion.

- Presidents George H.W. Bush, Obama and Trump each took actions that were progressively more authoritarian and President Biden is following in their footsteps. This increased authoritarianism has been partially rationalized by the disagreements in Congress which have resulted in legislative inaction.

- Former President Trump dismantled norms of governance and foreign policy, contributing to the breakdown of the old order, both in the U.S. and abroad. This breakdown of the old order is leading to increased anxiety and uncertainty about the future on the part of the citizens of the U.S. and the world.

- Attempting to find some salvation in increased government, the electorate is moving further and further to the left. Politicians' promises to relieve financial pressure though governmental programs are increasingly attractive to voters who are faced with economic uncertainty and are burdened with debt – particularly student loans.

- Cultural institutions, such as freedom of speech, are under attack. Particularly younger people, in response to increasing insecurity, are demanding protection, including protection from words.

- Icons, including some of the Founders of the U.S. and some individuals who were previously considered great people, are under attack for not having lived up to today's standards. This diminishes our society's mythology and eliminates its heroes, eroding our spiritual foundation.

- Life expectancy in the U.S. is declining. Cultural despair is manifesting in widespread opioid use and growing numbers of suicides.

- The younger generations' prospects are diminished by the load of student loans.

- Jobs are vanishing due to technology and outsourcing. Jobs are more than a source of income. For many people, satisfying and rewarding work is an integral part of their identity and their engagement with life. Many seem to be just giving up. Although official unemployment in the U.S. was near record lows in 2019, the manipulation of employment data results in a more optimistic result than is reflected in the underlying data. Labor force participation is a simple calculation, which is not subject to manipulation – those employed in a group divided by the total number of members in the group being measured. Limiting the group to males in their prime eliminates the effects of the women's movement and of retiring males. Prime-age male labor force participation rate declined from about 98% in 1954 to about 88% in 2015. This is the third lowest rate among developed countries, ahead of only Italy and Israel. It is significantly below the 95% of Switzerland, the Czech Republic and Japan.[298] Although reasons for non-participation include illness and disability, Didem Tüzemen, in a study analyzing the reasons for the decline for the Kansas City Federal Reserve, concludes, "that a decline in the demand for middle-skill workers accounts for most of the decline in participation among prime-age men."[299]

- As a result of the pandemic, unemployment levels increased to levels sometimes exceeding those experienced in the Great Depression. This economic insecurity is directly undermining social cohesion and stability.

- For Millennials, the ability to own a home is growing further and further out of reach. This part of the "American Dream" is becoming unattainable, leading to frustration and despair.

- People are experiencing an overall loss of meaning because of the loss of religion.

- Family structure is eroding, and people are struggling to find an effective replacement.

- An ever-increasing burden of debt at individual, corporate and governmental levels is weighing on the future and on our views of prospects for the future.

- Electronic communications, including texting and engagement on social media, and participating in online gaming, are separating people from society. Indicators of loneliness are increasing.

- Leadership in the U.S. and the rest of the world is uninspiring, raising questions about the quality of the future. Those aspiring to leadership are, at best, ordinary people. This is part of our destruction of and loss of heroes.

- The financial and military hegemony of the U.S. is being challenged on several fronts, particularly by China, and our position as sole economic and military superpower is eroding. That this erosion will continue seems inevitable, leading to anxiety about the future.

- The U.S. is experiencing a deteriorating education system, contributing to diminished prospects for the future.

- Increasing violence in the form of mass shootings is becoming a frequent occurrence. In addition to sadness and empathy for those who incur loss in these shootings, there is the question of what kind of society enables these things?

- Cities such, as Los Angeles, New York, San Francisco, Seattle and many more, are experiencing the extreme negative effects of homelessness. Pictures of filth and human suffering are discouraging.

- In the U.S., the tragedy of our inner cities seems to be unsolvable. Murder rates and human suffering add to the general level of despair.

- The Great Recession of 2008-2009 fundamentally compromised many U.S. citizens' faith in both the economic system and in the government.

- There is a general erosion in trust – trust in government; trust in social institutions, such as the Catholic Church and the Boy Scouts; trust in capitalism and trust in fellow humans.

- To add insult to injury, nature piled on in the form of a pandemic, which ushered in economic misery.

It is too early to tell whether these factors are harbingers of a continuing deterioration of quality of life and the beginning of widespread misery. That may be the case. It has required an extreme amount of debt to get the economy going again.

But since history moves in cycles and not in straight lines, each of these symptoms may signify low points in a cycle that will soon turn up. However, although history does not move in straight lines, the way to bet is a future containing more and deeper financial declines and a continual increase in human despair.

It is my view that we built an over-constrained, hyper-efficient, hyperindividualistic, hyper-connected system that is breaking down under its own weight.

GPI for the U.S. did peak in the 1970s and has been in decline ever since. Happiness in the U.S. did peak in the 1950s and has been in decline ever since. The ability for increased debt to contribute to increased GDP did turn negative in 1999. And in 2016, Trump was elected President, reflecting the desperation of a large proportion of U.S. voters.

One significant determinant of the future will be the amount of resources remaining when humans decide to take sustainability seriously. "Taking sustainability seriously" simplistically means that citizens of the U.S. will have to reduce consumption by more than 75 percent and the rest of the Western world will need to reduce consumption significantly, although less than in the U.S.

The Bottom Line

We have been gathering data toward answering the question of whether human population is in Overshoot and if it is not, when, if ever, it will be in Overshoot. It appears from the data that we are now in Overshoot or if not, we will be shortly. Different parts of the Earth will experience it differently, as each region squeezes the most resources out of the Earth that it is capable of squeezing.

Carrying current trends into the future yields an increasingly dystopian view. The path we are on leads to increasingly denuding parts of the Earth and increasing conflicts for resources - with technology in the background, attempting to mitigate the effects of Overshoot.

The *New Scientist* magazine (11/19/16), summarized a potential future as follows:

> We keep all the balls in the air using densely coupled
> networks of manufacturing, trade, money, employment,
> food, water, transport, energy, technology, healthcare,
> geopolitics and law and order.

> Civilization is an adaptive, complex system – and such
> systems are susceptible to catastrophic failure.

The problem is that once complex systems collapse, they stay collapsed. The lesson from history is that a less complex, alternative, stable state from our past would re-emerge. It could be small, authoritarian city states or even a return to hunting and gathering.[300]

Isaac Asimov, the great science fiction writer, put it this way:

It [the dignity of the human species if population growth continues] will be completely destroyed. I like to use what I call my bathroom metaphor: if two people live in an apartment and there are two bathrooms, then both have freedom of the bathroom. You can go to the bathroom anytime you want to stay as long as you want for whatever you need. And everyone believes in freedom of the bathroom; it should be right there in the Constitution.

But if you have twenty people in the apartment and two bathrooms, no matter how much every person believes in freedom of the bathroom, there is no such thing. You have to set up times for each person, you have to bang on the door, "Aren't you through yet?" and so on. ...

In the same way, democracy cannot survive overpopulation. Human dignity cannot survive [overpopulation]. Convenience and decency cannot survive [overpopulation]. As you put more and more people onto the world, the value of life not only declines, it disappears. It doesn't matter if someone dies, the more people there are, the less one person matters.[301]

Humans will likely organize around the fields that can sustain them, and will attempt to protect those fields from all others. Population and consumption will collapse over time into a steady state.

In a world of natural disasters, epidemics, wars and revolutions, there is no such thing as a steady state in the long term, just as there was not a steady state in our past. In the future, as opposed to the past, there will be no resources that can be used for growth or to provide a buffer for uncertainty.

The future will reflect complexity theory, with one unstable equilibrium being disturbed to create yet another unstable equilibrium.

Capitalistic consumerism just happened to be the mother of all unstable equilibria.

What to Do?

There are a few, straightforward steps that humanity could take to begin to address sustainability – these are necessary but not sufficient, and should be implemented as soon as possible:

- Prices must be adjusted to levels that reflect total impacts and depletion – no subsidies of any kind allowed; the Tragedy of the Commons must be abolished.
- Each woman must be restricted to no more than one child in her lifetime – population must decline.
- Each human must be restricted in their consumption to no more than the present-day average citizen of Myanmar (occupy an eco-footprint of no greater than 1.7 global hectares (4.2 acres)).

Should all of this come to pass, economies and lives would be disrupted and a large number of people would die. However, these deaths and disruptions would occur in any event and controlling the transition is arguably preferable to letting the process evolve on its own.

It Gets Worse

Although beyond the scope of this book, over the next 20 - 40 years, human society, will be shaken to its core by the Rise of the Robots and increasing use of artificial intelligence. This transcendence of technology will lead to the increasing obsolescence of human labor, loss of privacy and increased power of the state. The crisis of unemployment arising from a no-growth economy will be exacerbated by the relentless automation of human jobs.

A No-Growth Economy

"The increase of wealth is not boundless. The end of growth leads to a stationary state... a stationary condition of capital and population implies no stationary state of human improvement. There would be as much scope as ever for all kinds of mental culture, and moral and social progress; as much room for improving the art of living, and much more likelihood of it being improved, when minds ceased to be engrossed by the art of getting on." John Stewart Mill, Principles of Political Economy[302]

The Story, So Far

The Earth system is too large and too complex to calculate carrying capacity with any degree of accuracy. Looking at the data reviewed in this book, there is a reasonable chance we are already in Overshoot. However, if we are not, we will be in the next few decades.

Overshoot is a relative term. For a given level of population in Overshoot, a reduction in consumption could potentially return it to sustainability; for a given level of consumption, a reduction in population could potentially return it to sustainability.

The future appears to be a race between population growth and increased consumption, and the effects of conservation, effective pricing, degrowth and technology. Human populations will exist on the edge of Overshoot, which will be exacerbated by destabilizing events such as changes in weather patterns and disease and, possibly, war.

Because wealth, technology, weather and military capabilities will not be evenly distributed, some humans will likely experience better lives than most of the rest. Pockets of excess consumption can exist within the general context of denuding the environment as biocapacity is transferred from one region to another. Population collapse will be a constant threat. It is likely that some populations will collapse, increasing migration pressure, while other groups either maintain or (relatively) thrive.

We are there or almost there.

Revisiting Growth

Our current way of life depends on the satisfaction of an ever-expanding list of wants. Of adopting newer, more clever technology. Of conquering new markets. Of throwing out the old, or even the recently-new, in favor of the new. Of addressing our relentless need for novelty. Of enhancing our social status through the acquisition of stuff.

We have created institutions, culture, lifestyles and expectations based on the religion of economic growth and consumerism. If there is no growth, then as population increases, wealth per person decreases. In order for people to be continually "better off," economic growth must increase more rapidly than the rate of population increase.

Growth is only possible if there is spare capacity to be used and consumed in that growth. Once the spare capacity is gone, the potential for growth is also gone. "Sustainable growth" and "green growth" are oxymorons.

As capacity limits are reached for various resources in various parts of the world, either those resources must be imported or captured or the growth that relies on those resources will end.

In the financial arena, one way to repay the gargantuan debts we have incurred, other than default and inflation, is through growth. Without growth, debt cannot be repaid and entitlement and pension promises cannot be kept.

The overall picture is one of increasing scarcity and stress from the combination of limits to resources and increasing populations.

Society is faced with a profound dilemma. To resist growth is to risk economic and social collapse. To pursue it relentlessly is to endanger the ecosystems and natural resources on which we depend for long-term survival, risking economic and social collapse.

It is possible that the only way growth will stop is that the accumulated misery from growth becomes sufficiently acute.

Growth must end.

Growth will end.

Capitalism will end.

What, exactly, does that mean for the economy and for society?

A No-Growth Economy

The economic system that supports sustainability and replaces capitalism will, of necessity and ultimately, be the no-growth economy, although we will likely attempt multiple alternatives along the way.

Growth is so ingrained in our lives and our assumptions about our lives that a no-growth life will seem very strange. It will be like living in a foreign country or a different universe.

How do we live in a finite, bounded world in which the limits to growth are not theoretical but impose themselves because we did not decide to reach sustainability until we met or passed the critical-sustainability boundary?

Following is a high-level description of some of the implications of a no-growth economy:

- If something cannot grow, it cannot grow – except at the expense of something else. The entire world becomes a huge, zero-sum game. For every winner, there is a loser.

- There will be relentless tradeoffs between population and consumption. Simplistically, the product of population times consumption must be a constant or must decrease in magnitude. More consumption requires less population, and more people means less consumption.

- Society will function not so much on a needs basis or a wants basis but on a what's-available basis.

- Any attempts to move beyond the steady state leads to denuding. This denuding lowers the level of available resources, which in turn lowers the steady state that can be sustained, going forward.

- A sustainable steady state requires excess resources to be used for maintenance. Whatever stock of goods, e.g., roads, tools, houses, clothing, etc., which exists at steady state, must be maintained, or that stock will decline and eventually disappear. Steady state must be maintained at the level of long-term sustainability, not sustainability in the short term. Resources must be kept in reserve for maintenance. Since maintenance will be required for a long time, the amount of currently-usable resource will be significantly less than the amount of practically- or economically-available resources.

- A sustainable steady state also requires that there be excess resources beyond those used for current personal consumption for the common good, such as sanitation, sewage and defense. Consumption extends beyond the personal to include those governmental and structural requirements a society demands.

- Many natural resources are not sustainable. Any process or product which relies on a depleting natural resource, such as titanium, coal, phosphorus or molybdenum, will, for all practical purposes, ultimately disappear, not in the sense that they will be used up, but in the sense that they will not be available for use.

- Energy must be renewable. Given the dependence of wind and solar energy on depleting natural resources, the supply of energy will be complex to forecast. For example, wind energy generation, as it is currently undertaken, requires steel, carbon fibers, fiberglass and a lubricant. Energy transmission requires copper. It is not clear that either wind or solar energy is renewable over the long term. The only renewable sources of energy are solar, water, tide, properly-maintained forests and geothermal.

- The economy will shrink significantly. There will not be enough work, even ignoring the Rise of the Robots. It is unlikely that robots will be viable in a steady-state economy.

- If debt is consumption brought forward and the economy is at a steady state, there would be no surplus production to be brought forward.

- Increased productivity will be impossible in the sense of doing more with less human input. There is no more to be done. Doing the same with less human input would theoretically be possible, but potentially impractical, and would require energy and technology / materials to accomplish.

- Saving to spend more later on something assumes that the thing to be purchased later is sustainably available; that is, no one is currently claiming it. In a no-growth world, there will be no future goods to save for.

- The steady state is not, in reality, steady. Levels and relationships must be adjusted to reflect shocks to the system, such as weather, disease, natural disasters and conflicts.

- Innovation must be channeled into non-material forms, such as culture.

Steady State for the Long Run

Resources

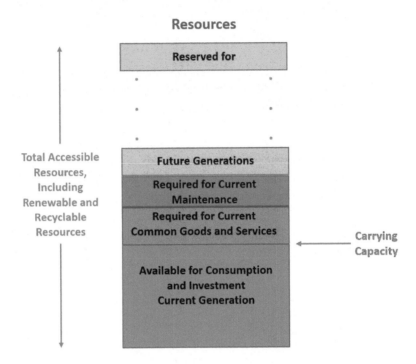

Figure 72 – Simple allocation of resources in a steady-state economy[303]

When considering available resources in a zero-sum game, one of the allocations is between current consumption and future consumption. (Actually, that allocation is occurring now, only we are, for all intents and purposes, ignoring the requirements related to future consumption.)

Let's do a thought experiment.

In our thought experiment, the world has reached steady state and there are exactly enough resources to sustain the current population at some standard of living. My shirt wears out. Or a road needs repair. If all resources are allocated - if there is no more cotton because the land is allocated to grain - then I cannot have a new shirt. The world just slowly grinds to a halt as existing assets are eroded away.

Therefore, I must reserve natural resources for the indefinite future or they must be renewable in sufficient amounts to support current and future consumption and maintenance. The greater the quantity of resources I reserve for the future, the fewer I can consume now, and the lower the sustainable carrying capacity. The farther in the future I want to ensure has sufficient resources, the greater the amount of resources I must reserve from current consumption and the lower the resulting carrying capacity.

The conclusions of this thought experiment, given that the "length" of the future is unknowable, are that the only resources available for an extended future are renewable resources, and that carrying capacity must encompass a reserve of renewable natural resources for the repair and replacement of existing assets, such as tools and clothing. Recycled assets are also available, so long as the material and energy required for recycling are properly accounted for and so far as the recycled output is "worth" the invested input.

Everything is Connected

Let's use milk as an example. What happens to milk in a steady-state economy?

In a steady state, all things are linked together in an endless web of zero-sum games. Having milk will mean that land is devoted to cows for grazing instead of crops. The good news is that some land can sustain grazing, but not crops. However, if more cows are desired than can be supported by grazing land, tradeoffs will have to be made. Cows require water, which cannot then be used for other things. They must be milked and the milk stored. Milk storage requires pasteurization and refrigeration, which, in turn, require refrigerators, coolant and power. The materials in the refrigerator and coolant, and the power that is used, cannot be used elsewhere. The milk may be transported, so there must be roads, vehicles and power, again creating zero-sum games. The milk may be sold in stores, which require materials, land and power.

Health care requires medicines and life-saving equipment. Education needs books and computers. Musicians need instruments. Gardeners need tools. Even the lightest recreation activities – dance, yoga, tai chi, martial arts – have to take place somewhere. There is an irreducible, material component to essentially every good or service.

We are accustomed to having the market, with government's "assistance," deploy its invisible hand to allocate resources. The market, in turn, was enabled by the availability of excess materials, resources, land and energy to be allocated.

If there is no excess, the market can still function, so long as there are no subsidies and prices encompass the Tragedy of the Commons. At steady state, prices must reflect actual value.

A model for society might be America or Europe in the 1700s. Markets were local. Most people lived on farms, usually with access to small cities. Those cities were connected with other cities, locally and even internationally. If someone wanted salt or some kind of cloth or medicine, it could be ordered and eventually supplied. However, the basic goods of everyday life were generated and marketed locally. There were very few strawberries in December. And the eventual availability of the salt or cloth or medicine assumed that there was excess somewhere that could be brought to a local market. Steady state at the border of sustainability means there is no excess to be brought in.

Local carrying capacity will once again become relevant to local areas as the definition of the field shrinks and connections become increasingly expensive.

Institutions and every-day life will change dramatically, including employment.

Employment in a No-Growth Economy

There are two principal timeframes for discussing employment in a no-growth economy: the transition and the end game.

During the transition from a consumption-oriented economy to a steady-state economy, economic activity will decrease as consumption becomes a smaller and smaller part of the economy. Not only will consumption decrease, but those parts of the economy, such as government, that rely on the profits from consumption, will also decrease.

Again, let's oversimplify and do the math and revisit a previous thought experiment.

Assume that consumption makes up 70% of the U.S. economy. Also assume that the eco-footprint calculations are correct and that the U.S. must decrease consumption by more than 75% in order to be sustainable. Consumption (actually, some combination of population and consumption, but I am keeping it simple) would have to decrease by more than half. Continuing to over-simplify, and ignoring second-order effects, such as the associated decline in government jobs, more than 50% of the jobs in the U.S. must either be eliminated or somehow transformed.

When thinking about the Rise of the Robots and the potential, significant, related destruction of human jobs, some commentators are recommending a basic income for all citizens. Ignoring the question of where this income would come from, there are larger issues. For millennia, humans have defined themselves in a large part by their work. They have devoted significant amounts of their lives to work. Taking these jobs away, even if part of the associated income is retained, would result in a large number of idle, unfulfilled people. It would result in a new quest for a new kind of meaning to fill the void that was once occupied by work.

One partial solution is to divide the economy into part-time jobs, which the entire population can share.

It will also be increasingly important for people to find fulfillment through activities that are not job related and will probably be more community and culturally oriented.

In the end game, a much smaller population will primarily be comprised of hunter-gatherers and farmers, the only occupations compatible with the need for all resources to be renewable resources. These hunter-gatherers and farmers may decide to set aside resources to support some common services, such as doctors (in turn reducing the number of sustainable hunter-gatherers and farmers).

The transition from a consumer society to a shared economy to a farming economy will be wrenching and will require population decreases at every step.

Institutions and the economy will also have to dramatically change.

Components of a No-Growth Economy

Once work and the economy begin to change, assumptions around government will also begin to change. As economies become increasingly local, over time the most relevant government will also become local. Remote governmental authority will become increasingly irrelevant as communication and transportation become more and more difficult.

The chaos and hardships associated with the transition would most likely foster centralized government on larger scales, but these adversities could also foster direct democracy on smaller scales as groups come together to survive. It will be important for groups to organize to defend themselves.

Following are some of the characteristics of the transition to a steady-state economy:

- Complexity will decrease as EROI, natural resources, processes and institutions required to support it deteriorate.
- The progress of technology will slow and then reverse as the materials, processes and refined energy required to create technology become unavailable.
- The availability of medicine and medical technology will decrease.
- Lifespans will decrease.
- There will be increasing exposure to "barbarians" on the frontier.
- Support systems and infrastructure will increase in fragility.
- Mercantilism, gaining access to resources located outside of your area, and war will increase as competition for resources intensifies.

Conclusion

Scorpions, Greek Tragedy, Overpopulation and the Human Condition

"Only a crisis - actual or perceived - produces real change. When that crisis occurs, the actions that are taken depend on the ideas that are lying around. That, I believe, is our basic function: to develop alternatives to existing policies, to keep them alive and available until the politically impossible becomes the politically inevitable." –
Milton Friedman[304]

I will wind up this section on sustainability on a quasi-philosophical note.

There is a fable about a scorpion and a frog. "A scorpion asks a frog to carry it across a river. The frog hesitates, afraid of being stung, but the scorpion argues that if it did so, they would both drown. Considering this, the frog agrees, but midway across the river the scorpion does indeed sting the frog, dooming them both. When the frog asks the scorpion why, the scorpion replies that it was in its nature to do so."[305]

Human nature is complex, however, the ancient Greeks often saw human nature through the lens of hubris – excessive pride or arrogance. Hubris is in our nature and is a primary cause of our tendency toward self-destruction.

We are a strange bunch. We have the intelligence to understand that certain actions are destructive. Yet we smoke, eat until we are obese, drive while drunk, do not get vaccinated, have unprotected sex, engage in continual warfare … The list goes on and on.

A significant part of human nature is destructive.

One of the most intelligent and thoughtful scientists of our time, the late Stephen Hawking, noted that our search for intelligent life in the universe could end in tragedy. Given the distances involved in, and therefore time required for, communication with other species, it is likely that anything that is listening or can respond is more technologically advanced than we are. They could and might approach humans as humans approach ants.

His logic is, to me, compelling, however, we will continue to risk destruction in the interest of intellectual pursuit of an idea as we continue to search for extraterrestrial life.

There is a lot of talk in the press that we are on the cusp of creating artificial intelligence that could exceed our own, and robots that will eliminate the jobs of millions of people. Human life could be fundamentally and utterly transformed. And yet we continue.

We continue to experiment with the human genome. In 2019, researchers in China announced that a human-monkey hybrid had been created in the laboratory.

Hubris.

It is in our nature.

It is also in our nature that our views of the world are sufficiently different that it is difficult to reach agreement on most subjects. Abortion, tax policy, how to approach China, which religion is true, which political party has the right ideas, which channel to watch, where to have lunch … This tendency to disagree, combined with uncertainty and with human intellectual limitations and emotional biases, makes action extremely difficult.

Which, in most cases, is probably a good thing, because bad ideas and emotions tend to significantly outnumber good ideas and logical thinking.

With regard to overpopulation and overconsumption, and one of their symptoms – climate change – we are in the worst of all positions:

- The data are highly indicative but not conclusive.
- Any clearly objective proof would occur in decades, significantly past the time when effective solutions could be implemented.
- In any event, we would disagree.
- We are biologically, and most of us are culturally, biased toward procreation, so controlling population will be very difficult.
- Consumption is fun, up to a point dramatically enhancing quality of life.
- Taking things away from people – diminishing their quality of life – is extraordinarily difficult in the absence of a clear emergency.

The way to bet is that we will engage in denial until the crisis imposes itself on us. Then we will act, but then it will be too late. Our field will be denuded, and we will be left with preserving what we can of the remainder.

Things to Think About

Thinking about sustainability tends to proceed in four, broad phases:

- Phase 1 – there are no constraints, and, in any case, technology is our salvation. Concerns are dismissed. This is where we are, today, culturally.
- Phase 2 – there are sustainable constraints, and technology may be our salvation. Concerns are worthy of discussion. This is beginning to slowly creep into our consciousness and conscience.
- Phase 3 – sustainability is important, and technology needs to help – fast. Concerns increase in number and in magnitude. This is where we are, today, in reality.
- Phase 4 – the only sustainable economy is in a steady state, using only renewable and recyclable resources, and technology is either minimally or no longer available due to its demands on resources and energy. This is where we will inevitably go, absent a technological revolution.

It is worth considering that this new steady state will be different than the quasi-steady states of ancient Greece or 18th century America. In all previous quasi-steady states, while growth was slow, there were resources available to accommodate expansion, growth and innovation. Bronze was available for the Bronze Age and iron for the Iron Age. American settlers had access to what seemed to be unlimited trees and land.

In the steady state to come, there will be no excess resources beyond renewable and recyclable resources. This lack of excess resources will place severe constraints on possible outcomes for the human population and the human material condition.

My conclusions with regard to sustainability from creating this book are

- There is no way to accurately model sustainability – it is too complex and chaotic.

- Things are going the wrong way.
- The finiteness of natural resources can be improved, somewhat, through technology. But in the end, together with EROI, as applies to energy and as conceptually applies to other resources, finite resources become the limiting factor to sustaining a complex society.
- Technology can help, and there is a tremendous amount of new technology on the horizon.
- The cost of implementing all of this technology will be huge in terms of money, material and energy.
- Westerners are unlikely to voluntarily drastically reduce their standards of living for a future, theoretical outcome.
- Humans in undeveloped countries are unlikely to voluntarily significantly reduce their rate of procreation because some Westerner has theories about an uncertain future.
- In almost any reasonable case, even with new technology, consumption will have to be severely constrained.
- The probability of wars to control resources is very high.
- The most likely outcome appears to be Overshoot / denuding / collapse.
- Following collapse, the most likely outcome is that population will reach equilibrium with resources at zero growth, utilizing renewable and recyclable resources.
- An alternative economy must be constructed that is sustainably based instead of based on the desires of the individual. Creating this alternative economy through planning and purpose will be difficult and perhaps impossible, but it will happen even if we do not manage the process – following a catastrophe.

These are the primary, but not the only, reasons capitalism is past its sell-by date.

In the End

My best estimate of carrying capacity from researching this book is that Earth's current carrying capacity, with everyone at the same, low standard of living, is between 7 and 7.5 billion people. We are probably in Overshoot and are denuding our field. We must quit generating more humans and we must consume less – much less - immediately. Additionally or alternatively, we have to rely on the technology cavalry to save us. Capitalism, wonderful capitalism, has been too successful and is past its sell-by date. It is the engine of growth, and we cannot grow anymore, either in population or in the size of the economy.

The machinery that has created the incredibly exceptional previous 300 years will begin to inexorably go into reverse as layer after layer is removed until we return to a steady state, living off renewable and recyclable resources.

We face two choices.

1. The first is by far the more likely. We will experience a slow descent into dystopia, punctuated by crises that could possibly provide the incentive and framework for action.

2. The second is the social transformation emphasized by many environmentalists: the creation of a new, global consciousness, will preempt the descent into dystopia. Although this is possible, it is highly unlikely. There are few, if any, examples of even small-scale, persistent utopias. For social transformation to succeed, it must be global. A more than daunting prospect.

Dealing with the Sell-By Date

Economist Milton Friedman notably said: "Only a crisis - actual or perceived - produces real change. *When that crisis occurs, the actions that are taken depend on the ideas that are lying around.* That, I believe, is our basic function: to develop alternatives to existing policies, to keep them alive and available until the politically impossible becomes the politically inevitable." (Emphasis mine.)

My objective has been to provide the basis for informed conversations on the twilight of capitalism, primarily emphasizing the implications of a lack of sustainability. The crisis has likely begun. The solutions to the crisis will arise from ideas that are lying around. It will be critical to develop the ideas that will provide the foundation for that future solution.

The ideas I have proposed as a starter kit are

- Prices must be adjusted to levels that reflect total impacts and depletion – no subsidies of any kind will be allowed; the Tragedy of the Commons must be abolished.

- Each woman must be restricted to no more than one child in her lifetime – population must decline.
- Each human must be restricted in their consumption to no more than the present-day average citizen of Myanmar (occupy an eco-footprint of no greater than 1.7 global hectares (4.2 acres)).

The challenging nature of these three ideas is an indication of the severity of the underlying problem.

The first two ideas will be daunting but are not outside the realm of conceptualization. The foundations and boundaries of these discussions are known, and useful conversations can begin about each. The third idea, although crucial and valid, is overwhelming. The amount of change required to achieve this degree of reduction in consumption is almost beyond the realm of imagination.

Time is short and there is much to be done. The first imperative is to start. The perfect cannot be the enemy of the good.

Therefore, I would add the following conversational points to the third idea:

- Enough is plenty – in both our corporate and personal lives. Clothes, cars, food, vacations, electronics – the GPI demonstrates that the developed countries have pursued excess to the detriment of both their well-being and of the environment.

- Consumption profoundly affects the environment and the path to Overshoot. Each and every act of consumption should reflect a conscious consideration of the environment and its sustainability.

- Repair. Do not replace.

- Recycle where recycling makes sense.

The Millennial Generation is providing a foundation on which we can begin to build some of these ideas. They seem to be less focused on consumption and are more environmentally aware than earlier generations. Some of this change is the result of the natural, intergenerational cultural swings described in Strauss' and Howe's *The Fourth Turning*, and will be to some extent modified or negated by future generations. Some of this awareness may represent a lasting cultural shift. In any event, commitment to a simpler life and concern for the environment, while far from sufficient, do represent a change in the right direction, a foundation to build upon and an opportunity for focus of conversation.

We have taken capitalism to its extremes and it is now destroying itself. It has become and is becoming increasingly dysfunctional.

Existentially, and therefore much more importantly, the fact that we are in Overshoot means that capitalism has been too successful and is past its sell-by date. As a culture and as a species, we must not focus on more and clearly not on growth. We must focus on the sustainability of our natural resources, including energy, that can provide the basis for support of as much of the existing population as possible. At the same time, we should consider the distribution of resources globally, not just within the U.S., something that has all but escaped our attention.

Because we must does not mean that we will.

Which leads to a prediction of a dystopian devolution to a future steady state that is significantly lower than our current standard of living.

Unless the technology cavalry can turn the tide.

Special Offer

Get my free weekly newsletter on capitalism and sustainability.

Visit my website at http://www.pastsellbydate.com/subscribe and sign up for my weekly newsletter about capitalism and sustainability, and I will send you my book on climate change, *The Only Ten Things You Need To Know About Global Warming*, for free! My book on climate change is available in either pdf or eBook format.

Acknowledgements

It is always humbling when someone volunteers to read and edit your book. Elota Patton, you are a great friend.

Vicki Goat, thanks for reading the book, making comments and giving encouragement.

Laura Yorke, thanks for fighting the good fight as my agent to get this book published. Your feedback was invaluable.

About the Author

I have spent my professional life as Chief Executive Officer, President or Chief Financial Officer of privately- and publicly-held companies. I have a Master of Electrical Engineering degree from Rice University and am a Certified Public Accountant. This unlikely combination summarizes my broad interests, including a deep love of history and of the theater, and a fascination with religion and with humanity's relationships with reality.

I enjoy teaching and have occasionally been a lecturer at the University of Texas at Austin, including teaching courses on finance and on information technology management in its MBA school, and on entrepreneurship and on corporate change in its undergraduate business school.

References – Partial List

I am reluctant to provide references because it is close to impossible to gain a balanced view from reading one author, much less one paper or article. I cannot emphasize enough the need to read from multiple sources and to think about what you have just read.

It is also not clear how useful a list of references or an index is in the age of Google and the ability to search text inside books.

I did not find one, much less a few, books that I categorize as "must-reads."

The Fourth Turning, Immoderate Greatness and *The Great Rupture* provide overviews of historical processes that will challenge and provide much food for thought.

Most of the books on capitalism are either strident or, in my opinion, focused on the wrong issues. *The Limits to Growth, the 30-Year Update* comes the closest to a must-read. *Supply Shock* is well considered, although I disagree with the author on several key points. Professor Al Bartlett's *Reflections* is a gem. The KPMG report provides an excellent analysis from a business perspective. The O'Neill paper in *Nature Sustainability* is the best analysis of carrying capacity. *Doughnut Economics* is a flawed book, complete with mistakes, misunderstandings and straw men. However, it is one place to find a series of thoughts and arguments that will challenge your thinking. And that is the point for me. To take a good argument and embrace it, and to take an argument that I think is flawed and understand and counter its flaws. Viktor Shvets' *The Great Rupture* is well worth the read.

Many authors make good points about certain areas, but many make assertions without facts or statistics to back up those assertions, assuming that what they view as common knowledge is and must be true. It is obvious to them that "the Earth is full" or that "we are running out of water," when very few non-environmentalists would accept either proposition. Many works are optimistic in tone and conclusions, based on faith in humanity. They believe that we will all come together in the end, and that societies based on community, culture and knowledge will be easily created.

Technology is the wild card in these discussions, but most technologists approach their subjects with a religious fervor and a utopian faith that there is a technological solution to every problem.

Again, it is important to consider and weigh various opinions from various sources.

Avoid essentially all articles in the popular press, and pronouncements by politicians and movie stars. Politically-correct discussion is less than useless, it is misleading.

One of my personal complaints about articles in the popular press or television news segments, including some cited below, is that they have headlines such as, "Something or other could cause something." The word, could, without associated statistics or probabilities, renders essentially any premise as useless. The world could end tomorrow; eating organic vegetables could cause cancer. I always modify these headlines in my mind to read: "Something or other could *or could not* cause something."

Following is a partial list of books and articles I have referenced:

Bartlett, Al, "Reflections on Sustainability, Population Growth and the Environment," http://www.albartlett.org/articles/art_reflections_part_1.html

Borucke, Michael, et. al, "Accounting for demand and supply of the Biosphere's regenerative capacity: the National Footprint Accounts' underlying methodology and framework," https://www.footprintnetwork.org/content/images/NFA%20Method%20Paper%202011%20Submitted%20for%20Publication.pdf

Brill, Steven, *Tailspin: The People and Forces Behind America's Fifty-Year Fall – and Those Fighting to Reverse It*, Knopf, May 29, 2018.

Calvo, Guiomar, et. al., "Decreasing Ore Grades in Global Metallic Mining: A Theoretical Issue or a Global Reality?" Resources, November 7, 2016, http://www.mdpi.com/2079-9276/5/4/36/htm

Capital Institute, http://capitalinstitute.org/about-us/

Cohen, Joel, *How Many People Can the Earth Support?*, WW. Norton & Company, November 1, 1995

Cook, Lynn and Elena Cherney, "Get Ready for Peak Oil Demand," The Wall Street Journal, May 26, 2011, https://www.wsj.com/articles/get-ready-for-peak-oil-demand-1495419061

Connor, Richard, and Marc Paquin, "Water and Jobs," United Nations World Water Development Report 2016, http://unesdoc.unesco.org/images/0024/002440/244040e.pdf

Cowen, Tyler, *Stubborn Attachments: A Vision for a Society of Free, Prosperous, and Responsible Individuals*, Stripe Press, October 2018.

Cribb, Julian, *The Coming Famine: The Global Food Crisis and What We Can Do to Avoid It*, University of California Press, August 10, 2010

Dahl, Arthur Lyon, "Alternatives to the Consumer Society," International Environment Forum, March 19, 2012, http://iefworld.org/ddahl12a

Desert Sun, "Pumped Dry, The Global Crisis of Vanishing Groundwater," https://www.desertsun.com/story/news/environment/2015/12/10/how-unchecked-pumping-sucking-aquifers-dry-india/74634336/

Desjardines, Jeff, "The Extraordinary Raw Materials in an Iphone 6s," Visual Capitalist, March 8, 2016, http://www.visualcapitalist.com/extraordinary-raw-materials-iphone-6s/

Diamandis, Peter H. and Steven Kotler, *Abundance, The Future is Better Than You Think,* Free Press, February 21, 2012

Diamond, Jared, *Collapse: How Societies Choose to Fail or Succeed*, Penguin Group U.S.A, December 31, 2004

Ehrlich, Paul, *The Population Bomb*, Amereon Press, February 1, 1976, originally published 1968

Ehrilich, Paul, John P. Holdren and Anne H. Ehrlich, *Ecoscience: Population, Resources, Environment*, W. H. Freeman & Co., July 3, 1978

Ellis, Erle C. "Overpopulation Is Not the Problem," *The New York Times*, September 15, 2015, http://www.nytimes.com/2013/09/14/opinion/overpopulation-is-not-the-problem.html

Epstein, Alex, *The Moral Case for Fossil Fuels*, Portfolio Press, November 13, 2014

Eschenbach, Willis, "Animal, Vegetable, or E. O. Wilson," WUWT, September 11, 2010, https://wattsupwiththat.com/2010/09/11/animal-vegetable-or-e-o-wilson/ - discusses E.O. Wilson's calculation of carrying capacity, primarily with regard to vegetarianism

"Expect the Unexpected: Building business value in a changing world," KPMG, https://home.kpmg.com/content/dam/kpmg/pdf/2012/08/building-business-value-part-1.pdf

Freedman, David H., "The Truth about Genetically Modified Food," *Scientific American*, September 1, 2013, " https://www.scientificamerican.com/article/the-truth-about-genetically-modified-food/

Gleick, Peter H. and Meena Palaniappan, "Peak water limits to freshwater withdrawal and use," Proceedings of the National Academy of Sciences of the United States of America, June 22, 2010, http://www.pnas.org/content/107/25/11155

Global Footprint Network, https://www.footprintnetwork.org/

Goldberg, Jonah, *Suicide of the West: How the Rebirth of Tribalism, Populism, Nationalism, and Identity Politics is Destroying American Democracy*, Crown Forum, April 24, 2018.

Gordon, Robert, *The Rise and Fall of American Growth: The U.S. Standard of Living since the Civil War,* Princeton University Press, January, 2016.

Grace Communications Foundation, "The Water Footprint of Food," http://www.gracelinks.org/1361/the-water-footprint-of-food

Grassini, Patricio, et. al., "Distinguishing between yield advances and yield plateaus in historical crop production trends," Nature Communications,

December 17, 2013,
http://www.nature.com/ncomms/2013/131217/ncomms3918/full/ncomms39
18.html

Hall, Charles A. S., et. al., "EROI of different fuels and the implications for
society," ScienceDirect, January 2014,
https://www.sciencedirect.com/science/article/pii/S0301421513003856

Handbook on Growth and Sustainability, Edward Elgar Publishing, June 30,
2017

Haspel, Tamar, "Is Organic Agriculture Really Better for the Environment?,"
The Washington Post, May 15, 2016,
https://www.washingtonpost.com/lifestyle/food/is-organic-agriculture-really-
better-for-the-environment/2016/05/14/e9996dce-17be-11e6-924d-
838753295f9a_story.html?tid=a_inl&utm_term=.b723edca6e93

Heinberg, Richard, *The End of Growth*, New Society Publishers, August 9,
2011

Heinberg, Richard, *Powerdown*, New Society Publishers, September 1, 2004

Henderson, Rebecca, "Reimagining Capitalism, Purpose & the Big
Problems, https://www.youtube.com/watch?v=6-SXYAcBTBw"

Intergovernmental Panel on Climate Change, "Sixth Assessment Report"
2021, https://www.ipcc.ch/assessment-report/ar6/

Jackson, Tim, *Prosperity without Growth: Foundations for the Economy of
Tomorrow*, Routledge, December 29, 2016

Katusa, Marin, and Erik Townsend, "Copper, Uranium and the EV
Revolution," MacroVoices podcast, April 26, 2018,
https://www.macrovoices.com/

Kelly, Kevin, *The Inevitable: Understanding the 12 Technological Forces
That Will Shape Our Future*, Viking Press, June 7, 2016

Klein, Naomi, *This Changes Everything: capitalism vs. The Climate*, Simon
& Schuster, September 16, 2014.

Kolbert, Elizabeth, *The Sixth Extinction: An Unnatural History*, Henry Holt and Co., February 11, 2014

Larkin, Amy, *Environmental Debt: The Hidden Costs of a Changing Global Economy*, St. Martin's Press, June 25, 2013

Long, Cheryl, "Industrially Farmed Foods Have Lower Nutritional Content," Mother Earth News, June/July 2009, https://www.motherearthnews.com/nature-and-environment/nutritional-content-zmaz09jjzraw

Malthus, Thomas, *An Essay on the Principle of Population*, Oxford World Classics, August 1, 2008, originally published 1798.

Mason, Paul, *Postcapitalism: A Guide to Our Future*, Farrar, Straus and Giroux, February 9, 2016

Meadows, Donella H., et. al., *The Limits to Growth*, Potomac Associates, 1972.

Meadows, Donella, et. al., *The Limits to Growth: The 30-Year Update*, Chelsea Green Publishing Co., June 1, 2004

Mills, Richard, "Earth Overshoot Day," AheadOfTheHerd.com, http://aheadoftheherd.com/Newsletter/2017/Earth-Overshoot-Day.htm

Mykleby, Mark, and Patrick Doherty, *The New Grand Strategy: Restoring America's Properity, Security, and Sustainability in the 21st Century*, St. Martin's Press, June 14, 2016.

Nelson, Arthur, "EU on brink of historic decision on pervasive glyphosate weedkiller," *The Guardian*, October 24, 2017, https://www.theguardian.com/environment/2017/oct/24/eu-brink-historic-decision-pervasive-glyphosate-weedkiller
Ophuls, William, *Immoderate Greatness – Why Civilizations Fail*, Self-published, 2012.

Niman, Nicolette Hahn, *Defending Beef: The Case for Sustainable Meat Production*, Chelsea Green Publishing, October 21, 2014

Parfitt, Julian, et. al, "Food waste within food supply chains: quantification and potential for change to 2050," The Royal Society Publishing, August 16, 2010, , http://rstb.royalsocietypublishing.org/content/365/1554/3065.short#ref-62

Parker, Laura, "What Happens to the U.S. Midwest When the Water's Gone?" *National Geographic*, August 2016.

Pearlstein, Steven, *Can American Capitalism Survive?*, St. Martin's Press, September 25, 2018

Porritt, Jonathon, *Capitalism as if the World Matters*, Routledge, February 4, 2016

Peinardo-Vara, Estrella, "The Circular Economy: Butterflies and the Fourth Industrial Revolution," Economonitor, May 4, 2016, http://www.economonitor.com/blog/2016/05/the-circular-economy-butterflies-and-the-fourth-industrial-revolution/?utm_medium=twitter&utm_source=twitterfeed

Pimentel, et. al., "Natural Resources and an Optimum Human Population," *Earth Island Journal*, Summer 1994, (reprinted by Minnesotans for Sustainability), http://www.mnforsustain.org/pimentel_d_natural_resources_and_optimum_population.htm

Pinker, Steven, *Enlightenment Now: The Case for Reason, Science, Humanism and Progress,* Viking Press, February 13, 2018.

Prieto, Pedro, and Charles Hall, *Spain's Photovoltaic Revolution: The Energy Return on Investment*, Springer, January 5, 2013

"Pristine Seas," National Geographic Society, https://www.nationalgeographic.org/projects/pristine-seas/

Raworth, Kate, *Doughnut Economics: Seven Ways to Think Like a 21st Century Economist*, Chelsea Green Publishing, March 29, 2018.

Red List, International Union for Conservation of Nature, http://www.iucnredlist.org/

"Regenerative Agriculture," Drawdown.org, http://www.drawdown.org/solutions/food/regenerative-agriculture

"Reimagining capitalism," https://www.youtube.com/watch?v=2KPs8gLuDF8

Rockstom, J., et. al., "Planetary Boundaries: Exploring the Safe Operating Space for Humanity," *Ecology and Society*, 2009, https://www.ecologyandsociety.org/vol14/iss2/art32/

Russell, Karl, and Danny Hakim, "Broken Promises of Genetically Modified Crops," *The New York Times*, October 29, 2016, http://www.nytimes.com/interactive/2016/10/30/business/gmo-crops-pesticides.html?_r=0

Shvets, Viktor, *The Great Rupture – Do we need to be FREE?*, Boyle Dalton, 2020

Skidelsky, Robert, and Edward Skidelsky, *How Much is Enough? Money and the Good Life*, Other Press, June 19, 2012

Speth, James Gustave, *The Bridge at the Edge of the World, Capitalism, the Environment, and Crossing from Crisis to Sustainability*, Yale University Press, March 28, 2008.

Strauss, William, and Neil Howe, *The Fourth Turning: An American Prophecy – What the Cycles of History Tell Us About America's Next Rendezvous with Destiny*, Bantam, U.S.A, December 29, 1997

Shvets, Viktor, *The Great Rupture, Three Empires, Four Turning Points, and the Future of Humanity*, Boyle & Dalton, 2020

Treeck, Wolfgang, *How Will Capitalism End?*, Verso, November 29, 2016

Talberth, John, and Michael Weisdorf, "Genuine Progress Indicator 2.0: Pilot Accounts for the U.S., Maryland, and Cty of Baltimore 2012-2014,"

Ecological Economics, https://sustainable-economy.org/wp-content/uploads/2017/07/Genuine-Progress-Indicator-2.0.pdf

Tainter, Joseph A., *The Collapse of Complex Societies*, Cambridge University Press, March 30, 1990.

Taleb, Nassim, *Fooled by Randomness*, Random House, October 14, 2008.

Tepper, Jonathan, and Denise Hearn, *The Myth of capitalism: Monopolies and the Death of Competition*, Wiley, November 20, 2018

Turner, Graham, "Is Global Collapse Imminent? An Updated Comparison of *The Limits to Growth* with Historical Data," Melbourne Sustainable Society Institute, August 4, 2014, http://sustainable.unimelb.edu.au/sites/default/files/docs/MSSI-ResearchPaper-4_Turner_2014.pdf

United Nations Environment Programme, "GEO5, Global Environment Outlook, Environment for the future we want," 2012, http://www.unep.org/geo/sites/unep.org.geo/files/documents/geo5_report_full_en_0.pdf

Van Huis, Arnold, et. al., "Edible Insects: future prospects for food and feed security,", Food and Agriculture Organization of the United Nations, 2013, http://www.fao.org/docrep/018/i3253e/i3253e.pdf

Washington, Haydn, and Paul Twomey, editors, *A Future Beyond Growth: Towards a steady state economy*, Routledge, April 12, 2016

Webster, Kit, *The Only 10 Things You Need to Know About Global Warming,* http://www.tenthingswarming.com

Wilson, Edward O., *The Future of Life*, Vintage Press, March 11, 2003

Worldwatch Institute, "Global Population Reduction: Confronting the Inevitable," April 24, 2018, http://www.worldwatch.org/node/563

Zabarenko, Deborah, "Overfishing may wipe seafood off menu," Reuters, November 3, 2006, http://www.abc.net.au/science/news/stories/2006/1780487.htm

Zaraska, Marta, "Lab-grown meat is in your future, and it may be healthier than the real stuff," *The Washington Post*, May 2, 2016, https://www.washingtonpost.com/national/health-science/lab-grown-meat-is-in-your-future-and-it-may-be-healthier-than-the-real-stuff/2016/05/02/aa893f34-e630-11e5-a6f3-21ccdbc5f74e_story.html?noredirect=on&utm_term=.6b03f2cdf76e

Endnotes

[1] Thomas Hobbes in his book, *Leviathan*, published in 1651.

[2] Strauss, William, and Neil Howe, *The Fourth Turning*, January 13, 1998, Broadway Books.

[3] Stephen King, quoted at https://www.elephantjournal.com/2017/08/i-write-to-find-out-what-i-think-not-the-other-way-around-stephen-king/

[4] Meadows, Donella H., et. al., *The Limits to Growth*, Potomac Associates, 1972. Also, http://www.donellameadows.org/wp-content/userfiles/Limits-to-Growth-digital-scan-version.pdf

[5] Klein, Naomi, *This Changes Everything: capitalism vs. The Climate*, Simon & Schuster, September 16, 2014.

[6] Stoppard, Tom, *Arcadia*, a play.

[7] Hobbes, Thomas, *Leviathan*, 1651

[8] "Life Expectancy," Wikipedia, https://en.wikipedia.org/wiki/Life_expectancy

[9] Lavin, James, "Before 20th Century, doctors did more harm than good," March 11, 2009, http://www.jameslavin.com/articles/2009/11/11/before-20th-century-doctors-did-more-harm-than-good/

[10] https://www1.umassd.edu/ir/resources/laboreducation/literacy.pdf

[11] Lomborg, Bjørn, *The Skeptical Environmentalist,* Cambridge University Press, 2001

[12] https://en.wikipedia.org/wiki/Extreme_poverty#/media/File:World-population-in-extreme-poverty-absolute.svg

[13] "Poverty," World Bank Group, https://www.worldbank.org/en/topic/poverty/overview

[14] Ridley, Matt, "Fossil Fuels will Save the World (Really)," The Wall Street Journal, December 5, 2018, https://www.wsj.com/articles/fossil-fuels-will-save-the-world-really-1426282420

[15] "capitalism," *Wikipedia*, https://en.wikipedia.org/wiki/capitalism

[16] Marx, Karl and Friedrich Engles, *Das Kapital: A Critique of Political Economy*, originally published in 1867.

[17] Smith, Adam, *The Wealth of Nations*, originally published in 1776.

[18] Stigler, George J., "The Successes and Failures of Professor Smith," *Journal of Political Economy, 84(6)*, p. 1202, 1976

[19] Stigler, George J., "The Division of Labor is Limited by the Extent of the Market," *Journal of Political Economy*, 59(3), pp. 185,193, 1951,

[20] Wei, Lingling, "Xi Jinping Aims to Rein in Chinese Capitalism, Hew to Mao's Socialist Vision, *The Wall Street Journal*, September 20, 2021, https://www.wsj.com/articles/xi-jinping-aims-to-rein-in-chinese-capitalism-hew-to-maos-socialist-vision-11632150725?st=fcpld164enez9tg&reflink=article_copyURL_share

[21] Shvets, Victor, in an interview on the podcast www.macrovoices.com , July 8, 2021

[22] Shvets, Viktor, *The Great Rupture, Three Empires, Four Turning Points, and the Future of Humanity*, Boyle & Dalton, 2020.

[23] Henerson, David, *The Concise Encyclopedia of Economics*, Liberty Fund, Inc., August 1, 2008

[24] Data from https://www.usgovernmentspending.com/spending_chart_1900_2020U.S.p_XXs2li011tcn_F0t_U.S._Total_Government_Spending

[25] "2018 Annual Report of the Boards of Trustees of the Federal Hospital Insurance and Federal Supplementary Medical Insurance Trust Funds," https://www.cms.gov/Research-Statistics-Data-and-Systems/Statistics-Trends-and-Reports/ReportsTrustFunds/Downloads/TR2018.pdf

[26] Yandle, Bruce, "Yes, the System is 'Rigged" – the Question is How," American Institute for Economic Research, May 8, 2019, https://www.aier.org/article/yes-system-%E2%80%9Crigged%E2%80%9D-question-how

[27] Pope Saint John Paul II, "Centesimus Annus," May 1, 1991, http://w2.vatican.va/content/john-paul-ii/en/encyclicals/documents/hf_jp-ii_enc_01051991_centesimus-annus.html

[28] Meghji, Lina, "Islam and Economics, is Islam compatible with capitalism?", May 20, 2015, https://themuslimvibe.com/muslim-lifestyle-matters/money/islam-and-economics-khurshid-ahmad-on-capitalism-and-islam

[29] Evers, Williamson M., "California Wants to Teach Your Kids that capitalism is Racist," *The Wall Street Journal*, July 29, 2019, https://www.wsj.com/articles/california-wants-to-teach-your-kids-that-capitalism-is-racist-11564441342

[30] "Joseph Alois Schumpeter," Library of Economics and Liberty, https://www.econlib.org/library/Enc/bios/Schumpeter.html#:~:text=Schumpeter%20believed%20that%20capitalism%20would,for%20the%20intellectual%20class's%20existence.

[31] Niall Ferguson, interview on the Remnant podcast, Lil Jacobins, July 3, 2020, https://remnant.thedispatch.com/

[32] Shvets, Viktor, in an interview on the www.macrovoices.com podcast, July 8, 2021.

[33] "List of recessions in the United States," Wikipedia, https://en.wikipedia.org/wiki/List_of_recessions_in_the_United_States

[34] "Civilian Unemployment Rate," FRED, https://fred.stlouisfed.org/series/UNRATE/

[35] "Unemployment Rate by Year Since 1929 Compared to Inflation and GDP," the balance, https://www.thebalance.com/unemployment-rate-by-year-3305506

[36] Minsky, Hyman, "The Financial Instability Hypothesis," Levy Economics Institute, May 1992, http://www.levyinstitute.org/pubs/wp74.pdf

[37] Kessler, Glenn, "How many pages of regulations for 'Obamacare'?," *The Washington Post*, May 15, 2013, https://www.washingtonpost.com/blogs/fact-checker/post/how-many-pages-of-regulations-for-obamacare/2013/05/14/61eec914-bcf9-11e2-9b09-1638acc3942e_blog.html?utm_term=.30d7f9faf07e

[38] Daven, David, "The New Economic Concentration," The American Prospect, January 16, 2019, https://prospect.org/article/new-economic-concentration

[39] Hunt, Ben, "This is Water," April 17, 2019, https://www.epsilontheory.com/this-is-water/#.XLhisAbUky0.twitter (may be behind pay wall)

[40] Jaynes, Dwight, "Equal pay for women's World Cup players? Seriously?, NBC Sports Northwest, July 9, 2015, https://www.nbcsports.com/northwest/world-cup/equal-pay-womens-world-cup-players-seriously

[41] Donnelly, Grace, "Top CEOs Make More in Two Days Than An Average Employee Does in One Year," July 20, 2017, http://fortune.com/2017/07/20/ceo-pay-ratio-2016/

[42] Gavett, Gretchen, "CEOs Get Paid Too Much, According to Pretty Much Everyone in the World," Harvard Business Review, September 23, 2014, https://hbr.org/2014/09/ceos-get-paid-too-much-according-to-pretty-much-everyone-in-the-world

[43] "Wealth inequality in the United States," Wikipedia, https://en.wikipedia.org/wiki/Wealth_inequality_in_the_United_States

[44] Goldberg, Jonah, Suicide of the West: How the Rebirth of Tribalism, Populism, Nationalism, and Identity Politics is Destroying American Democracy, Crown Forum, April 24, 2018

[45] Scheidel, Walter, The Great Leveler, Violence and the History of Inequality from the Stone Age to the Twenty-First Century, Princeton University Press, September 18, 2018

[46] Schumpeter, Joseph A., capitalism, socialism and Democracy. Routledge, 1942.

[47] https://blog.robotiq.com/a-look-into-fully-automated-futuristic-factories

[48] Taleb, Nicholas Nassim, Antifragile: Things that Gain from Disorder (Incerto, Book 3), November 26, 2012, Random House.

[49] Reinhart, Carmen M. and Kenneth S. Rogoff, This Time is Different, Eight Centuries of Financial Folly, 1672, January 1, 2009

[50] Heyneke, Neels and Mehul Daya, "The Rise and Fall of the Eurodollar System, Nedbank, September 2016, https://www.nedbank.co.za/content/dam/nedbank-crp/reports/Strategy/NeelsAndMehul/2016/September/TheRiseAndFallOfTheEurodollarSystem_160907.pdf

[51] "M2 Money Stock", Federal Reserve Bank of St. Louis, https://fred.stlouisfed.org/series/M2

[52] Ophuls, William, Immoderate Greatness – Why Civilizations Fail, Self-published, 2012.

[53] Gordon, Robert, "Perspectives on the Rise and Fall of American Growth," American Economic Review, May, 2016, https://www.researchgate.net/publication/302973038_Perspectives_on_The_Rise_and_Fall_of_American_Growth

[54] Saad, Lydia, "socialism as Popular as capitalism Among Young Adults in

U.S.," Gallup, November 25, 2019,
https://news.gallup.com/poll/268766/socialism-popular-capitalism-among-young-adults.aspx
[55] Desilver, Drew, "For most U.S. workers, real wages have barely budged in decades," August 7, 2018, Pew Research Center, https://www.pewresearch.org/fact-tank/2018/08/07/for-most-us-workers-real-wages-have-barely-budged-for-decades/
[56] "B Corporation (certification), Wikipedia, https://en.wikipedia.org/wiki/B_Corporation_(certification)
[57] Misra, Subodh, "An Early Look at 2019 U.S. Shareholder Proposals, March 5, 2019, https://corpgov.law.harvard.edu/2019/03/05/an-early-look-at-2019-us-shareholder-proposals/
[58] "Measuring Stakeholder capitalism Towards Common Metrics and Consistent Reporting of Sustainable Value Creation," World Economic Forum, September 2020, http://www3.weforum.org/docs/WEF_IBC_Measuring_Stakeholder_capitalism_Report_2020.pdf
[59] "The environment and our global economy; The Sustainable Markets Initiative places sustainability on par with profitability," Bank of America, January 22, 2021, https://about.bankofamerica.com/en-us/what-guides-us/sustainable-markets-initiative.html#fbid=noyVKqCXHYT
[60] "Economist Says Manufacturing Job Loss Driven by Technology, Not Gobalization," NPR, December 10, 2016, https://www.npr.org/2016/12/10/505079140/economist-says-manufacturing-job-loss-driven-by-advancing-technology-not-globali
[61] Shvets, Viktor, *The Great Rupture, Three Empires, Four Turning Points, and the Future of Humanity*, Boyle & Dalton, 2020.
[62] Reisinger, Don, "A.I. Expert Says Automation Could Replace 40% of Jobs in 15 Years, January 10, 2019, *Fortune*, http://fortune.com/2019/01/10/automation-replace-jobs/
[63] Farnish, Keith, *Time's Up!: An Uncivilized Solution to a Global Crisis*, January 31, 2009, UIT Cambridge, Ltd.
[64] Coyote Blog, January 22, 2010, http://coyoteblog.com/coyote_blog/tag/keith-farnish?doing_wp_cron=1556377590.2098929882049560546875
[65] Hume, David, *Of Public Credit*, essay published 1792.
[66] Davidson, Kate and Jon Hilsenrath, "How Washington Learned to Love Debt and Deficits," *The Wall Street Journal,* June 13, 2019, https://www.wsj.com/articles/how-washington-learned-to-love-the-deficit-11560436380
[67] Mauldin, John, "These 6 charts explain the world's looming demographic crisis," Business Insider, May 1, 2016, https://www.businessinsider.com/6-charts-explain-worlds-demographic-crisis-2016-4
[68] Hunt, Lacy, interview on http://www.macrovoices.com , broadcasted on April 25, 2019.
[69] "World Life Expectancy (2019),

http://www.geoba.se/population.php?pc=world&type=015&year=2019&st=c
ountry&asde=&page=1
[70] "World Happiness Report 2019,"
https://worldhappiness.report/ed/2019/#read
[71] "2019 Index of Individual Freedom," Heritage Foundation,
https://www.heritage.org/index/book/chapter-3
[72] "2019 World Press Freedom Index," Reporters Without Borders,
https://rsf.org/en/ranking
[73] Phelps, Glenn and Steve Crabtree, "Worldwide, Median Household
Income About $10,000," December 16, 2013,
https://news.gallup.com/poll/166211/worldwide-median-household-income-
000.aspx
[74] Brock, Dr. Woody, presentation to the John Mauldin Strategic Investment
Conference, May 2019.
[75] Ophuls, William, *Immoderate Greatness – Why Civilizations Fail*, Self-
published, 2012.
[76] Capretta, James, C., "Opinion: The financial hole for Social Security and
Medicare is even deeper than the experts say," June 16, 2018,
https://www.marketwatch.com/story/the-financial-hole-for-social-security-
and-medicare-is-even-deeper-than-the-experts-say-2018-06-15
[77] https://www.macrotrends.net/1381/debt-to-gdp-ratio-historical-chart
[78] Foundation for the Study of Cycles,
https://foundationforthestudyofcycles.org/
[79] https://www.seeitmarket.com/ever-accumulating-debt-trade-deficits-triffin-
warned-us-17866/
[80] Bergman, David, "Less is More, More or Less," Resilience, February 8,
2013, http://www.resilience.org/stories/2013-02-08/less-is-more-more-or-
less/
[81] Bernstein, Joseph, "Alienated, Alone And Angry: What The Digital
Revolution Really Did To Us," BuzzFeed, December 17, 2019,
https://www.buzzfeednews.com/article/josephbernstein/in-the-2010s-decade-
we-became-alienated-by-technology
[82] "Preston curve," Wikipedia, https://en.wikipedia.org/wiki/Preston_curve
[83] Floramonti, Lorenzo, "We Can't Eat GDP: Global Trends on Alternative
Indicators," DailyGood, August 22, 2015,
http://www.dailygood.org/story/1105/we-can-t-eat-gdp-global-trends-on-
alternative-indicators-lorenzo-fioramonti/
[84] Lawn, Phillip and Matthew Clarke, *Sustainable Welfare In The Asia-
Pacific: Studies Using the Genuine Progress Indicator*, Edward Elgar
Publishing, September 30, 2008
[85] "Public Trust in Governmnet: 1958-2021," Pew Research Center, May 17,
2021, https://www.pewresearch.org/politics/2021/05/17/public-trust-in-
government-1958-2021/
[86] Color print from an 1860s edition of *Gulliver's Travels*
[87] LaBarre, Polly, Reimagining capitalism, Harvard Business Review,
February 27, 2012, https://hbr.org/2012/02/reimagining-capitalism

[88] Dalio, Ray, "Why and How capitalism Needs to be Reformed," April 5, 2019, https://www.linkedin.com/pulse/why-how-capitalism-needs-reformed-parts-1-2-ray-dalio/?published=t

[89] Ferguson, Niall, interview on RealVision, https://www.realvision.com/tv/shows/the-larry-mcdonald-series/videos/a-historical-perpective-on-populist-politics

[90] Diamandis, Peter H. and Steven Kotler, *Abundance, The Future is Better Than You Think,* Free Press, February 21, 2012

[91] Pinker, Steven, *Enlightenment Now: The Case for Reason, Science, Humanism and Progress,* Viking Press, February 13, 2018.

[92] Desjardins, Jeff, "The Extraordinary Raw Materials in an Iphone 6s," Visual Capitalist, March 8, 2016, http://www.visualcapitalist.com/extraordinary-raw-materials-iphone-6s/

[93] Wilson, Edward O., *The Future of Life,* Vintage Press, March 11, 2003

[94] Intergovernmental Panel on Climate Change, *Sixth Assessment Report, 2021,* https://www.ipcc.ch/assessment-report/ar6/

[95] Frank, Patrick, "Uncertainty in the Global Average Surface Air Temperature Index: A Representative Lower Limit," https://www.jstor.org/stable/43734979?seq=1

[96] Ellis, Arthur K., *Teaching and learning Elementary Social Studies*, Allyn & Bacon, 1970, 431

[97] Hubbert, M.K., "Nuclear Energy and the Fossil Fuels," Presented before the Spring Meeting of the Southern District, American Petroleum Institute, Plaza Hotel, San Antonio, Texas, March 1956, https://web.archive.org/web/20080527233843/http://www.hubbertpeak.com/hubbert/1956/1956.pdf

[98] U.S. Energy Information Administration, https://www.eia.gov/dnav/pet/hist/LeafHandler.ashx?n=PET&s=MCRFPU.S.1&f=M

[99] "Crude Oil Prices – 70 Year Historical Chart," Macrotrends , https://www.macrotrends.net/1369/crude-oil-price-history-chart

[100] Rosenberg, Eric, "Can Fracking Survive at $60 a Barrel?," Investopedia, August 26, 2017, https://inflationdata.com/Inflation/Inflation_Rate/Historical_Oil_Prices_Chart.asp

[101] "Cost of Oil Production by Country," Knoema, November 29, 2017, https://knoema.com/vyronoe/cost-of-oil-production-by-country

[102] Ibid

[103] Aublinger, Christof, "How Much Does It Cost to Produce 1 Barrel of Oil," Seeking Alpha, May 11, 2015, https://seekingalpha.com/article/3168006-how-much-does-it-cost-to-produce-1-barrel-of-oil-chinese-oil-producers-cnooc-petrochina-and-sinopec-in-2014

[104] Barbucia, David, "Saudi Arabia needs oil at $85-$87 a barrel to balance budget: IMF official," Reuters, May 2, 2018, https://seekingalpha.com/article/3168006-how-much-does-it-cost-to-

produce-1-barrel-of-oil-chinese-oil-producers-cnooc-petrochina-and-sinopec-in-2014
[105] Knoema
[106] "Daily demand for crude oil worldwide from 2006 to 2018," Statistica, https://www.statista.com/statistics/271823/daily-global-crude-oil-demand-since-2006/
[107] Visser, Steve, "Mammoth Texas oil discovery biggest ever in U.S.A." CNN, November 18, 2016, https://www.cnn.com/2016/11/17/us/midland-texas-mammoth-oil-discovery/index.html
[108] "EROI and the Energy Cliff," The Next Turn, November 4, 2014, http://thenextturn.com/eroei-energy-cliff/
[109] Hall, Charles A. S., et. al., "EROI of different fuels and the implications for society," ScienceDirect, January 2014, https://www.sciencedirect.com/science/article/pii/S0301421513003856
[110] "Energy returned on energy invested," Wikipedia, https://en.wikipedia.org/wiki/Energy_returned_on_energy_invested
[111] Prieto, Pedro, and Charles Hall, *Spain's Photovoltaic Revolution: The Energy Return on Investment*, Springer, January 5, 2013, 118
[112] Frangoul, Anmar, "Forget 'Peak Oil': We could reach 'Peak Demand' for energy before 2030," CNBC, October 10, 2016, https://www.cnbc.com/2016/10/10/forget-peak-oil-we-could-reach-peak-demand-for-energy-before-2030.html
[113] Voelcker, John, "1.2 Billion Vehicles On World's Roads Now, 2 Billion By 2035: Report," Green Car Reports, July 29, 2014, https://www.greencarreports.com/news/1093560_1-2-billion-vehicles-on-worlds-roads-now-2-billion-by-2035-report
[114] "Average gas mileage of new cars rises in January, U.S.AToday, February 6, 2015, https://www.usatoday.com/story/money/cars/2015/02/06/gas-mileage-january-cars/22967509/
[115] Burks, Fred, "Car Mileage: 1908 /fird Nidek /////t – 25 MPG," WANTtoKNOW.info, https://www.wanttoknow.info/050711carmileageaveragempg
[116] Edelstein, Stephen, "Global oil demand could peak by 2020, says Shell," November 9, 2016, https://www.greencarreports.com/news/1107158_global-oil-demand-could-peak-by-2020-says-shell
[117] Cook, Lynn and Elena Cherney, "Get Ready for Peak Oil Demand," The Wall Street Journal, May 26, 2011, https://www.wsj.com/articles/get-ready-for-peak-oil-demand-1495419061
[118] Hood, Marlowe, "One million species risk extinction due to humans: draft UN report," AFP, April 23, 2019, AFP, https://news.yahoo.com/one-million-species-risk-extinction-due-humans-draft-131407174.html
[119] Ritchie, Hannah, "Wild mammals have declined by 85% since the rise of humans, but there is a possible future where they flourish," Our World in Data, April 20, 2021, https://ourworldindata.org/wild-mammal-decline
[120] Rosane, Olivia, "Humans and ig Ag Livestock Now Account for 96 Percent of Mammal Biomass," EcoWatch, May 23, 2018,

https://www.ecowatch.com/biomass-humans-animals-2571413930.html
[121] Kelly, Kevin, *The Inevitable: Understanding the 12 Technological Forces That Will Shape Our Future*, Viking Press, June 7, 2016
[122] Nordhaus, Ted, "The Earth's carrying capacity for human life is not fixed," AEON, July 5, 2018, https://aeon.co/ideas/the-earths-carrying-capacity-for-human-life-is-not-fixed
[123] Taleb, Nassim, *Fooled by Randomness*, Random House, October 14, 2008
[124] Malthus, Thomas, *An Essay on the Principle of Population*, Oxford World Classics, August 1, 2008, originally published 1798
[125] Ehrlich, Paul, *The Population Bomb*, Amereon Press, February 1, 1976, originally published 1968
[126] World Population by Year, WorldOMeter, https://www.worldometers.info/world-population/world-population-by-year/
[127] World Population Prospects 2019, United Nations DESA/Population Division, https://population.un.org/wpp/
[128] Klatz, Dr. Ronald, and Dr. Robert Goldman, Editors, *Anti-Aging Therapeutics, Volume XVI, Volume 16*, American Academy of Ani-Aging Medicine, A4M Publications, 2016.
[129] Turner, Graham, "Is Global Collapse Imminent? An Updated Comparison of *The Limits to Growth* with Historical Data," Melbourne Sustainable Society Institute, August 4, 2014, http://sustainable.unimelb.edu.au/sites/default/files/docs/MSSI-ResearchPaper-4_Turner_2014.pdf
[130] Meadows, Dennis and Chris Martenson, Peak Prosperity's Featured Voices podcast, December 17, 2019, https://www.youtube.com/watch?v=hBmjIIWPj3w&feature=youtu.be
[131] Herrington, Gaya, "Update to limits to growth: Comparing the World3 model with empirical data," *Journal of Industrial Ecology*, June 3, 2021, https://advisory.kpmg.us/articles/2021/limits-to-growth.html
[132] Global Footprint Network, https://www.footprintnetwork.org/
[133] "Reimagining capitalism," https://www.youtube.com/watch?v=2KPs8gLuDF8
[134] "List of countries by ecological footprint," Wikipedia, https://en.wikipedia.org/wiki/List_of_countries_by_ecological_footprint
[135] http://data.footprintnetwork.org/#/
[136] "Grain: World Markets and Trade," U.S. Department of Agriculture, April 2018, https://apps.fas.usda.gov/psdonline/circulars/grain.pdf
[137] Ebikeme, Charles, "Eyes on Environment," Scitable, July 25, 2013, https://www.nature.com/scitable/blog/eyes-on-environment/water_world
[138] O'Neill, Daniel W., et. al., "A good life for all within planetary boundaries," Nature Sustainability, February 5, 2018, https://www.nature.com/articles/s41893-018-0021-4
[139] Bologna, Mauro and Gerardo Aquno, "Deforestation and world population sustainability: a quantitative analysis," *Nature*, May 4, 2020,

https://www.nature.com/articles/s41598-020-63657-6

[140] Gerten, Dieter, et. al, "Feeding the world without wrecking the planet is possible," Potsdam Institute for Climate Impact Research, January 20, 2020, https://www.pik-potsdam.de/news/press-releases/feeding-the-world-without-wrecking-the-planet-is-possible

[141] Cohen, Joel, *How Many People Can the Earth Support?*, WW. Norton & Company, November 1, 1995, 363

[142] Pimentel, et. al., "Natural Resources and an Optimum Human Population," *Earth Island Journal*, Summer 1994, (reprinted by Minnesotans for Sustainability), http://www.mnforsustain.org/pimentel_d_natural_resources_and_optimum_population.htm

[143] Worldwatch Institute, "Global Population Reduction: Confronting the Inevitable," April 24, 2018, http://www.worldwatch.org/node/563

[144] Webb, Richard, "Paul Ehrlich: There are too many super-consumers on the planet," *New Scientist* magazine, November 11, 2020, https://www.newscientist.com/article/2232011-paul-ehrlich-there-are-too-many-super-consumers-on-the-planet/?utm_source=nsday&utm_medium=email&utm_campaign=NSDAY_171120

[145] Rees, William E, "Ecological economics for humanity's plague phase," *Ecological Economics*, volume 169, March 2020, https://www.sciencedirect.com/science/article/pii/S0921800919310699

[146] Image created by the author

[147] Washingron, Haydn, and Paul Twomey, editors, *A Future Beyond Growth: Towards a steady state economy*, Routledge, April 12, 2016, 52

[148] Ellis, Erle C. "Overpopulation Is Not the Problem," *The New York Times*, September 15, 2015, http://www.nytimes.com/2013/09/14/opinion/overpopulation-is-not-the-problem.html

[149] Rockstom, J., et. al., "Planetary Boundaries: Exploring the Safe Operating Space for Humanity," *Ecology and Society*, 2009, https://www.ecologyandsociety.org/vol14/iss2/art32/

[150] "Global agriculture towards 2050," United Nations Food and Agriculture Organization, October 13, 2009, http://www.fao.org/fileadmin/templates/wsfs/docs/Issues_papers/HLEF2050_Global_Agriculture.pdf

[151] "Environment for the future we want," United Nations Environment Programme, 2012, http://web.unep.org/geo/sites/unep.org.geo/files/documents/geo5_report_full_en_0.pdf

[152] "Benjamin Franklin, Quotes," goodreads,

https://www.goodreads.com/quotes/53013-when-the-well-is-dry-we-know-the-worth-of

[153] "Water resources," Wikipedia, https://en.wikipedia.org/wiki/Water_resources

[154] "Water cycle," Wikipedia, https://en.wikipedia.org/wiki/Water_cycle

[155] "Water scarcity," Wikipedia, https://en.wikipedia.org/wiki/Water_scarcity

[156] "The Water Footprint of Food," Grace Communications Foundation, http://www.gracelinks.org/1361/the-water-footprint-of-food

[157] Ritchie, Hannah, and Max Roser, "Water Access, Resources & Sanitation, Our World in Data, https://ourworldindata.org/water-access-resources-sanitation#water-footprint-of-food-products

[158] "Bottled water consumption worldwide from 2007 to 2017," Statista, https://www.statista.com/statistics/387255/global-bottled-water-consumption/

[159] "The Hidden Water in Everyday Products," Water Footprint Calculator, July 1, 2017, https://www.watercalculator.org/water-use/the-hidden-water-in-everyday-products/

[160] "Uses of water," Wikispaces.com, https://ih-igcse-geography.wikispaces.com/1.6.+Uses+of+water

[161] "8 Mighty Rivers Run Dry from Overuse," National Geographic, https://www.nationalgeographic.com/environment/photos/rivers-run-dry/

[162] Glennon, Robert Jerome, *Unquenchable: America's Water Crisis and What To Do About It*, Inland Press, May 11, 2009, 106

[163] Bandoim, Lan, "Groundwater levels are down in South Dakota," DakotaFire Media, September 17, 2013, http://dakotafire.net/land/groundwater-levels-are-down-in-south-dakota/5607/

[164] Guru, Manjula, and James E. Horne, "The Ogallala Aquifer," Kerr Center for Sustainable Agriculture, July, 2000, http://kerrcenter.com/wp-content/uploads/2014/11/ogallala_aquifer.pdf

[165] Hegeman, Roxana, "High Plains Aquifer will be 69 percent depleted in 50 years, K-State study says," *The Wichita Eagle*, August 26, 2013, http://www.kansas.com/news/article1121517.html

[166] Khandal, Dr. R. K., "Water: Sources and Sustainability," June 26, 2014, https://www.slideshare.net/RakeshKhandal/water-final , Slide 22

[167] "Study: Third of Big Groundwater Basins in Distress," NASA Jet Propulsion Laboratory, June 16, 2016, https://www.jpl.nasa.gov/news/news.php?feature=4626

[168] James, Ian, "How unchecked pumping is sucking aquifers dry in India," Desert Sun, December 10, 2015, https://www.desertsun.com/story/news/environment/2015/12/10/how-unchecked-pumping-sucking-aquifers-dry-india/74634336/

[169] "What Happens to the U.S. Midwest When the Water's Gone?"," *National Geographic*, August, 2016, https://www.nationalgeographic.com/magazine/2016/08/vanishing-midwest-ogallala-aquifer-drought/

[170] Ian

[171] "The Problems of water stress," European Environment Agency, April 20, 2016, https://www.eea.europa.eu/publications/92-9167-025-1/page003.html

[172] "Confronting the Global Water Crisis Through Research," SciVal, March 2011, https://www.elsevier.com/__data/assets/pdf_file/0018/53082/Water-Resources_WP_lr.pdf

[173] "Indonesia's planning minister announces capital city move," BBC News, April 29, 2019, https://www.bbc.com/news/world-asia-48093431

[174] "Chennai water crisis: City's reservoirs run dry," BBC, June 18, 2019, https://www.bbc.com/news/world-asia-india-48672330?utm_source=GPF+-+Paid+Newsletter&utm_campaign=45c88c129f-EMAIL_CAMPAIGN_2019_06_20_02_28&utm_medium=email&utm_term=0_72b76c0285-45c88c129f-240035277

[175] "Land Subsidence, U.S. Geological Survey, https://water.usgs.gov/edu/earthgwlandsubside.html

[176] Frankson, Liesl, "80% of world's wastewater goes untreated," InfrastructureNews, February 9, 2015, http://www.infrastructurene.ws/2015/02/09/80-of-worlds-wastewater-goes-untreated/

[177] "Billions around the world lack safe water, proper sanitation facilities, reveals UN report," UN News, July 12, 2017, https://news.un.org/en/story/2017/07/561362-billions-around-world-lack-safe-water-proper-sanitation-facilities-reveals-un

[178] Pokharel, Krishna, and Preetika Rana, "The World's Next Environmental Disaster," *The Wall Street Journal*, October 20, 2017, https://www.wsj.com/articles/the-worlds-next-environmental-disaster-1508511743

[179] "Quality not quantity problem for Indo-Gangetic Basin groundwater," *Nature Geoscience*, August 30, 2016, https://www.natureasia.com/en/research/highlight/10942

[180] "Four-fifths of China's water from wells 'unsafe because of pollution'," *The Guardian*, April 12, 2016, https://www.theguardian.com/environment/2016/apr/12/four-fifths-of-chinas-water-from-wells-unsafe-because-of-pollution

[181] "Water in Crisis," Ocion Water Sciences Group, http://ocion.com/the-environment/21st-century-water-issues/

[182] St. Fleur, Nicholas, "Two-Thirds of the World Faces Severe Water Shortages," *The New York Times*, February 12, 2016, https://www.nytimes.com/2016/02/13/science/two-thirds-of-the-world-faces-severe-water-shortages.html

[183] Vaughan, Adam, "Carbon-negative crops may mean water shortages for 4.5 billion people," New Scientist Newsletter, March 8, 2021, https://www.newscientist.com/article/2270227-carbon-negative-crops-may-mean-water-shortages-for-4-5-billion-people/?utm_source=nsday&utm_medium=email&utm_campaign=NSDAY_090321

[184] Tran, Michael, et. al.,"The United Nations World Water Development Report 2016," UNESCO,

[185] Chen, Stephen, "Chinese engineers plan 1,000 km tunnel to make Xinjiang desert bloom," *South China Morning Post*, October 30, 2017, http://www.scmp.com/news/china/society/article/2116750/chinese-engineers-plan-1000km-tunnel-make-xinjiang-desert-bloom

[186] Gelt, Joe, "Sharing Colorado River Water: History, Public Policy and the Colorado River Compact," University of Arizona Water Resources Research Center, August 1997, https://wrrc.arizona.edu/publications/arroyo-newsletter/sharing-colorado-river-water-history-public-policy-and-colorado-river

[187] "Durden, Tyler (pseudonym), "Rick Rule: "Water Is The Most Mispriced Commodity In The World," Zero Hedgd, February 25, 2018, https://www.zerohedge.com/news/2018-02-25/rick-rule-water-most-mispriced-commodity-world

[188] Kaplan, Melanie, "Aging water infrastructure wastes 1.7 trillion gallons a year," ZDNet, November 1, 2010, https://www.zdnet.com/article/aging-water-infrastructure-wastes-17-trillion-gallons-a-year/

[189] "Factory Fresh," *Economist*, June 9, 2016, https://www.economist.com/technology-quarterly/2016-06-09/factory-fresh

[190] "Israel Recycles 90% of Its Wastewater, Four Times More Than Any Other Country," The Tower, December 25, 2016, http://www.thetower.org/4305oc-israel-recycles-90-of-its-wastewater-four-times-more-than-any-other-country/

[191] Rogers, Paul, "Drought or no drought: Jerry Brown sets permanent water conservation rules for Californians," The Mercury News, May 31, 2018, https://www.mercurynews.com/2018/05/31/california-drought-jerry-brown-sets-permanent-water-conservation-rules-with-new-laws/

[192] "Topsoil," Wikipedia, https://en.wikipedia.org/wiki/Topsoil

[193] Lang, Susan S., "'Slow, insidious' soil erosion threatens human health and welfare as well as the environment, Cornell study asserts," Cornell Chronicle, March 20, 2006, http://news.cornell.edu/stories/2006/03/slow-insidious-soil-erosion-threatens-human-health-and-welfare

[194] "What If the World's Soil Runs Out?", World Economic Form and Time, December 14, 2012, http://world.time.com/2012/12/14/what-if-the-worlds-soil-runs-out/

[195] Lang

[196] "New World Atlas of Desertification shows unprecedented pressure on planet's resources," Science News, June 21, 2018, https://www.sciencedaily.com/releases/2018/06/180621111958.htm

[197] D'Amour, Bren, et. al., "Future urban land expansion and implications for global croplands," National Center for Biotechnology Information, December 27, 2016, https://www.ncbi.nlm.nih.gov/pubmed/28028219

[198] Rosemarin, Arno, "Peak Phosphorus, The Next Inconvenient Truth?", Presentation to the World Bank, October 15, 2010, http://www.susana.org/_resources/documents/default/2-819-en-rosemarin-

peak-phosphorus-manila-2010.pdf

[199] Ibid

[200] Charles, Dan, "The Gulf of Mexico's Dead Zone is the Biggest Ever Seen," NPR, August 3, 2017, https://www.npr.org/sections/thesalt/2017/08/03/541222717/the-gulf-of-mexicos-dead-zone-is-the-biggest-ever-seen

[201] "Environment for the future we want," United Nations Environment Programme, 2012, http://web.unep.org/geo/sites/unep.org.geo/files/documents/geo5_report_full_en_0.pdf

[202] "State of World Fisheries and Aquaculture 2016," Food and Agriculture Organization of the United Nations, http://www.fao.org/3/a-i5555e.pdf

[203] Nickson, Amanda, "New Science Puts Decline of Pacific Bluefin at 97.4 Percent," Pew Charitable Trusts, April 25, 2016, http://www.pewtrusts.org/en/research-and-analysis/analysis/2016/04/25/new-science-puts-decline-of-pacific-bluefin-at-974-percent

[204] I prepared this chart with data from https://www.st.nmfs.noaa.gov/pls/webpls/FT_HELP.SPECIES

[205] "The IUCN Red List of Threatened Species," International Union for Conservation of Nature, http://www.iucnredlist.org/

[206] "Thousands of turtles netted off South America," Science Daily, June 5, 2018, https://www.sciencedaily.com/releases/2018/06/180605083040.htm

[207] Zabarenko, Deborah, "Pverfishing may wipe seafood off menu," Reuters, Australian Brodcasting Company, http://www.abc.net.au/science/news/stories/2006/1780487.htm

[208] "Getting serious about overfishing," The Economist, May 27, 2017, https://www.economist.com/news/briefing/21722629-oceans-face-dire-threats-better-regulated-fisheries-would-help-getting-serious-about

[209] Hennigar, Melissa, "Photoplankton in Retreat," Dalhousie University, July 28, 2010, https://www.dal.ca/news/2010/07/28/photoplank.html

[210] Hallmann, Caspar, et. al., "More than 75 percent decline over 27 years in total flying insect biomass in protected areas," PlosOne, October 18, 2017, http://journals.plos.org/plosone/article?id=10.1371/journal.pone.0185809

[211] Carrington, Damian, "Warning of 'ecological Armageddon' after dramatic plunge in insect numbers," *The Guardian*, October 18, 2017, https://www.theguardian.com/environment/2017/oct/18/warning-of-ecological-armageddon-after-dramatic-plunge-in-insect-numbers

[212] Shellenberger, Michael, "Why Climate Activists Threaten Endangered Species With Extinction," Forbes, June 26, 2019, https://www.forbes.com/sites/michaelshellenberger/2019/06/26/why-climate-activists-threaten-endangered-species-with-extinction/#564d2cde23aa

[213] Zimmer, Carl, "Birds Are Vanishing from North America," *The New York Times*, September 19, 2019, https://www.nytimes.com/2019/09/19/science/bird-populations-america-canada.html?smtyp=cur&smid=tw-nytimes

[214] "'Catastrophe' as France's bird population collapses due to pesticides,"

The Guardian, March 20,2018,
https://www.theguardian.com/world/2018/mar/21/catastrophe-as-frances-bird-population-collapses-due-to-pesticides
[215] "Beekeepers see 42% of U.S. honeybee colonies die off in a single year," *The Guardian*, May 13, 2015,
https://www.theguardian.com/environment/2015/may/13/honeybee-deaths-colonies-beekeepers
[216] Freedman, David H., "The Truth about Genetically Modified Food," *Scientific American*, September 1, 2013,
https://www.scientificamerican.com/article/the-truth-about-genetically-modified-food/
[217] Hilbeck, Angelika, et. al., "No scientific consensus on GMO safety," Environmental Sciences Europe,
https://link.springer.com/content/pdf/10.1186/s12302-014-0034-1.pdf
[218] Hakim, Danny, "Broken Promises of Genetically Modified Crops," *The New York Times*, October 29, 2016.
https://www.nytimes.com/interactive/2016/10/30/business/gmo-crops-pesticides.html
[219] Charles, Dan, "GMOs Are Safe, But Don't Always Deliver On Promises, Top Scientists Say," The Salt, May 17, 2016,
https://www.npr.org/sections/thesalt/2016/05/17/478415310/top-scientists-say-gmos-are-safe-but-dont-always-deliver-on-promises
[220] Durden, Tyler, "CRISPR Crashes After Study Highlights Potential Cancer Risk from Gene-Editing," Zero Hedge, June 11, 2018,
https://www.zerohedge.com/news/2018-06-11/crispr-crashes-after-study-highlights-potential-cancer-risk-gene-editing?utm_source=feedburner&utm_medium=feed&utm_campaign=Feed%3A+zerohedge%2Ffeed+%28zero+hedge+-+on+a+long+enough+timeline%2C+the+survival+rate+for+everyone+drops+to+zero%29
[221] Long, Cheyl, "Industrially Farmed Foods Have Lower Nutritional Content," Mother Earth News, June/July 2009,
https://www.motherearthnews.com/nature-and-environment/nutritional-content-zmaz09jjzraw
[222] Neslen, Arthur, "EU on brink of historic decision on pervasive glyphosate weedkiller," The Guardian, October 24, 2017,
https://www.theguardian.com/environment/2017/oct/24/eu-brink-historic-decision-pervasive-glyphosate-weedkiller
[223] "IARC Monographs Volume 112: evaluation of five organophosphate insecticides and herbicides," world Health Organization, March 20, 2015,
https://www.iarc.fr/wp-content/uploads/2018/07/MonographVolume112-1.pdf
[224] Brown, H. Claire, "Attack of the Superweeds," *The New York Times Magazine*, August 18, 2021,
https://www.nytimes.com/2021/08/18/magazine/superweeds-monsanto.html?campaign_id=9&emc=edit_nn_20210819&instance_id=382

93&nl=the-morning&regi_id=57816322&segment_id=66654&te=1&user_id=06db51d4 f00f79283845a9e4a71b881c

[225] "Is meatless meat really better for your health and the planet," CBC Radio, September 13, 2019, https://www.cbc.ca/radio/thesundayedition/the-sunday-edition-for-september-15-2019-1.5282280/is-meatless-meat-really-better-for-your-health-and-the-planet-1.5283185

[226] "Rabbi says meat from genetically cloned pig could be eaten by Jews – including with milk," Jewish Telegraphic Agency, March 22, 2018, https://www.jta.org/2018/03/22/israel/rabbi-says-meat-genetically-cloned-pig-eaten-jews-including-milk

[227] Parfitt, Julian, Mark Barthel and Sarah Macnaughton, "Food waste within food supply chains: quantification and potential for change to 2050,", The Royal Society, http://rstb.royalsocietypublishing.org/content/365/1554/3065.short#ref-62

[228] "Obesity," World Health Organization, http://www.afro.who.int/health-topics/obesity

[229] Haspel, Tamar, "Is organic agriculture really better for the environment?", *The Washington Post*, May 14, 2016, https://www.washingtonpost.com/lifestyle/food/is-organic-agriculture-really-better-for-the-environment/2016/05/14/e9996dce-17be-11e6-924d-838753295f9a_story.html?utm_term=.f5e00c874a91

[230] "Regenerative Agriculture," Drawdown, http://www.drawdown.org/solutions/food/regenerative-agriculture

[231] Van Huis, Arnold, et. al., "Edible insects: future prospects for food and feed security," Food and Agriculture Organization of the United Nations, 2013, http://www.fao.org/docrep/018/i3253e/i3253e.pdf

[232] Ratner, Paul, "Swedish scientist advocates eating humans to combat climate change," September 9, 2019, https://bigthink.com/surprising-science/swedish-scientist-eating-humans-climate-change?rebelltitem=1#rebelltitem1

[233] Grassini,Patricio, Kent M. Eskridge, and Kenneth G. Cassman, "Distinguishing between yield advances and yield plateaus in historical crop production trends, Nature Communications, December 17, 2013, https://www.nature.com/articles/ncomms3918

[234] "BP Energy Outlook, 2017 Edition," BP, https://www.bp.com/content/dam/bp/pdf/energy-economics/energy-outlook-2017/bp-energy-outlook-2017.pdf

[235] Guilford, Megan C., et. al., "A new Long Term Assessment of Energy Return on Investment (EROI) for U.S. Oil and Gas Discovery and Production," *Sustainability*, October 14, 2011, http://www.mdpi.com/2071-1050/3/10/1866/htm

[236] "Energy returned on energy invested," Wikipedia, https://en.wikipedia.org/wiki/Energy_returned_on_energy_invested

[237] Weiβbach, et al., "Energy intensities, EROIs (energy returned on invested), and energy payback times of electricity generating power plants,"

Elsevier Energy, March 13, 2013.
[238] Trainer, Ted, "Estimating the EROI of whole systems for 100% renewable electricity supply capable of dealing with intermittency," Elsevier Energy Policy, 2018, https://www.journals.elsevier.com/energy-policy
[239] "Expect the Unexpected: Building business value in a changing world," KPMG, https://home.kpmg.com/content/dam/kpmg/pdf/2012/08/building-business-value-part-1.pdf, 10
[240] Mills, Mark P., "If You Want 'Renewable Energy,' Get Ready to Dig," *The Wall Street Journal*, August 5, 2019, https://www.wsj.com/articles/if-you-want-renewable-energy-get-ready-to-dig-11565045328
[241] Bennett, Nelson, "Global energy transition powers surge in demand for metals," Business in Vancouver, January 29, 2019, https://www.mining.com/global-energy-transition-powers-surge-demand-metals/6269/
[242] "The Role of Critical Materials in Clean Energy Transtions," IEA, 2021, https://iea.blob.core.windows.net/assets/278ae0c8-28b8-402b-b9ab-6e45463c273f/TheRoleofCriticalMineralsinCleanEnergyTransitions.pdf
[243] McLelland, Christine V., "What Earth Materials are in My Subaru?, https://core.ac.uk/download/pdf/5213665.pdf
[244] https://mineraleducationcoalition.org/mining-minerals-information/mining-mineral-statistics/
[245] Els, Erik, "All the mines Tesla needs to build 20 million cars a year," Mining.com, January 27, 2021,
[246] "Draft List of Critical Minerals," Federal Register, February 16, 2018, https://www.mining.com/all-the-mines-tesla-needs-to-build-20-million-cars-a-year/https://www.federalregister.gov/documents/2018/02/16/2018-03219/draft-list-of-critical-minerals
[247] Calvo, Guiomar, et. al., "Decreasing Ore Grades in Global Metallic Mining: A Theoretical Issue or a Global Reality?", MDPI, November 7, 2016, http://www.mdpi.com/2079-9276/5/4/36/htm
[248] "Photos: Bingham Canyon rebuilds after landslide," http://www.mining.com/bingham-47835/
[249] Ibid
[250] "Haul truck," Wikipedia, https://www.google.com/search?q=mining+truck&rlz=1C1CHBF_enU.S.788U.S.789&source=lnms&tbm=isch&sa=X&ved=0ahUKEwiO6YPrmLPbAhWpx4MKHQGmDgoQ_AUICigB&biw=1922&bih=1096#imgrc=xc-5lFqpWsV9NM:
[251] Hagens, N.J., "Economics for the future – Beyond the superorganism," Ecological Economics, March 2020, https://www.sciencedirect.com/science/article/pii/S0921800919310067
[252] "How Long Will It Last?", New Scientist, https://www.newscientist.com/data/images/archive/2605/26051202.jpg
[253] Peinado-Vera, Estrella, "The Circular Economy: Butterflies and the Fourth Industrial Revolution," EconoMonitor, May 4, 2016, http://archive.economonitor.com/blog/2016/05/the-circular-economy-

butterflies-and-the-fourth-industrial-revolution/?utm_medium=twitter&utm_source=twitterfeed

[254] "Engine Efficiency," Wikipedia, https://en.wikipedia.org/wiki/Engine_efficiency

[255] Chasan, Emily and Hema Parmar, "Starbucks, Dunkin Race Against Bans, Taxes on Disposable Cups," https://www.bloomberg.com/news/articles/2019-04-28/starbucks-sbux-dunkin-dnkn-brace-for-coffee-cup-bans-fees

[256] Pettit, Harry, "Paradise lost: Shocking video shows the miles-wide sea of plastic and trash covering a section of the Caribbean," http://www.dailymail.co.uk/sciencetech/article-5070397/Video-shows-Caribbean-sea-choked-death-human-waste.html

[257] "How Much Trash is in Our Ocean?," https://4ocean.com/blogs/blog/how-much-trash-is-in-our-ocean?gclid=EAIaIQobChMI76-d3JO42wIVTyWBCh236w7_EAAYASAAEgJGE_D_BwE

[258] Oli, Swikar, "Landfills are turning trash into energy and cleaning the environment", https://theplaidzebra.com/landfills-are-turning-trash-into-energy-and-cleaning-the-environment/

[259] "Microplastics," Wikipedia, https://en.wikipedia.org/wiki/Microplastics

[260] Scutti, Susan, "If you drink bottled water, you could double how many microplastic particles you ingest, study says," CNN, June 5, 2019, https://www.cnn.com/2019/06/05/health/microplastic-particle-ingestion-study/index.html

[261] Kulpinski, Dan, "Human Footprint: Where does All the Stuff Go?," http://channel.nationalgeographic.com/channel/human-footprint/trash-talk.html

[262] "Seven charts that explain the plastic pollution problem, BBC, December 10, 2017, https://www.bbc.com/news/science-environment-42264788

[263] "Diwali Cracker Is Not The Only Culprit For Delhi Air Pollution," https://www.skymetweather.com/content/weather-news-and-analysis/diwali-cracker-is-not-the-sole-culprit-for-delhi-air-pollution/

[264] Smith, Oliver, "Is Delhi the most polluted city on Earth? Not quite," https://www.telegraph.co.uk/travel/destinations/asia/india/articles/delhi-most-polluted-city-in-the-world/

[265] Khemani, Ankush, https://www.youtube.com/watch?v=AHnC5v34S-o

[266] Manu, "The most polluted rivers in the world," https://www.whatagreenlife.com/polluted-rivers-world/

[267] Buchholtx, Katharina, "Unsafe Water Kills More People Than Disasters and Conflict," Statista, March 22, 2019, https://www.statista.com/chart/17445/global-access-to-safe-drinking-water/

[268] Harrington, Rebecca, "Here's what the U.S. actually agreed to in the Paris climate deal," Business Insider, June 1, 2017, http://www.businessinsider.com/what-did-us-agree-to-paris-climate-deal-2017-5

[269] "Upton Sinclair," New World Encyclopedia,

http://www.newworldencyclopedia.org/entry/Upton_Sinclair
[270] Butcher, Jim, *Turn Coat*, Roc, April 7, 2009.
[271] Kelly, Walt, Poster for Earth Day, April 22, 1970
[272] Bartlett, Al, "Reflections on Sustainability, Population Growth, and the Environment," January 1998, http://www.albartlett.org/articles/art_reflections_part_1.html
[273] Larkin, Amy, *Environmental Debt: The Hidden Costs of a Changing Global Economy*, St. Martin's Press, June 25, 2013, 7 (Kindle)
[274] O'Neill, Daniel W., et. al., "A good life for all within planetary boundaries," Nature Sustainability, February 5, 2018, https://www.nature.com/articles/s41893-018-0021-4
[275] "Nine Population Strategies to Stop Short of 9 Billion," Worldwatch Institute, May 5, 2018, http://www.worldwatch.org/nine-population-strategies-stop-short-9-billion
[276] "One child policy," Wikigender, https://www.wikigender.org/wiki/one-child-policy/
[277] Ehrlich, Paul, John P. Holdren ad Anne H. Ehrlich, *Ecoscience: Population, Resources, Environment*, W. H. Freeman & Co., July 3, 1978
[278] Carli, Jame, "It's Time to Discuss the Ethics of Subjecting New Humans to the Climate Change Era," HuffPost, December 18, 2017, voluntarily removed from website by the author on February 2, 2018, https://medium.com/@jamescarli/its-time-to-discuss-the-ethics-of-subjecting-new-humans-to-the-climate-change-era-db84db59d37d
[279] "Household final consumption expenditure, etc. (% of GDP)," The World Bank, https://data.worldbank.org/indicator/NE.CON.PETC.ZS
[280] Keen, Steve, "Incorporating energy into production functions," Steve Keen's Debtwatch, August 19, 2016, http://www.debtdeflation.com/blogs/2016/08/19/incorporating-energy-into-production-functions/
[281] "Energy subsidies," Wikipedia, https://en.wikipedia.org/wiki/Energy_subsidies
[282] Mann, Charles, "Can Plaet Earth Feed 10 Billion People?", *The Atlantic*, March 2018, https://www.theatlantic.com/magazine/archive/2018/03/charles-mann-can-planet-earth-feed-10-billion-people/550928/
[283] "Expect the Unexpected: Building business value in a changing world," KPMG, https://home.kpmg.com/content/dam/kpmg/pdf/2012/08/building-business-value-part-1.pdf , 4
[284] Mauldin, John, "Why 2017 Was a Year to Celebrate," Mauldin Economics, December 17, 2017, https://www.mauldineconomics.com/frontlinethoughts/why-2017-was-a-year-to-celebrate
[285] Skidelsky, Robert, and Edward Skidelsky, *How Much is Enough? Money and the Good Life*, Other Press, June 19, 2012
[286] Fromm, Erich, *To Have or to Be?*, Harper & Row, December 1, 1976.
[287] Dahl, Arthur Lyon, "Alternatives to the Consumer Society, International

Environment Forum, March 19, 2012, http://iefworld.org/ddahl12a
[288] Goldberg, Jonah, *Suicide of the West: How the Rebirth of Tribalism, Populism Nationalism, and Identity Politics is Destroying American Democracy*, Crown Forum, April 24, 2018
[289] I created this chart
[290] Tainter, Joseph A., "Complexity, Problem Solving, and Sustainable Societies," 1996, https://www.goldonomic.com/tainter.htm
[291] "Convention on the Organisation for Economic Co-operation and Development," OECD, December 14, http://www.oecd.org/general/conventionontheorganisationforeconomicco-operationanddevelopment.htm1960
[292] *Handbook on Growth and Sustainability*, Edward Elgar Publishing, June 30, 2017
[293] Ibid
[294] Hickel, Jason, "Why Growth Can't Be Green," https://foreignpolicy.com/2018/09/12/why-growth-cant-be-green/?utm_source=Sightline%20Institute&utm_medium=web-email&utm_campaign=Sightline%20News%20Selections
[295] McLeod, Saul, "Maslow's Hierarchy of Needs," SimplyPsychology, 2017, https://www.simplypsychology.org/maslow.html
[296] "List of countries by GDP (PPP) per capita," Wikipedia, https://en.wikipedia.org/wiki/List_of_countries_by_GDP_(PPP)_per_capita
[297] *Handbook on Growth and Sustainability*, Edward Elgar Publishing, June 30, 2017
[298] "The Long-Term Decline in Prime-Age Male Labor Force Participation," The Obama White House, June 2016, https://obamawhitehouse.archives.gov/sites/default/files/page/files/20160620_cea_primeage_male_lfp.pdf
[299] Tuzemen, Didem, "Why Are Prime-Age Men Vanishing from the Labor Force?," Kansas City Federal Reserve, first quarter 2018, https://www.kansascityfed.org/~/media/files/publicat/econrev/econrevarchive/2018/1q18tuzemen.pdf
[300] MacKenzie, Debora, "The world in 2076: Civilisation was more fragile than we thought," New Scientist, November 16, 2016, https://www.newscientist.com/article/mg23231001-700-the-world-in-2076-civilisation-was-more-fragile-than-we-thought/
[301] Asimov, Isaac, quoted in *A World of Ideas* by Bill Moyers, May 26, 1989, 276
[302] Mill, John Stewart, *Principles of Political Economy*, Book IV, Chapter VI, http://www.econlib.org/library/Mill/mlP61.html
[303] Illustration by the author
[304] Friedman, Milton, *capitalism and Freedom: 40th Edition*, University of Chicago Press, November 28, 2002, Introduction.
[305] "The Scorpion and The Frog," Wikipedia, https://en.wikipedia.org/wiki/The_Scorpion_and_the_Frog

Made in the USA
Columbia, SC
29 November 2021

50006052R00180